Bible Studies

for

A Firm Foundation

Bob and Rose Weiner

weinermedia.com

weiner**ministries**.org

maranatha *publications*

Over 30 Years of Publishing

A Maranatha Book

2017 Edition

Available in Other Languages

**For More Study Books
and Daily Inspiration**

Visit Our Websites:

www.weinermedia.com

www.weinerministries.org

Library of Congress Number: 80081915

For more information write or call:
WeinerMedia@gmail.com

Maranatha Publications
P.O. Box 1799
Gainesville, Florida 32614

(352) 375-6000

Printed in the United States of America

ISBN: 978-0-938558-66-8

Table of Contents

How to Study God's Word

Paul Taught the Church How to Understand the Word and Will of God:

Eye has not seen and ear has not heard and it has not entered into the heart of man, all that God has prepared for those who love Him and hold Him in affectionate reverence, promptly obeying Him, and gratefully recognizing the benefits He has bestowed.

Yet to us, God has unveiled and revealed them by His Spirit. For the Holy Spirit searches diligently, exploring and examining everything, even sounding the profound and bottomless things of God. The Spirit looks into His Divine counsels and things hidden and beyond man's scrutiny.

For what person knows and understands what passes through a man's thoughts except the man's own spirit within him? Just so no one discerns or comes to know and comprehend the thoughts of God except the Spirit of God.

We have received the Holy Spirit that we might understand and appreciate the gifts of divine favor and blessing so freely and lavishly bestowed on us by God.

And we are setting these truths forth in words not taught by human wisdom but taught by the Holy Spirit combining and interpreting spiritual truths with spiritual language to those who possess the Holy Spirit.

But the natural, non-spiritual man does not accept or welcome or admit into his heart the gifts and teachings and revelations of the Spirit of God, for they are folly and meaningless nonsense to him; and He is incapable of knowing them because they are spiritually discerned. (1 Corinthians 2:9-15, *Amplified Version*)

From This Passage We Learn:

- God's Truth can only be understood by revelation.

- God reveals His Truth to those who love Him - those who reverence Him, obey Him, and thank Him.

- The Holy Spirit will lead us into all Truth.

- The Holy Spirit teaches us by comparing Spiritual Truth with spiritual words, by comparing scripture with scripture.

- Don't assign arbitrary meaning to Bible words or allegories. The Bible is a dictionary interpreting its own words and images. Let the Bible interpret its own symbols.

In this Bible Study, we will compare scripture with scripture to understand God's meaning. To get the most out of studying the Bible, it is essential to pray for the revelation of God's Word. Ask the Holy Spirit to lead you into all Truth and give you spiritual understanding. On the next page are two of the Bible's greatest prayers for revelation and understanding. We recommend that you pray these prayers each time you open up your Bible.

Jesus promised that the Holy Spirit would lead us into all truth, reveal Jesus to us, and show us the future. Ask the Holy Spirit to be your Teacher. Ask Him to guide you into all Truth and to give you revelation and spiritual understanding. Here are two of the Bible's greatest prayers. They were Paul's prayers for the Early Church.

Dear Father of Glory, God of our Lord Jesus Christ,

I ask for the spirit of wisdom and revelation, of insight into mysteries and secrets, in the deep and intimate knowledge of Jesus.

Flood my heart with your light. Let me understand the wonderful future You have planned for me. Let me realize what a rich and glorious inheritance You have given me.

Help me understand the incredible greatness of Your power toward me, the same power that raised Christ from the dead and seated Him high above every principality and power, and put all things under His feet.

Lord fill me with the fullness of Your Presence. I ask this in Jesus' name.

Ephesians 1:15-19

Paul writes: "Because of Christ and our faith in Him, we can now come boldly and confidently into God's Presence. When I think of all this, I fall to my knees and pray to the Father, the Creator of everything in heaven and on earth."

Dear Lord Jesus,
I pray that from Your glorious, unlimited resources You will empower me with inner strength through Your Spirit. I pray that You will make Your home in my heart as I trust in You.

Let my roots grow down into Your love and keep me strong. Give me the power to understand, as all God's people should, how wide, how long, how high, and how deep Your love is.

Let me experience Your great love and make me complete with all the fullness of life and power that comes from You.

I give all glory to You my God, who is able, through Your mighty power at work within me, to accomplish infinitely more than I might ask or think.
May the glory of God be manifested in the church and in Christ Jesus through all generations forever and ever! Amen.

Ephesians 3:14-20

Study 1: Set Free from Sin!
The Sacrifice of the Lamb

As far back as you can imagine, before the dawn of time, God was there calling worlds into existence and filling the universe with His Living Presence. Like a mighty river, God's Eternal Spirit swept forward, engulfed this present moment, and surged into the future. His Presence encompasses all time, fills all of eternity, and vibrates in every fiber of the universe. In one glance, He comprehends all things past and present to a thousand ages from now. All of life is in Him, flows from Him, and returns to Him again. He is from everlasting, He was there in our past, He stands in our now, and He is waiting in our tomorrow.

When God created this jeweled planet earth, it was a riot of color, texture, and architectural wonder, filled with fragrance and the most delicate perfumes. It was, and still is, a thing of exquisite beauty. At the sound of God's voice, light appeared out of the darkness, supernovas burst on the scene, galaxies went whirling and spinning into space, and the heavens were spangled with stars of all colors, sizes, and magnitudes.

Great sea monsters began to swim in the deep, and the seas and the oceans swirled and teamed with speckled, striped, and mottled fish of every color and shape. Birds of brilliant hues and unusual forms took flight and dived and soared in the dazzling blue skies above. Animals of every description came leaping, walking, crawling, swinging and springing out of the earth. They had long necks, short necks, longs tusks, big trunks, flowing manes, thick fur, and funny ears of all shapes and sizes. "The voice of the Lord" sounded again and "caused the deer to calf"; the earth teemed with wildlife, as each animal gave birth and brought forth their young after their own kind to be nursed and cuddled at their sides.

One can imagine what it must have been like to have been on our planet in its infancy. To be outnumbered by wildlife of sometimes monstrous proportions and to be engulfed at night in the cascading beauty of the diamond-studded heavens - a scene which many city dwellers are unfamiliar with in this day of electric lights that blot out the view - must certainly have been overwhelming to the early tribes of men. As they looked at this, the abode of God, the ancients cried out, "Who is man that You are mindful of him, and the son of man that You visit him" (Psalm 8:4).

God created all of this magnificent beauty with just the sound of His voice. But when God created man, He formed him in His very own image and breathed into him His very life. And all this was because God's greatest desire was to have a family to share His likeness, to have someone He could dream with and share His life, love, and plans. The whole created universe was a giant birthday gift for His Beloved. Then God gave the race of man, both male and female, dominion over the earth and the privilege of being co-creators with Him in the future of this planet.

On the sixth day of creation, when God made man and woman in His image and gave them the breath of life, He placed them in a beautiful garden that had four rivers running through it and filled it with His blessings. The garden was furnished with every variety of plants and trees that were good for food and beauty, and the ground was covered with very pure gold and sparkling gems of every hue and radiance. In the middle of the garden, God placed the tree of life, and beside it, He placed another tree, the tree of the knowledge of good and evil. God gave Adam and Eve permission to eat from any tree in the garden, including the tree of life. However, there was one tree from which God commanded them not to eat; for if they ate from it they would die.

In that command, God gave His beloved ones a choice of whether to obey Him, love Him, and live - or to disobey Him, not love Him, and die. It was never His will to force man to love Him - or serve Him. He wanted Adam and Eve to be free to choose to love Him from their heart. There was one more thing that He did. Before the foundation of the world, outside of time, He provided a slain Lamb to heal the breach that He knew would inevitably come (Revelation 13:8).

The Fall of Man

1. What did Adam and Eve choose to do? (Genesis 3:3-6) _____

_____

We see that Adam and Eve chose not to love God and obey Him, but they chose to rebel against God and disobey Him.

2. What was the secret motive of their heart? (Genesis 3:5; Isaiah. 14:13-14)

_____

_____

_____

When a person imitates the sin of Adam and Eve, exalting "self" above the will of God, then that person by his own free will has become a sinner.

3. On what three things were Adam and Eve's sin based? (Genesis 3:6; 1 John 2:16)

a._____

b._____

c._____

The lust of the flesh, the lust of the eyes and the boastful pride of life are the root causes of all sin in this world.

4. What do we find God doing in the garden, and what was the desire of His heart? (Genesis 3:8-9) _____

_____

The God of heaven and earth came to the garden seeking fellowship with His children whom He loved. But they had broken His commandment and had gone their own independent way. By turning away from God in disobedience, the man and woman lost the blessing and protection of God and came under a curse and the power of the devil. They were cast out of the garden so they would not eat from the tree of life and live eternally in sin. They lost their beautiful garments of light along with their fellowship with the Father. Because of Adam and Eve's transgression, the knowledge of good and evil has come to all men; every unregenerate person has desires bent toward self-exaltation.

5. What does the Scripture teach about the spiritual condition of a person who willfully sins against God? (Romans 3:10-19, 23)

a. (10) _____

b. (11) _____

c. (11) _____

d. (12) _____

e. (12) _____

f. (13-14)_____

g. (15) _____

h. (16) _____

i. (17) _____

j. (18) _____

k. (23) _____

Restoration

6. If all have sinned willfully and are *not* seeking God, then how can men come to God? (Isaiah 19:20; Luke 19:10; John 6:44)_____

_____

7. Therefore what is it that brings men to repentance? (Romans 2:4)_____

It is the love and kindness of God that goes out and seeks rebellious men and women. It is the love of God that strives with our heart, convicting us of sin and drawing us to Himself. It is the love of God that continues to push the stubborn and rebellious person into a corner until that person gives up and surrenders his or her life of sin and death. Yet, God has given every person a free will to choose Him and live or to reject His provision and die.

8. Can we save ourselves by our own good works? (Ephesians 2:8-9; Titus 3:5)

9. Can we be saved by keeping the law? (Galatians 3:21; Romans 3:20)

10. What was Paul's testimony about himself in regard to the law and to sin? (Philippians 3:6; 1 Timothy 1:15)

11. What was the purpose of the law? (Romans 3:19-20)

12. Under the Old Covenant, how did a person receive forgiveness and cleansing from sin and enter into a right relationship with God? (Ezekiel 18:27-32; Leviticus 17:11)

a.

b.

The Bible defines repentance as turning away from sin and keeping God's commandments. This is biblical repentance. The blood sacrifice as the atonement and covering for sin, was instituted by God from the beginning of time. Adam, Abel, Noah, Job, Abraham, Jacob, and finally the nation of Israel all offered blood sacrifices for the atonement of sin. God required animal sacrifices, for their blood is pure, innocent and undefiled; it is free from the nature that is bent toward sin. Under the Old Covenant, God received the shedding of this blood which provided a covering and atonement for sin.

13. What does the book of Hebrews tell us about the blood sacrifices that were offered under the Old Covenant? (Hebrews 9:19-22)

14. What did the blood of animals do under the Old Covenant? (Hebrews. 9:13; Ezekiel. 19:9; Leviticus 16:15-17)

Deliverance from Sin

15. What did Jesus come to do? (Matthew 1:20-23; 1 John 3:5)_____

_____

16. Who did John the Baptist say Jesus was? (John 1:29)_____

_____

The bloodline comes from the father. The Bible tells us that the life of the flesh is in the blood. In Jesus there was no sin. He was *not* born from Adam, but from a virgin who was with child by the Holy Spirit. The blood of God ran through Jesus' veins, and it was that blood which was shed for the sins of the world.

The forgiveness of sins was available through true repentance and the blood of animals under the Old Covenant. The atonement that Jesus made was greater than the atonement under the Old Covenant. Jesus' atonement was more than just an offering for the forgiveness of sins.

17. What did the blood of Jesus do? (Hebrews 9:14) _____

_____

18. What did Jesus do for us on the cross? (1 Peter 2:24; Galatians 3:13; Romans 6:6-7)

a. _____

b. _____

c. _____

d. _____

Consequently, we see that the atonement of Jesus not only provided forgiveness but brought complete deliverance from sin, sickness, and the curse.

The New Covenant

19. What is the "New Covenant" that Jesus established and made available through His blood? (Hebrews 8:8-12; Ezekiel 36:26-27)

a. (10) _____

b. (10) _____

c. (11) _____

d. (12) _____

e. (26) _____

f. (26) _____

20. How can we become partakers of the New Covenant? (Acts 3:19; Romans 10:9-10)

a. _____

b. _____

21. Why did Jesus come? (John 3:16-17) _____

_____

Rejecting God's Provision for Sin

22. Who are under God's judgment? (John 3:18-19) _____

_____

    If people reject God's provision for sin under the New Covenant there is no way they can be saved; for there is no other atonement apart from the blood of Jesus Christ.

23. What is the final end of all unrepentant sinners? (Matthew 25:41; Revelation 20: 12-15)

_____

_____

Memory Verses: Romans 5:9; Galatians 1:4

_____

_____

_____

_____

There is a Fountain Filled with Blood

- William Cowper - 1772

There is a fountain filled with blood
Drawn from Emmanuel's veins;
And sinners plunged beneath that flood
Lose all their guilty stains.

E'er since, by faith, I saw the stream
Thy flowing wounds supply,
Redeeming love has been my theme,
And shall be till I die.

Worship with Selah - *There is a Fountain Filled with Blood* <http://goo.gl/4nMbB5>

Worship with Vicki Yohe - *Mercy Seat* <http://goo.gl/BycoFM>

Worship with Steve Green, *Enter In* <http://goo.gl/9hBTsT>

Worship with Keith Green, *There is a Redeemer* <http://goo.gl/iE2HU2>

Study 2: What is True Repentance?
The Lordship of Jesus Christ

1. In preaching the Gospel to the Jews, what did Peter say about Jesus? (Acts 2:36)

_____

2. When the Jews heard this preaching, what happened and what was their response? (Acts 2:37) _____

_____

3. What did Peter say that they must do? (Acts 2:38)

a. _____

b. _____

c. _____

In this series we will deal separately with each of these three basic truths. The first one we will consider is repentance.

4. How does the Word of God define repentance?

a. (Psalm 32:3-5) _____

b. (Proverbs 28:13)_____

c. (Ezekiel. 18:21-23,27-28) _____

Repentance is not only confessing and admitting to God that we are guilty, it is forsaking sin.

5. What causes us to be separated from God? (Isaiah 59:2)

_____

Outward Sin

6. Sin is disobedience to God's commandments. What are the Ten Commandments that God has given to people to follow? (Exodus 20:1-17)

1)_____

2)_____

3)_____

4)_____

5)_____

6)_____

7)_____

8)_____

9)_____

10)_____

If you have broken any of these commandments then you have sinned against God.

7. What did Jesus say about the importance of the Ten Commandments? (Matthew 5:17-19)

_____

_____

_____

However, Jesus taught that sin is more than outward actions and its presence is revealed in the attitudes and motives of the heart.

Inward Sin

8. What are some of these sinful attitudes? (Matthew 5:21-28)

a. (v 21-22)_____

b. (v 27) _____

c. (v 43-47)_____

9. Paul and John list attitudes where the sinful self is ruling. What are they? (Galatians 5:19-20, 1 John 2:15-17, 1 Corinthians 6:9,18-20)_____

_____

_____

10. What does James say about sin? (James 4:17) _____

_____

11. What do we see Adam and Eve doing in the garden? (Genesis 3:3-6)_____

_____

Idolatry of Self

All sin carries with it the penalty of God's judgment. While outward and inward sin and impurity mark the presence of sin in the soul, sin is much deeper than outward actions and heart attitudes and can be present in the morally upright as well as the wicked. Since Adam and Eve made their break with the High Will of Heaven, sin has run through human nature like a gigantic fault line. Sin is revealed in my claim to my rights to myself.

In pride we have said, "I will." We have exalted ourselves above God. We have rebelled against God and have chosen to go our own stubborn, independent way. This is the root of sin that has broken our fellowship with God. We have taken the place as the ruler of our heart that belongs to God alone. We live our lives according to our own self-will. We follow our own plans and focus on our own self-interest.

Our stubborn opposition to God's laws of life often brings a sharp crisis in our affairs. We blame God for the circumstances that are the result of our own actions, and then we cry out, "O God, why did You do this to me?"

We demand that our wishes be satisfied. We seek to get ourselves in the highest position. We want to exercise control over other people. We want everyone to bow to our judgment and accept our declarations as law. We want power. We want to be popular. We have a deep thirst for the recognition of our excellence that we so desperately need in order to avoid despair. We seek the praise of others that belongs to God alone.   The idolatry of self is the sin of man. This is the true nature of evil.

12. Jesus greatest rebukes were to the leaders of Israel. Why? (Matthew 23:1-7)

_____

_____

13. What did Jesus tell His disciples not to do? (Matthew 23:8-11)

_____

_____

14. If you seek the honor of men, what did Jesus say you wouldn't be able to do? (John 5:44)

_____

_____

According to Jesus, as long as we are seeking to be noticed or approved of by others, as long as we seek to maintain our popularity and seek the honor of our friends, we can't believe. Following Jesus is not the way to win a popularity contest. All those who live godly in Christ Jesus will suffer persecution. Those who follow Jesus will be persecuted for righteousness' sake.

15. What did Jesus say about persecution? (John 15:20, Matthew 5:10-11)

_____

Laying the Ax to the Root of Sin

16. What does Jesus require of those who want to follow Him? (Matthew 10:37-38). Why do you think Jesus requires this? _____

_____

17. Jesus came to lay the ax to the root of sin, therefore what did Jesus tell all those who wanted to be His disciples to do? (Matthew 16:24-25) _____

_____

18. If we confess our sin, what will God do? (1 John 1:9; Isaiah 1:18, 20)

_____

_____

19. What did Jesus say to the woman who was brought to Him who had been caught in the act of adultery? (John 8:10-12)_____

_____

20. In repentance, what else must we be willing to do? (Ezekiel 33:15)

_____

This restitution must be made as the Spirit of God instructs and leads.

21. When Jesus said to Zaccheus that He would come to his house, what was Zaccheus' response that showed his repentant heart? (Luke 19:1-8)

_____

Zaccheus was a very wicked man, a tax collector; and had treated many men unjustly. However, as a Jew, Zaccheus was familiar with Ezekiel's teaching of repentance and restitution and knew what God required as evidence of his repentance.

22. What did Jesus say to Zaccheus? (Luke 19:9-10)

a._____

b._____

23. What conditions does God set for receiving us and being a Father to us?
(2 Corinthians 6:14-18)

a._____

b._____

c._____

The Lost Son

This condition for repentance is demonstrated very clearly in a parable Jesus told about a wayward son who decided to leave his father's house and go his own way.

24. What had the son done? (Luke 15:11-16) _____

_____

This is a picture of those who are involved in worldliness and sin.

Forsaking Worldliness

25. What did the wayward son decide to do when he realized his state? (Luke 15:17-19) _____

_____

Notice that there had to be a decision on his part to come out from the world and be separate and to go to his father's house.

26. When the son made the decision in his heart to separate himself from the unclean thing and to go to his father to confess his sin, what did the father do? (Luke 15:20)

_____

_____

27. The son was hoping only to be allowed to become a hired servant of the father, yet what did the father make him? (Luke 15:22-24) _____

_____

So also will the Heavenly Father do for us, as it is written:

> Come out from their midst and be separate," says the Lord, "and do not touch what is unclean; and I will welcome you. And I will be a Father to you, and you shall be sons and daughters to Me," says the Lord Almighty. (2 Corinthians 6:17-18)

28. We see the same requirement made of the Israelites when they were going in to possess the land that God had given them. What did God require them to do because of the heathen nations? (Deuteronomy 7:1-3)

a._____

b._____

c._____

29. Why did God require this? (Deuteronomy 7:4,6; 8:1)

a._____

b._____

c. _____

We too have a spiritual land to possess and very real spiritual enemies to overcome.

30. God has always desired a holy people for His own possession. How does God compare the relationship between Jesus and His church? (Ephesians 5:25-32)

_____

_____

31. Describe God's attitude toward this marriage covenant. (Isaiah 62:4-5)

_____

_____

32. When Israel went astray from her covenant with God, what did God call her? (Hosea 9:1; 4:12) _____

_____

When God's people break the covenant they have with God, God calls this harlotry and adultery.

33. What three things does James say about those who have friendship with the ways of the world? (James 4:4)

a._____

b._____

c._____

34. What is the Lord's attitude towards His bride? (James 4:5)_____

_____

_____

35. If anyone loves the ways of the world, what does John say about him? (1 John 2: 15)

_____

36. What is in the world? (1 John 2:16)

a._____

b._____

c._____

37. What happens to those who do the will of God? (1 John 2: 17)_____

_____

38. What commandment did Jesus give for us to follow, and what did He say for us to seek first? (Mark 12:28-31; Matthew 6:33)

a._____

b._____

Forsaking All I Take Him

39. What must a man do to be a disciple of Jesus? (Luke 14:26-33)

_____

_____

_____

Briefly summarized, we can say that unless a man is willing to forsake all that he has, he cannot be a disciple of Jesus. The first command is this, "You shall have no other gods before me." To hate your parents, friends, relatives, and even your own life means that you do not exalt your love for them or desire to please them above the will of God, nor exalt your own will above God's will.

40. Therefore, before we decide to become a disciple and follower of Jesus: what are we exhorted to do? (Luke 14:28-30) _____

_____

We see this principle demonstrated in Jesus' interaction with the rich young ruler.

41. What did the rich young ruler want? (Matthew 19:16) _____

_____

Jesus' response was that he should keep the commandments.

42. What was the young ruler's response? (Matthew 19:20) _____

_____

Notice that although the rich young ruler had been morally upright and obedient to God's commandments, he still recognized that something in his relationship with God was lacking.

43. What requirement did Jesus make of him? (Matthew 19:21) _____

_____

_____

Jesus put His finger on this man's idolatry. According to commentaries, most rulers in Israel were older men. Because this young man was a ruler, he had gained his position by his alms giving and beneficence. If he had given up his wealth, he would no longer have anything to commend him as a leader in Israel.

44. What did the rich young ruler do that proved that he was serving himself? (Matthew 19:22) _____

_____

Notice that Jesus did not run after this man to make a compromise or make the requirement less severe. The first and greatest commandment is this: "You shall love the Lord your God and Him only shall you serve." Anything less than this is not acceptable and is nothing less than idolatry.

45. What will the Lordship of Jesus bring? (Matthew 10:34) _____

Jesus came to make peace between an individual and God, yet in a world that is at enmity with Him, conflicts will arise.

46. What does Jesus point out as the three main areas of this conflict? (Matthew 10:17-22,35-36)

a._____

b._____

c._____

47. What did Paul say we must do to be saved? (Romans 10:9)

a._____

b._____

To confess that someone is your Lord and Master means that you are committing your entire life to that person to be His slave for life; you are committing your own will and desires to Him to do His bidding. When you give your all to Jesus you get back much more than you ever could give.

The Blessings of Full Surrender

48. What will those who have forsaken all to follow Jesus receive? (Matthew 19:27-29; Mark 10:29-30)

a._____

b._____

c._____

49. What does Jesus give to all those who will receive Him? (John 1:12)

_____

50. If we open our hearts to receive Jesus, what promise has He given us? (Revelation 3:20)_____

_____

51. What experience will we have as a result? (John 3:3-7)

52. When we receive Jesus, what does God give us ? (1 John 5:11; Romans 6:23)

Memory Verses: 2 Corinthians 6:17-18

I Surrender All

- Judson VanDeventer, 1896

All to Jesus, I surrender,
All to Him I freely give
I will ever love and serve Him
In His presence, daily live.

All to Jesus, I surrender
Humbly at his feet I bow,
Worldly pleasures all forsaken
Take me Jesus, take me now.

Worship with Brian Doerksen, *Just As I Am* <http://goo.gl/5Xw0XW>

Worship, *I Surrender All* <http://goo.gl/A88uCH>

Watch this scene from *You Raise Me Up* <https://youtu.be/VTByzluCtMo>

Worship with Lindell Coolley, *Holy Holy Holy* <http://goo.gl/jP0VY9>

Worship with Michael W. Smith, *Lord This is My Desire* <http://goo.gl/4mgYcz>

Worship with Chris Tomlin, *Amazing Grace,* <http://goo.gl/mycLTA>

Study 3: The Power in Water Baptism
The Sign of the New Covenant

When we turn to Jesus, repent of our sins, and accept Him as our Lord and Savior, we enter into what the Bible calls the "born again" experience. We experience a "new birth" and receive a new heart. Jesus comes to dwell in our hearts by faith. We become partakers of eternal life, for eternal life is in the Son. When we depart from this life, we shall go to be with the Lord.

1. What are three vital elements of the Christian life? (Acts 2:38)

a.

b.

c.

We come now to our second vital truth, water baptism, in which we bury our old nature and rise to walk with Christ in newness of life. If you have received Jesus as your Lord and Savior you will want to be baptized. Both Jesus and the Apostles command it. Why? Because water baptism is a supernatural experience that is imperative for experiencing new life in God's kingdom.

2. What was the Great Commission that Jesus gave His disciples? (Matthew 28:19)

3. Why was our old sin-loving nature crucified with Him? (Romans 6:6)

a.

b.

The *Amplified Version* says it this way:

We know that our old unrenewed self was nailed to the cross with Him in order that our body, which is the instrument of sin, might be made ineffective and inactive for evil, that we might no longer be the slaves of sin.

4. What provision did Jesus make for the "putting off" or burial of the sin-loving nature? (Colossians 2:11)_____

5. What is the circumcision of Christ? (Colossians 2:11-12)_____

The *New Living Translation* says it this way:

When you came to Christ, you were "circumcised," but not by a physical procedure. Christ performed a spiritual circumcision - the cutting away of your sinful nature. For you were buried with Christ when you were baptized. And with Him you were raised to new life because you trusted the mighty power of God, who raised Christ from the dead.

This circumcision, made without hands, is a supernatural work of God. In a sense, in the waters of baptism, God supernaturally takes His scalpel and cuts away from our heart the old nature that was in bondage to sin and buries it. Baptism in water is a grave where you bury *the old self-serving life* that has died. It is the reign of "self" in my life as king and lord of all that must be buried. It is my independence from God, my right to myself that must be laid in the grave forever. When we do this, a tremendous deliverance and victory takes place in the waters of baptism to those who believe. If we do not place our faith in this, we can get baptized every year and absolutely nothing will happen.

Water baptism is prefigured in the Old Covenant. To get a better understanding of water baptism, let's examine some of the types and figures of water baptism in the Old Covenant.

Old Covenant Circumcision

6. What was circumcision a sign of under the Old Covenant? (Genesis 17:10-11)

_____

7. Under the Old Covenant, what happened to someone who was not circumcised and why? (Genesis 17:13-14)

a._____

b._____

8. With whom did God establish this covenant of circumcision? (Genesis 17:19)

_____

9. From whom are we descended as the offspring of Christ? (Romans 9:6-8; Galatians 3:29)

_____

10. Who did Paul say were the true circumcision? (Philippians 3:3) _____

New Covenant Circumcision

11. Moses spoke prophetically of New Covenant circumcision. What did he call this circumcision, and what would this circumcision do for those who receive it? (Deuteronomy 30:6a)

a._____

b._____

12. Ezekiel spoke prophetically of the New Covenant and of the new heart that God was going to give. What did he say that God was going to remove? (Ezekiel 11:19; 36:26)

_____

13. What is circumcision in the New Covenant? (Colossians 2:11-13)

_____

In the Old Covenant, circumcision is the cutting away of the foreskin of the male reproductive organ. In the New Covenant, circumcision is a cutting away of the whole body of sins, the sin-loving nature. Even more, baptism is a burial and resurrection - a burial of the old sin-loving self (the heart of stone) and a real and present rising again of the believer in union with Christ to a new life and new nature.

Delivered from Slavery

Another beautiful picture of water baptism is found in the Old Testament. It is a type and shadow of the meaning of baptism under the New Covenant. The Israelites had been held in bondage in Egypt for many years enslaved to Pharaoh, the cruel King. When the Lord brought them forth from bondage in the Exodus, He parted the Red Sea before them. The water was like a wall on either side of them as the Israelites passed through to the other side on dry land.

Pharaoh and his armies pursued the Israelites and followed them into the water to bring them back into slavery. The Lord caused the water to roll back together, cutting the Egyptians off, and causing them to drown. Those who were pursuing Israel in her new relationship with God to enslave her again were buried in the waters of the Red Sea. The Israelites were left alone on the other side of the water, free from slavery, free to be servants of their God. If the sea had not buried the Egyptians, the threat of slavery would have followed Israel into the Promised Land. Not only would Israel have to fight her new enemies in the Promised Land, she would have to fight her old enemy trying to bring her back into slavery and bondage.

In the same way, if you have come to faith in Christ in self-surrender and have been buried with Him through water baptism, you have been made free from the power and bondage of sin, set free from the taskmaster of *self*. The power of the old self-centered drives are broken, the heart has been "made new." Those who have accepted the truth and the power of the Gospel, who were once enslaved to sin, have been made free from the slavery to sin by the life, death, and resurrection of Jesus Christ. We enter into the Promised Land as sons and daughters of God, able to meet and conquer our enemies and inhabit the land of spiritual promises.

14. In fact, what does Paul say about Israel's experience at the Red Sea? (1 Corinthians 10:1-2) _____

Rolling off the Reproach of Slavery

Consider another Old Testament example. After forty years of wandering, the generation of Israelites whom God had originally brought out of Egypt died in the wilderness. Because of their continual disobedience to God, they did not get to go into the Promised Land. Their children went into the Promised Land in their place. The Lord rolled back the waters of the Jordan River, just as He had done at the Red Sea, and a new generation walked through the Jordan River on dry land into the land of God's promise.

15. What was the first thing that they did after they crossed through the river? (Joshua 5:2)

_____

_____

16. Why did they do this? (Joshua 5:5-7) _____

_____

17. What did the Lord say that He did when they were circumcised? (Joshua 5:9)

_____

Before the Israelites could go up and possess the Promised Land, they had to be circumcised so that the reproach of Egypt might be rolled away from them. That circumcision was a sign in their flesh of their covenant with God.

Rolling off the Reproach and Power of Sin

Likewise, under the New Covenant before we can go up and possess our promised inheritance, we must receive what the Bible calls the circumcision of Jesus.

18. How do we receive the circumcision of Jesus, and what is removed? (Colossians 2:11-12)

a. _____

b. _____

The New Testament circumcision is supernatural, it is *made without hands*, in putting off the "the sin loving nature." Through this circumcision, the spirit of God uproots us from the world, of which both Egypt and the wilderness of wandering is a picture, and the reproach of the world is rolled away from us.

Burial and Resurrection

19. When believers are baptized, they are following Jesus into what experience? (Romans 6:4)

a._____

b._____

20. If we have been united with Him in the likeness of His death, in what else will we be united with Him?

a. (Romans 6:5) _____

b. What did Ezekiel prophesy God would remove? (Ezekiel 11:19)_____

21. Jesus took on flesh and blood and died. Why did He do this? (Hebrews 2:14-15)

a._____

b._____

22. Jesus hung on the cross and became sin for us. Why? (2 Corinthians 5:21)

_____

Jesus died on the cross to make a perfect atonement for man's sinful and lost condition. On the third day, He arose from the dead and triumphed over Satan, providing for man's salvation. Because we receive His life when we make Jesus Lord, our relationship to God is made alive, and we live in fellowship with God.

As we go down and come up out of the waters of baptism, we share in Jesus' burial and resurrection. Just as the angel rolled away the stone from the tomb and the resurrected Christ walked out, so as we are baptized into his death, the stony heart that keeps us bound to the law of sin and death is rolled away and we rise to new life in Christ. Because we now share the resurrection life of Jesus, sin no longer has dominion over us.

Paul exhorts us to pray every day that we will understand the incredible greatness of the power of His resurrection life we are called to experience as God's children: "I pray that you will begin to understand the incredible greatness of His power for us who believe Him. This is the same mighty power that raised Christ from the dead and seated Him in the place of honor at God's right hand in the heavenly realms" (Ephesians 1:19-20).

Now that we have established the scriptural meaning of baptism, let's look into the application of it.

Believe and be Baptized

23. What did the people who received the Word of God do? (Acts 2:41)_____

_____

24. What did the people of Samaria do after they believed Philip's teaching? (Acts 8:12)

_____

25. What did the Ethiopian eunuch want to do after he had heard the message of Philip about Jesus the Messiah? (Acts 8:35-36)_____

26. In what way, or by what method, was the eunuch baptized? (Acts 8:38-39)

_____

The baptisms throughout the New Testament, including the baptisms of John, were all done by immersion. The Scriptures tell us that the people all went down into the water and came up again. The water represents the grave where the burial takes place.

27. What did the Philippian jailer do after believing Paul's message? (Acts 16:29-33)

_____

28. When was he baptized? (Acts 16:33) _____

29. When were those who heard Peter's message baptized? (Acts 2:41)

_____

Notice the immediacy of all the baptisms recorded in the book of Acts. Likewise, there should be no delay in the baptism of believers today.

30. In what name did Jesus tell the disciples to baptize? (Matthew 28:19)

_____

Baptized in His Name

31. In what name did the disciples baptize?
a.(Acts 2:38) _____
b.(Acts 8:14-16)_____
c.(Acts 10:45-48)_____
d.(Acts 19:5) _____

We may wonder why the apostles and the early church did not baptize in the name of the Father, Son, and Holy Spirit, but baptized in the name of the Lord Jesus Christ. Paul told the Colossians about Jesus: "For in Him all the fullness of Deity dwells in bodily form" (Colossians 2:9).

Jesus' disciples understood this; for having His command, they went everywhere baptizing new believers. They were baptizing in the Name which is above all names in which all authority of heaven and earth is invested, and that name is the Lord Jesus Christ. In the name of the Lord Jesus Christ demons are cast out, the sick are healed, and the lame walk. We are saved in the name of the Lord Jesus Christ and by the power of His blood.

32. Into whom are we to be baptized? (Romans 6:3)

33. Many believers have gone through the motions of baptism, yet have not experienced a genuine New Testament baptism. What have they experienced? (Acts 19:3-4)

In the Old Covenant, an account is given of Naaman, the captain of the army of the King of Syria, who had leprosy. He went to Elisha, the prophet of God, to ask for healing. Leprosy in the Scripture is a type of the "sin-loving nature" or of the bondage of the power of sin, At that time there was no cure for this disease apart from the mercy of God. The whole flesh was infected, the whole body was corrupted, and the end of it was certain death.

34. What did Elisha tell Naaman to do? (2 Kings 5:9-10) _____

35. What was his response? (2 Kings 5:11-12)_____

Likewise, many people are insulted by God's command for water baptism, thinking it is silly and ridiculous.

36. What was the servant's advice to him, and what did he do? (2 Kings 5:13-14)

We must become as little children and obey the simple things that God asks us to do. His ways are far above our ways. We must not depend on our own understanding. We must be willing to humble ourselves to God's way of doing things.

Living Under Open Heavens

37. What happened when Jesus was baptized? (Matthew 3:16)

When Jesus was baptized, the heavens were opened. There is no record of them closing again.

38. How have we shared in that baptism with Christ? (Romans 6:3-4)

When you believe and are baptized, you share in Christ's baptism, and you have been raised up to new life in Christ. You have the privilege of living and walking under an "open heaven.

39. Where are you now seated? (Ephesians 2:6)

We are seated with Him in heavenly realms all because we are one with Christ. There is nothing that stands between you and God.

40. What did Paul conclude? (Romans 8:35-39)

Memory Verses: Colossians 2:11-12

Water Grave

- The Imperials

In my house there's been a mercy killing.
The man I used to be has been crucified.
And the death of this man
Was the final way of revealing,
In the spiritual way to live, I had to die.

Now if I let that dead man linger in me,
I might get a little idle in my way.
So, I'm going down to the celebration river,
And take this dead man down to a water grave.

I'm going down to the river.
And I'm going to be buried alive.
I want to show my Heavenly Father,
The man I use to be has finally died.

Now when I think of where I'm going,
In terms of where I've been,
It makes me glad to know, my Lord,
That I've been born again.

Yes, I'm going down to the river.
I'm going to be buried alive.
I want to show my Heavenly Father.
The man I use to be has finally died.

Worship, *Water Grave* <https://youtu.be/K82TQiHWD7w>

Worship with Chris Tomlin, *I Will Rise* <https://youtu.be/CKRF8UihM5s>

Worship with Alison Kraus, *Let's Go Down to the River to Pray,*
<https://youtu.be/zSif77IVQdY>

Worship with Love Song, *Water Baptism, The Jesus Movement 1970 Great Spiritual Awakening* <https://youtu.be/aW-2tbSiCWM>

Baptism of Jesus, The Bible MiniSeries <https://youtu.be/pKr0HfruNBk>

Water Baptism - *Moscow Spiritual Awakening 1990 right before the Collapse of Communism* <http://goo.gl/MZsRMW>

Study 4: What is the Baptism of the Holy Spirit?
Receiving Living Water & Power from on High

1. What instruction did Peter give to the Jewish people who were under conviction following his sermon at Pentecost? (Acts 2:37-38)

a. _____

b. _____

c. _____

The third vital truth in experiencing the fullness of Christ's salvation is receiving the gift of the Holy Spirit. After Jesus had risen from the dead, He found His eleven disciples and those who were with them gathered together, hiding for fear of the Jews. They had just learned the news that Jesus had been seen alive. Suddenly, Jesus appeared in the room and showed them His hands and His feet and His pierced side. He opened the Scripture and explained everything to them and He told them, "Thus it is written, that the Christ would suffer and rise again from the dead the third day, and that repentance for forgiveness of sins would be proclaimed in His name to all the nations, beginning from Jerusalem. You are witnesses of these things" (Luke 24:36-48).

Wait for the Power

2. What did Jesus tell His disciples to do before they went out into the world to preach repentance? (Luke 24:47-53)_____

The *New American Standard* says it this way: "And behold, I am sending forth the promise of My Father upon you; but you are to stay in the city until you are clothed with power from on high."

3. What type of proof had the disciples been given of Jesus' resurrection? (Acts 1:3; 1 Corinthians 15:3-8)_____

For the next forty days, Jesus appeared to His disciples and those who followed Him and explained to them about the kingdom of God. During this time, Jesus appeared to over five hundred people at the same time. Just before He ascended into heaven, Jesus called His disciples together and told them again not to leave Jerusalem, but to *wait for what the Father has promised.*

4. What was the "promise of the Father" they were to receive? (Acts 1:4-5)_____

_____

5. What did Jesus say would happen when the Holy Spirit came upon them? (Acts 1:8)

_____

Notice that the empowering of the Holy Spirit produces the ability to be a witness; that is, it gives us the ability to live the Christian life and imparts the power to preach the Gospel. The disciples had seen Jesus crucified, dead, and buried. They had walked and talked with the resurrected Christ. They had watched Jesus ascend into heaven and had talked to the angels who attended Him. Who wouldn't want to go and tell everyone the Good News?

Surprisingly, Jesus told them not to go and preach, but to wait. It was important for them to first be "baptized in the Holy Spirit and fire" so they would have "power to be a witness." If the Apostles and all the others who walked and talked with Jesus and had seen the risen Christ needed power to be a witness, how much more important it is for us today!

6. How did Jesus fulfill His ministry? (Acts 10:38) _____

_____

Paul explains that while the Old Covenant was glorious, it was exceeded in glory by the New Covenant, which is based on better promises than the Old (Hebrews 8:6). Looking at Jesus, John the Baptist proclaimed, "Behold the Lamb of God who *takes away the sin of the world*." Jesus came not only to forgive sin, He came to *take away* sin. He has *"put away sin* by the sacrifice of Himself "* (Hebrews 9:26).

7. But there was more that Jesus came to do. What did John the Baptist say about Jesus? (Matthew 3:11) _____

Living Water

Jesus continually talked about this Baptism of the Holy Spirit that He would give to all who would ask Him. The first person Jesus spoke to about the Holy Spirit of Promise was a Samaritan woman He met at a well. It is significant that Jesus gave this revelation to this woman. This woman represented the type of person the Pharisees believed was unqualified to receive anything directly from God. She was a woman and she was a Samaritan. Women were considered not worthy to learn. Samaritans were looked down on as a mixed breed who had distorted the worship of the true God. By revealing who He was to her, Jesus was demonstrating the new priesthood He had come to establish - the priesthood of the believer.

Anyone could come to know Him and speak to Him directly and receive a revelation without the need of some man acting as a priest. Through this one event Jesus laid the ax to the root of class warfare, gender discrimination, and male superiority. He laid the ax to the root of pride of place, position, and family. Paul would later explain that in Jesus "there is no longer Jew or Gentile, slave or free, male or female. For you are all Christians - you are one in Christ Jesus" (Galatians 3:28).

8. What did Jesus tell this woman that He could give her? (John 4:10, 13-14)_____

_____

9. What did Jesus say were two benefits of drinking the *living water* that He offered? (John 4:13-14)

a. _____

b. _____

At another time, Jesus was in Jerusalem for the Feast of Tabernacles. The Feast of Tabernacles was spectacular in its celebration of Israel's wandering through the wilderness, the end of their journey, and God's provision. The priests sacrificed seventy bullocks for the seventy nations that existed in the world at that time, signifying the day when the nations would be redeemed and worship the God of Israel (Isaiah 2:1-4).

The last day of the feast was the Day of the Great Hosannah. The crowds who had gathered sang the Psalms, shouted Hosanna, and waved palm branches. Suddenly, the trumpets began to blow as the designated priests entered through the Water Gate carrying large jars of water. As they walked up to the altar that was ladened with the burning sacrifice, they tipped over the jars of water and poured them out at the base of the altar. The water, which was mingled with wine, began to flow out of the temple into the Court of the Gentiles and down the steps of the temple. As the water poured out of the temple, it was a symbol of the outpouring of God's Spirit on all nations foretold by the prophets (Joel 2:28-29).

Just at this moment, Jesus stood up in the midst of the congregation and cried out.

10. What did Jesus cry out? (John 7:37-39)_____

_____

_____

11. How did Jesus say that we could receive the rivers of living water? (John 7:37; 4:10)

_____

12. What does John say that Jesus was talking about when He spoke about the living water that He would give? (John 7:39)_____

13. Why had the Holy Spirit not been given yet in human history? (John 7:39)

_____

This promise of the in-filling of the Spirit that quenches spiritual thirst and flows out as mighty rivers from the heart of the New Testament believer to bless the world has been made possible through the glorification of Jesus Christ. The Old Testament prophets foretold this event.

Ezekiel saw a vision of the outpouring of God's Spirit. He saw the temple in Jerusalem with a trickle of water flowing out of it. At first the water was ankle deep, then knee deep, then waist deep, and finally it became a river that could not be crossed - water enough to swim in.

14. Read Ezekiel's vision. Explain what happened wherever the waters from the temple flowed. (Ezekiel 47 answer from vs. 9-12)_____

_____

_____

_____

Notice that where the waters flowed out from the temple in Ezekiel's vision, there was a multitude of fish. The Jews in Jesus' day would have been familiar with this passage. The vision comes into focus in the light of Jesus' words and Paul's teaching on the temple of God.

15. What did Paul teach about the temple? (1 Corinthians 3:16)_____

_____

Fish in both the Old and New Testament symbolize _people._ One day after teaching on the beach, Jesus got into Peter's boat and told him to go out for a catch. Peter insisted that it was useless; they had already fished all night and caught nothing, but because the Master commanded it, Peter obeyed.

16. What happened when Peter cast out his net? (Luke 5:1-10)_____

_____

Power from on High

17. What did Jesus tell Peter? (Luke 5:10) _____

_____

Jesus equates _fish_ with _people_. When Jesus rose from the dead, He commissioned His disciples to go take the Good News to all nations. Jesus calls all of His followers, for all time, to be fishers of men. However, before He sent His disciples out to catch people (_fish_), Jesus told them to wait for the promised Holy Spirit, who would flow out from them in rivers of living water. It is the will of God that we not only fish for people but also catch them. If we try to go out in our own strength to serve the Lord and win people without having received the *power from on high,* we will find ourselves like Peter - fishing all night and catching nothing.

Jesus, the Second Adam, was fully man and fully God. Yet, Jesus needed to be anointed with the Holy Spirit and power to do the work He had come to do. The living water of the Holy Spirit flowing out from within is the power that will bring people into Christ's kingdom. When we receive this power from on High, we should expect to see people won to Jesus through our lives. This is the very thing that Jesus promised.

The imagery of *the river of the water of life* surfaces again in the book of Revelation.

18. Describe John's vision. (Revelation 22:1-3) _____

_____

_____

_____

_____

Notice that the river flows out from the *throne of God and of the Lamb.* As Jesus is enthroned in your life as King and Lord of all, God intends that from His throne in the sanctuary of your heart the Holy Spirit will flow out as rivers of life to reach those around you and ultimately reach the nations. Wherever men and women receive the Gospel, the curse is lifted from their lives and eventually the curse will be lifted from their nation. Healing, health, and blessing will follow.

The Manifest Presence of God

The Old Testament saints were familiar with the Holy Spirit's Presence. They believed that God was *Omnipresent* (everywhere Present).

19. What did David say about God's Presence? (Psalm 139:7-16)_____

_____

_____

20. What did Paul tell the idol worshipers of Athens about God? (Acts 17:22-28 answer from verses 27-28) _____

_____

_____

Paul, expressing the ancient view of the Scriptures, explained that God is present everywhere. However, God had promised Israel that as long as they kept His commandments and worshipped Him alone, He would dwell among them in a special way in His manifest Presence. God's manifest Presence hovered above the Mercy Seat in the Holy of Holies first in the tabernacle, and then in the temple.

The Old Testament saints prophesied by the Holy Spirit, did miracles by the Holy Spirit, and experienced the Spirit's Presence in their personal lives.

21. What did David say about his first hand knowledge of the Presence of God? (Psalm 16:11; 84:10)

a. _____

b. _____

_____

22. What was David's prayer? (Psalm 51:11) _____

_____

When Jesus was born, God pitched His *tent* of *human flesh* to tabernacle among men. Jesus was the Firstborn, the Father of the New Creation, the Second Adam, who came to bring forth many sons and daughters into His image.

23. Concerning the change He came to make in things, what did Jesus tell His disciples? (John 14:16-17) _____

_____

24. What spectacular promise did Jesus make about the home of the Holy Spirit? (John 14:17) _____

_____

In this passage, Jesus called the Holy Spirit the Helper, the Comforter, the Spirit of Truth. Israel knew and believed that God dwelt in their midst. Now Jesus declared a change in the order of things. "The Spirit of Truth," Jesus told them, "you know Him; He dwells with you, but He will be *in you*...and He will abide with you forever."

Under the Old Covenant, the center of worship was the temple in Jerusalem. Under the New Covenant, the center of worship is the heart of the individual believer whose body is now the temple of the Holy Spirit. Under the Old Covenant, God was so holy that the High Priest could only approach God's manifest Presence within the Holy of Holies in the temple once a year, and he had to bring blood. When the blood of Jesus is applied to our hearts through our faith in Him, His Holy Presence now makes His home in our heart. This is the very Spirit of Holiness that dwelt in the tabernacle and in the temple in Jerusalem. Jesus explained this to the woman He met at the well. She wanted to know the proper place to worship. Was it in Jerusalem or on the mountain in Samaria? Jesus explained to her about the change that was coming in true worship.

25. What was Jesus' answer to her question? (John 4:20-24)_____

The Holy Spirit is given so that He may help us worship in spirit and in truth.

26. To whom does Jesus promise the Holy Spirit? (John 14:15-16)_____

27. What are some of the many names of the Holy Spirit? Answer from the *Amplified* text: "I will ask the Father and He will give you another Comforter (Helper, Intercessor, Advocate, Strengthener, and Standby) that He may be with you forever - the Spirit of Truth." (John 14:15-16)
a._____
b._____
c._____
d._____
e._____
f._____

28. What are two other names for the Holy Spirit? (Matthew 10:20; Galatians 4:6)
a._____
b._____

The Leadership of the Holy Spirit

Jesus taught His disciples about the many blessings that would come as a result of the Baptism in the Holy Spirit.

29. As the Spirit of Truth, what will the Holy Spirit do for you? (John 16:13)
a._____
b._____

The Holy Spirit will lead you into all truth and will show you things to come. This means that the Holy Spirit will reveal to you things that are to come in your life and in doing this, He will guide you into God's will.

30. When the Holy Spirit was poured out on the day of Pentecost, what did Peter say would characterize the lives of those who received the Holy Spirit? (Acts 2:16-18)
a._____
b._____
c._____

31. What examples do we have of the Apostles being led by dreams, visions?
a. (Acts 9:10-12)_____
b. (Acts 9:12)_____

c. (Acts 10:9-20) _____

d. (Acts 16:9-10) _____

e. (Acts 18:5-12) _____

f. (Acts 26:12-19) _____

g. (Rev. 1:1-2,10-13,4:1-3) _____

32. What has God stored up for those who love Him, and how can these blessings be known? (1 Corinthians 2:9-11)

a. _____

b. _____

33. What did John teach about the Holy Spirit as the Teacher and Revealer of Truth, and what is His most important lesson? (1 John 2:27) Answer from the *New Living Translation*: "But you have received the Holy Spirit, and He lives within you, so you don't need anyone to teach you what is true. For the Spirit teaches you everything you need to know, and what He teaches is true - it is not a lie. So just as He has taught you, remain in fellowship with Christ."

a. _____

b. _____

_____

34. What does the Holy Spirit pour into our hearts? (Romans 5:5) _____

35. How does the Holy Spirit help us to become like Jesus? (2 Corinthians 3:18)

_____

_____

Although everyone can obey God's commandments of moral absolutes, according to the New Covenant, no matter how hard you try, by your own self-effort you cannot transform your heart and become more Christ-like. This can only be done by the transforming power of the Holy Spirit. As you look away from self and self-interest and behold God's glory, as revealed in Jesus Christ, you will be transformed supernaturally into the image of Jesus Christ by the power of the Holy Spirit from glory to glory. The love of God will be shed abroad in your heart by the Holy Spirit.

Memory Verses: John 4:10, 14

_____

_____

_____

Worship, Lindell Cooley - *Send the Fire* <http://goo.gl/y5smYA>

Worship with the Gaithers, *"There is a River"* <https://youtu.be/_Q8dYPNV4OQ>

Study 5: How to Receive the Baptism
In the Holy Spirit

1. What did Jesus say the Holy Spirit will give us power to do? (Acts 1:8) _____

_____

2. How did Jesus explain that the Holy Spirit will empower you to be a witness? (John 15:26-27, Matthew 10:18-20) _____

_____

_____

At such times as these, Jesus said that it will not even be you who is speaking, but the Spirit of our Father who will speak through you.

It is by the power of the Holy Spirit that you are to tell others about Jesus and what He has done for you. This is how the apostles and disciples spoke as they ministered in the church at its beginning. Five thousand people had accepted Jesus as their Messiah in a few short days. The high priests and rulers of the Jews were very worried that all the people were going to follow Jesus' apostles. Peter and John had just prayed for a lame man who was healed at the temple gate and Jerusalem was astir. They found Peter and John and demanded, "By what power or by what name have you done this?"

3. Peter was called before the religious leaders to testify. Who empowered Peter's response? (Acts 4:8) _____

4. What was Peter's response? (Acts 4:1-12)_____

_____

_____

5. What did the religious leaders see about Peter that astonished them? (Acts 4:13)

_____

They were amazed at Peter's boldness and knowledge, especially since they knew he had no formal training in religious matters. He hadn't been to their schools.

6. Later, what would Peter explain to the church about the preaching of the Gospel? (1 Peter 1:12) _____

Notice that although Peter and the rest of the disciples walked and talked with Jesus for three years and had been personally trained by Him, He did not point to this experience as the source of power to preach the Gospel. Peter pointed instead to the power of the Holy Spirit.

7. What pledge of allegiance and testimony of courage did Peter give to Jesus at the Last Supper? (Matthew 26:31-35) _____

_____

8. What did Peter actually do? (Matthew 26:56-75) _____

_____

The Baptism of the Holy Spirit changed Peter into a man of supernatural courage. He received power from on High to be a witness.

9. Paul also speaks of this empowering. What did he say about the Gospel, which he preached? (1 Corinthians 2:4)_____

_____

10. On what should your faith *not* rest? On what should your faith rest? (1 Corinthians 2:5)

a. _____

b. _____

11. Who anointed Jesus, and as a result, what was Jesus able to do as a man and why? (Acts 10:38)

a. _____

b. _____

c. _____

When Jesus began His ministry, He read from the scroll of the prophet Isaiah and proclaimed what He came to do.

12. What did Jesus say that He was anointed to do? (Luke 4:18-19)

a. _____

b. _____

c. _____

d. _____

e. _____

This is the same Spirit of Promise that the disciples were waiting to receive on the Day of Pentecost.

Clothed with Power from on High

13. Besides the eleven apostles, who else was waiting to receive the promise of the Holy Spirit? (Acts 1:13-15) _____

14. How many people were present who were waiting for the Promise of the Father? (Acts 1:15) _____

15. Although these people were staying in the upper room for lodging purposes, where were they continually meeting to praise the Lord? (Luke 24:52-53) _____

16. During this time, because of the Feast of Pentecost, who was present at Jerusalem and in the temple? (Acts 2:5) _____

17. What happened when the Holy Spirit was given? (Acts 2:1-4)

a. _____

b. _____

c. _____

The word *house* in Greek also means *temple*. When the Holy Spirit was poured out, the disciples were probably not hiding out in an upper room somewhere behind closed doors. More than likely, they were in the temple.

18. What happened when this sound occurred? (Acts 2:6)

_____

_____

Right in the midst of the temple, they were all filled with the Holy Spirit and began to speak with other tongues as the Spirit was giving them utterance. When this sound occurred, a great crowd of people who were also in the temple ran up to them to see what was happening.

19. How did Peter explain what was happening, and what was the result of his preaching? (Acts 2:14-21)

a. _____

b. _____

Tongues of Fire

20. What did the tongues of fire that rested upon the believers represent? (Matthew 3:11-12) _____

21. According to John the Baptist, what would Jesus do? (Matthew 3:11)

_____

_____

The baptism of the Holy Spirit is associated with fire. This fire of the Spirit is many-faceted. It first speaks of *boldness.*

22. When the Lord anoints someone to speak His Word in His name, what did He say His Word is like? (Jeremiah 23:29) _____

23. When God sends and anoints us to give His message, what will happen? (Jeremiah 23:32)_____

24. Although the prophet Jeremiah was not baptized in the Holy Spirit and fire, the fire of the Holy Spirit often came upon him. What did he say this experience was like?(Jeremiah 20:9)_____

The Purifying Work

The fire of the Holy Spirit also represents *the cleansing and purifying work* of the Spirit in the lives of believers.

When we are born again, we receive a brand new nature. "Old things are passed away and all things become new." We don't have two natures, an old one and a new one competing against each other. We have a new nature, like His glorious nature. Sin no longer dwells in us. However, we have a mind that has been shaped and molded by sin. We have old ways of thinking and habits of acting that do not glorify God and need to be transformed to become Christ-like.

25. How does John describe this transforming work? (Matthew 3:11-12) _____

_____

_____

26. The prophet Malachi speaks prophetically about these cleansing fires. Describe this refining and purifying work that is to be done by the Holy Spirit. (Malachi 3:1-3)

_____

_____

This is a process like that performed by of a refiner of precious metal. A refiner of silver heats the silver over a burning fire. As the silver becomes hot, all the dross and impurities rise to the top. He then skims them off. He continues heating and skimming off the dross until he can see his image reflected clearly in the silver. As trials and tests come your way, the Holy Spirit works in you and skims all the dross and impurities from your old way of thinking and acting so that the image of Jesus may be seen in you. As you trust in Jesus and His Word, your unrenewed mind is changed and fashioned into Jesus' way of thinking and acting.

27. In fact, what does Paul say the Spirit of the Lord has come to do? (2 Corinthians 3:18)_____

The Knowledge of His Will

Under the Old Covenant, the High Priest would go in before the Lord to seek God for answers for Israel. Inside the breastplate of the High Priest were two stones, *the Umin and Thummim*. Jewish rabbis explain that often these stones were used to gain answers from the Lord. One stone was the "yes" and the other the "no." When the High Priest came out of the Holy Place, he would take out the stones. The one with the answer would be lit up by a small flame of fire.

The flame of fire resting upon the disciples' heads also represents the fact that, through the power of the Holy Spirit, we have received the "yes" and the "no" of God. Through the power of the Holy Spirit, we can know what the will of God is.

28. What does the Bible say that we have? (1 Corinthians 2:12-16. Answer from v 16)

_____

The "yes" and the "no" of God has now been given to the believer so we can know God's will.

29. What did Jesus say about the ability of the believer to know His voice and follow Him? (John 10:2-5) _____

_____

How to Receive the Holy Spirit

30. How did the Gentiles receive the Holy Spirit? (Acts 10:44-45)

_____

31. How did they know the Gentiles had received the Holy Spirit? (Acts 10:45-46)

_____

When the Gentiles at the house of Cornelius began to speak with tongues, the Jews present realized that they had received the Holy Spirit. They realized that this was not just a Jewish thing; Jesus had opened up the Baptism of the Holy Spirit to the world.

32. How did the believers at Samaria receive the Holy Spirit? (Acts 8:17)

_____

33. How did the believers at Ephesus receive the Holy Spirit? (Acts 19:6)

_____

34. What happened when they received the Holy Spirit? (Acts 19:6)

_____

Everywhere the Word of God was preached, the Holy Spirit was given through the laying on of hands or the Holy Spirit fell upon those who heard the world as in the case of Cornelius. The people who received this heavenly gift spoke in tongues and prophesied.

35. What does the prophet Ezekiel say about the Holy Spirit when he is prophesying about the New Covenant? (Ezekiel 36:26-27)

_____

Receiving the Baptism of the Holy Spirit

This promise of the Holy Spirit is not just for the early church.

36. To whom is the promised gift of the Holy Spirit made available? (Acts 2:39)

_____

37. To whom will the Father give the Holy Spirit? (Luke 11:11-13, Answer from v 13)

_____

38. If we ask the Father for the Holy Spirit, do we have to fear receiving anything from the devil? (Luke 11:11-13)

_____

Receiving your Heavenly Prayer Language

39. What signs did Jesus say would follow those who believe? (Mark 16:17-18)

a._____

b._____

c._____

d._____

e._____

When you are baptized in the Holy Spirit, you will have the awesome privilege and opportunity of speaking in tongues. Remember the words of Jesus: "If you ask for a fish you are not going to receive a snake." You don't have to be afraid that you are going to receive something from the devil. The Father will give you what you ask for. The moment you are baptized in the Holy Spirit, you will do what the believers did on that Day of Pentecost and what the early believers did - you will have the opportunity to speak in tongues and glorify

God. From the moment you are filled with the Holy Spirit, you should expect to begin speaking in tongues.

We have learned that, biblically, the Holy Spirit is given in two ways. The Holy Spirit is given through "the laying on of hands" by those who have already received it. Second, the Holy Spirit can also fall upon you as it fell upon the 120 on the day of Pentecost and fell on the Gentiles in the house of Cornelius.

Surrennder your heart to the in-filling of the Holy Spirit, and when you do, a new heavenly language will flow out. At the beginning you may have just a few syllables, but as you continue in your worship, a wellspring of life will fill you, and from this well-spring your heavenly language (tongues of angels) will arise by the operation of the Holy Spirit. This heavenly prayer language will be yours to use for the rest of your life as your very own prayer language and will wonderfully enable you to communicate with God and pray for the exact need or action required in any situation.

40. As we pray in our heavenly prayer language, what is the Spirit of God doing through us? (Romans 8:26)

The Invitation

The Baptism in the Holy Spirit is the gateway into the life of the Spirit. In the last book and last chapter of the Bible, we are left with an invitation.

41. What is the invitation and who is giving the invitation? (Revelation 22:17)
a.
b.

Memory Verses: Acts 2:38-39

The First Great Awakening (1730-1760) sprung up in England, swept the early American colonies, and helped lay the Christian foundation of the American Republic. Charles Wesley, put the revelation that God was giving his brother John to music. Here is part of the hymn, *O for a Thousand Tongues to Sing*:

O For a Thousand Tongues to Sing

- Charles Wesley, 1739

O for a thousand tongues to sing
My great Redeemer's praise,
The glories of my God and King,
The triumphs of His grace!

My gracious Master and my God,
Assist me to proclaim,
To spread through all the earth abroad
The honors of Thy name.

Jesus! the name that charms our fears,
That bids our sorrows cease;
'Tis music in the sinner's ears,
'Tis life, and health, and peace.

He breaks the power of canceled sin,
He sets the prisoner free;
His blood can make the foulest clean,
His blood availed for me.

He speaks, and, listening to His voice,
New life the dead receive,
The mournful, broken hearts rejoice,
The humble poor believe.

Hear Him, ye deaf; His praise, ye dumb,
Your loosened tongues employ;
Ye blind, behold your Savior come,
And leap, ye lame, for joy.

Worship with David Crowder, *O for a Thousand Tongues to Sing*
<https://youtu.be/igvtsUfD5xM>

Worship with Darlene Sczech, *This Is the Air I Breathe* <http://goo.gl/RoG3tk_>

Worship with Paul Wilbur, *Burn in Me* < http://goo.gl/9rWniQ>

Watch Jesus call His Disciples and give them Spiritual Authority <http://goo.gl/quZkUm>

Worship, *Come Holy Spirit* <https://youtu.be/WPyqkFWqwTE>

Study 6: What are the Gifts of the Holy Spirit?

1. Who does Peter say that the Holy Spirit is? (Acts 2:38) _____

2. What does Paul say about the significance of the promised Holy Spirit who is given to us as believers? (Ephesians 1:13-14) _____

_____

The Holy Spirit is a pledge or an engagement ring of promise. It is given to us as a promise from God that He will redeem us completely - body, soul, and spirit. It is a promise of full redemption so that we might be a holy and perfect dwelling place for God in the Spirit, to the end that we might be transformed into the very image of Jesus. It is God's desire that we allow the Spirit of God to control our life so that His Presence floods our whole being, and we come to know the fullness of "resurrection life."

The Amplified Bible says it this way (Ephesians 1:14):

> That Spirit is the guarantee of our inheritance - the first fruit, the pledge and foretaste, the down payment of our inheritance and anticipation of its full redemption and our acquiring complete possession of it.

3. What is eternal life? (John 17:3) _____

4. What Spirit have we received? (Romans 8:15) _____

_____

5. To what does the Spirit within us bear witness? (Romans 8:16) _____

_____

6. Who are the sons of God? (Romans 8:14) _____

The Baptism in the Holy Spirit is the gateway into a life filled with fellowship and communion with the Father. It is the turning point from being enslaved to the spirit of this age and our fleshly desires to being energized by the power of God's Spirit. Through the Spirit's power, we may press on in God toward the fullness of resurrection life.

In our previous study, we found that besides bringing a revelation of Jesus, the Holy

Spirit was given to empower us for effective witness and service. Let's turn our thoughts toward the different gifts and graces that are resident in the gift of the Holy Spirit and that are available to us as believers.

7. What are a few of the glorious things that happened through the early church under the anointing of the Holy Spirit? (Acts 3:1-10; Acts 8:5-7; Acts 9:36-42)

a. _____

b. _____

c. _____

d. _____

8. How did Jesus Himself minister and preach to those in need? (Luke 4:18)

_____

9. How did Jesus cast out demons? (Matthew 12:28)_____

Preaching Confirmed by Signs

10. What signs did Jesus say would follow all those who believe? (Mark 16:17)

a. _____

b. _____

c. _____

d. _____

e. _____

11. What did the Lord confirm with these signs? (Mark 16:20)_____

12. What was the first manifestation of the Baptism in the Holy Spirit? (Acts 19:6)

_____

13. What was the second manifestation of the Baptism in the Holy Spirit? (Act 19:6)

_____

Understanding the Gift of Tongues

14. What does a believer do when he speaks in an unknown tongue? (1 Corinthians 14:2,4)

a._____

b._____

c._____

15. If a believer prays in an unknown tongue, what part of him is praying? (1 Corinthians 14:14) _____

16. If you pray in tongues, does your mind understand it? (1 Corinthians 14:14)

_____

When you pray in tongues, your mind does not know every word you are praying. However, often you can know what you are praying about. Suppose you want to pray for the salvation of your family. You may run out of your own words, but you can think about your family and begin to pray in tongues for them and the Spirit of God will intercede for them through you according to the will of God.

17. What benefit is praying in tongues or praying in the Spirit? (Romans 8:26-27; Jude 20)

a. _____

b. _____

This sign of tongues is given to all believers who are baptized in the Spirit. It is a personal prayer language between the believer and God.

18. What was Paul's attitude toward speaking with tongues? (1 Corinthians 14:5, 18)

_____

19. Even though the gift of tongues remains of great benefit to the individual believer and is essential in prayer, what gift is best for edifying the church? (1 Corinthians 14:4)

_____

The Gift of Prophecy

20. When prophecy is given, what happens to an unbeliever who may be present? (1 Corinthians 14:24-25)

a. _____

b. _____

c. _____

d. _____

e. _____

21. What is the spirit of prophecy? (Revelation 19:10)

_____

22. What are three other gifts that can be used to instruct the church? (1 Corinthians 14:6)

a. _____

b. _____

c. _____

23. What is equal to prophecy? (1 Corinthians 14:5)

_____

24. When we get together to worship God, what should we bring? (1 Corinthians 14:26)

a. _____

b. _____

c._____

d._____

25. Besides praying in the Spirit, what else can we do? (1 Corinthians 14:15)

_____   _____

The Gifts and Functions of the Holy Spirit

26. What are three distinct functions of the Holy Spirit in the church? (1 Corinthians 12:4-6)

a._____

b._____

c._____

27. What are nine basic gifts resident in the Holy Spirit that are available to us? (1 Corinthian 12:8-10)

1)_____   6)_____

2)_____   7)_____

3)_____   8)_____

4)_____   9)_____

5)_____

28. Beside each Scripture below, list the gifts that were operating by the Spirit in the lives of the believers in the book of Acts.

a. (Acts 3:1-10) _____

b. (Acts 5:1-6) _____

c. (Acts 9:33-35) _____

d. (Acts 16:16-18) _____

e. (Acts 21:10-11)_____

f. (Acts 2:4-11)_____

29. As a perfect man, Jesus operated under the anointing and power of the Spirit. When He gave an answer to the Pharisees concerning the woman caught in adultery, what gift was in operation? (John 8:3-11)_____

All nine gifts are resident within the Holy Spirit and are available to you as you have need of them. If a demon needs to be cast out, the gift of discerning of spirits is needed. If a person needs to be healed, the gift of healing is needed. The Holy Spirit manifests the different gifts as the need arises. These spiritual gifts generally operate in pairs or groups.

30. What are some of the varieties of ministries given to the church by the Holy Spirit? (Ephesians 4:11; 1 Corinthians 12:28)

a._____

b._____

c._____

d._____

e._____

f._____

g._____

h._____

i._____

j._____

These are a few of the ministries that are given to the church by the Holy Spirit. Not everyone is a prophet or an apostle. Not everyone has the ministry of tongues. The body of Christ would be useless if everyone was an eye or everyone was a mouth. Therefore, God has given each member in the body a separate ministry, function, and ability. Each is given a special anointing or office. The gifts, resident in the Holy Spirit, equip each person with the ability to function in the office that God has given to each believer.

31. What are some of the varieties of effects given to the church by the Holy Spirit? (Romans 12:7-8, 13)

a._____

b._____

c._____

d._____

e._____

f._____

g._____

These are but a few of the different effects that God establishes in His body. The body of Christ is like a many-faceted diamond with each member reflecting some aspect of the beauty and character of the Lord.

32. What are the nine fruits of the Holy Spirit? (Gal. 5:22-23)

1)_____   6)_____

2)_____   7)_____

3)_____   8)_____

4)_____   9)_____

5)_____

33. If we operate in spiritual gifts but don't have love, what does the Scripture tell us? (1 Corinthians 13: 1-2)_____

34. What should our attitude be toward spiritual gifts, and along with them what must we earnestly pursue? (1 Corinthians 12:31; 14:1)

_____

35. What are three ways that the Spirit of God will minister to believers in the last days? (Acts 2:17)

a._____

b._____

c._____

36. Why are the manifestations of the Spirit given? (1 Corinthians 12:7)

_____

37. What did Jesus say about those who had received the gift of the Holy Spirit? (John 4: 14; John 7:38-39) _____

Memory Verse: Ephesians 4:8

_____

_____

_____

Holy Spirit Truth Divine

- Samuel Longfellow - 1864

Holy Spirit, Truth divine,
Dawn upon this soul of mine;
Word of God and inward light
Wake my spirit, clear my sight.

Holy Spirit, Love divine,
Glow within this heart of mine;
Kindle every high desire;
Perish self in Thy pure fire.

Worship, *Spirit of the Living God* <http://goo.gl/kd7w6u>

Worship with Michael W. Smith *Holy, Holy Are You Lord God Almighty* <https://youtu.be/UWndDW_271g>

Worship, *Holy Spirit Thou Art Welcome in this Place* <https://youtu.be/LDaMVReR9gE>

Study 7: The Power in the New Covenant Supper
Holy Communion

Jesus gave very few ordinances to His disciples. But those He gave were faithfully observed by the early church. Among the ordinances practiced daily by the early church was the ordinance of Holy Communion or the Lord's Supper.

1. When the early church met from house to house, what did they do? (Acts 2:42, 46)

a. _____

b. _____

c. _____

d. _____

e. _____

The book of Acts tells us that one of the practices of the early church was "breaking bread from house to house." The *New Living Translation* says, "They met in homes for the Lord's Supper." Partaking of Holy Communion, or the Lord's Supper, was the centerpiece of New Covenant worship and fellowship and was central to the teaching of the Early Church Fathers.

Read Luke 22:14-20

2. From the New Testament record, what was the last religious feast that Jesus kept before He was crucified? (Luke 22:15)_____

3. When Jesus gave His disciples the bread, what did He declare? (Luke 22:19)

_____

4. When Jesus passed the cup of wine, what did He tell His disciples? (Luke 22:20)

_____

5. What did Jesus call this cup of wine that He passed around? (Luke 22:20)

_____

Jesus called the Passover cup, "The New Covenant." "This cup," He said, *"is the New Covenant."* Let's consider the significance and power of Jesus' statement, and what it might mean to us today. The only other time that Jesus talked about eating His body and drinking His blood was after He had fed the five thousand. The people who had partaken of the miracle of the multiplied bread sought Jesus the next day looking for more bread to eat.

6. What did Jesus say about Himself to the people who came to Him looking for more bread? (John 6:32-35) _____

Benefits of Holy Communion

7. What promise did Jesus give to all those who would come to Him and believe in Him? (John 6:35)

a. _____

b. _____

8. Jesus talked about Himself as *the Bread of Life,* telling His followers to eat His flesh and drink His blood and the benefits of doing so. These are the same benefits that we may receive today from partaking of the Lord's Supper. If we eat His flesh and drink His blood, what did Jesus say the benefits would be? (John 6: 54-57)

a. _____

b. _____

c. _____

d. _____

e. _____

Jesus pointed to eating His flesh and drinking His blood as a key to experiencing His abiding Presence and to knowing and consistently experiencing His life within.

9. What was the response of those who heard Jesus talk about eating His flesh and drinking His blood? (John 6:66) _____

10. The twelve disciples were bewildered at Jesus' sayings. What did Jesus ask them, and what was their response? (John 6:68-69)

a. _____

b. _____

Jesus' sayings remained a mystery until Jesus explained the meaning and instituted the practice of eating His flesh and drinking His blood at His last Passover Seder with His disciples.

To Abide in Him

11. At the Last Supper, why did Jesus tell His disciples to continue to celebrate and partake of His body and blood? (Luke 22:19) _____

_____

This command was given by our Lord just before He was lay down His life for our sakes. These are His dying words, and His expressed will to all His followers for all time. To neglect taking the Lord's Supper and treat this commandment lightly is to lightly esteem all that Jesus has done for us. As a result, we forfeit a great measure of God's blessings and promises.

If we trace the word "remember" back to its roots in the Greek, we find its root meaning is *to abide, dwell, be present.* (*Strong's Exhaustive Concordance of the Bible*, Greek Dictionary of the New Testament Entries # 364, 363, 3403, 3415, 3306). A rendering of this passage using the root meaning reads, "Do this as often as you will *to abide, to dwell, to be present* in Me. This meaning coincides with Jesus' teaching, "He who eats my flesh and drinks My blood *abides* in Me."

The Testimony of History

Martin Luther, the great Reformer of the 16th century, explained that the most important sacraments of the church that should never be done away with are water baptism and Holy Communion. Of Holy Communion, Luther explained that *the Presence of God* is communicated to the believers through the elements of the bread and the wine.

John Wesley, revivalist and founder of Methodism in the 18th century, encouraged everyone who desires to lead a new life following the commandments of Christ, all those who desire to receive God's promises, and those who are earnestly waiting for that salvation with a sincere heart, to take Holy Communion as often as possible. He writes that the practice of partaking of Holy Communion is *necessary for maintaining the Presence of God in your life* (from Sermon 101, *Sermons of John Wesley*, "The Duty of Constant Communion").

C. S. Lewis in *Mere Christianity* writes:

> There are three things that spread the Christ-life to us: baptism, belief, and that mysterious action which different people call by different names—Holy Communion, the Mass, the Lord's Supper...I cannot see why these things should be conductors of the new kind of life. We have to take reality as it comes. But though I cannot see why it should be so, I can tell you why I believe it is so. It seems plain as a matter of history that He taught His followers that the new life was communicated in this way. In other words, I believe it on His authority.

The Significance of the Veil

When the tabernacle and the early temple was in existence under the Old Covenant, the manifest Presence of God, the Shekinah, dwelt within the Holy of Holies, enshrined above the Mercy Seat which was on top of the Ark of the Covenant. A thick veil hung before the Holy of Holies. Into this holy place, no one was allowed to enter except the high priest, however the high priest could not enter the Holy of Holies any time he wanted. He could only enter once a year. When he entered into the Holiest of All, he had to wear special linen garments.

12. a. What did the high priest have to bring with him when he entered into the Holiest of Holies? (Hebrews 9:6-8) _____

During Old Covenant times, the veil that separated the Holy of Holies from the rest of the temple was embroidered with cherubim. The cherubim in Scripture are always seen guarding the Holy Presence of God.

b. When Adam and Eve fell in the garden, God placed cherubim with a flaming sword to guard something from the reach of fallen man. What were they guarding? (Genesis 3:24)_____

c. In David's description of the majesty and power of God, what did God ride on? (Psalms 18:6-15)_____

The cherubim are seen in Scripture as guarding God's Glory. The veil of the temple, which displayed the cherubim, reaches back in biblical symbol to the forbidden Tree of Life that fallen man was not allowed to eat. The veil was a continual testimony of man's ultimate separation from God and the fact that partaking of the very essence of God was forbidden because of sin.

13. What happened when Jesus was crucified on the cross? (Matthew 27:50-51)

_____

This veil once shut all of Israel out and prohibited the Israelites from gaining access into God's Holy Presence. The torn veil signifies that Jesus has opened up the way for all to enter into the very Presence of God. Under the New Covenant, that system has been done away with, and a new and living way into God's Holy Presence has been opened up.

14. Under the New Covenant, where is the temple of God today? (1 Corinthians 6:19-20)

_____

Although the body of the believer is now the very temple of the Living God, many Christians don't experience the deep reality of Christ's abiding Presence. Like Israel, they are busy in the Outer Court of noise. By law, no one could go any further in temple worship than the Outer Court. Now under the New Covenant Jesus "has made us a Kingdom of priests for God His Father" (Rev. 1:6). Jesus has cleansed us from our sins by His blood, and we are invited to come into His Holy Presence whenever we want to. However, very few people take the time to go in alone to commune with the Holy Presence that dwells within. Those who take time to seek Him are often disappointed in not always making the spiritual connection they had hoped for and sometimes become discouraged. Yet, God has made a way that we can experience His Presence every time we turn our hearts to spend time with Him.

You can't read the accounts of Old Covenant worship very long before you realize the importance that blood sacrifice had in the Israelites approach to the Holy Presence of God. Blood always had to be brought when men and women approached God. During the Feast of Tabernacles, one of the annual feasts of Israel, many animals were sacrificed as the nation of Israel came before God to worship. The first day, 13 bullocks were sacrificed along with two rams and 14 lambs. Each day following for seven days of the feast, one less bullock was sacrificed along with two rams and 14 lambs. The sacrifices were not just burned up, they were eaten. During that week, 194 animals were sacrificed as Israel approached God.

15. David found out very quickly the importance of blood and doing things God's way in dealing with God's Holy Presence. He wanted to bring the Ark of God up to Jerusalem so he put it on a new cart and had a team of oxen pull it. What happened? (2 Samuel 6:1-7)_____

David had organized a great worship service with 30,000 worshipers and instruments of every kind. As he brought up the Ark on the new cart, one of the priests was killed for touching it. The problem was that David did not follow the prescribed order that God had designated for transporting the Ark. Poles were to be placed through gold rings on the side of the ark, and the ark was to be carried on the shoulders of the priests.

16. What was the remedy? How many animals were sacrificed. (1 Chronicles 15:12-16, 26, 2 Samuel 6:13) _____

_____

Jesus has made the blood atonement once for all those who come to God through Him. However, the New Covenant is not without a prescribed order for entering into God's Presence. We all must come by the blood of Jesus. We can do this anywhere, any place, any time by faith in the shed blood of Jesus alone. However, there is a greater depth of fellowship and communion that Jesus invites us to experience. To experience His abiding Presence, Jesus tells us to eat His flesh and drink His blood. We have the great privilege of taking up the "cup of the New Covenant, in His blood" through the Lord's Supper. We can now eat from the Tree of Life because of the redemption through Christ's blood. The very essence of the New Covenant life is hidden in this.

17. Under the New Covenant, we are told to "enter boldly into the Holiest by the new and living way that Jesus has consecrated for us." How are we exhorted to do this? (Hebrews 10:19-20)

This passage is a clear reference to the Lord's Supper. Paul said that Jesus consecrated this way for us. To *consecrate* means *to dedicate for a sacred purpose.*

18. When did Jesus consecrate the new and living way? (1 Corinthians 11:23-25)

19. Paul was not present at the Last Supper since he had not yet believed in Jesus. Who taught Paul about the Lord's Supper? (1 Corinthians 11:23; Galatians 1:11-12)

We know from the Scriptures that Paul got his Gospel directly from Jesus, who personally appeared to him. The ordinance of partaking of the Lord's Supper was apparently very important to Jesus. As He related the Gospel message that Paul must preach to the Gentiles, Jesus specifically told Paul about the night He was betrayed and about the Last Supper which He instituted to be practiced by all of His followers in every age. Paul diligently taught the church to observe this celebration for all time.

Healing through the Lord's Supper

Jesus promised His disciples that if they would "eat His flesh and drink His blood," they would continually have "life," and if not, they would not have life within them (John 6: 53). From the pages of Scripture we learn that this "life" is both spiritual and physical. The Passover meal which Jesus and His disciples celebrated before Jesus' crucifixion commemorated Israel's deliverance from their slavery of Egypt. The bondage in Egypt symbolizes bondage to sin.

20. The night before their Exodus from Egypt, what were the Israelites commanded to do? (Exodus 12:5-8)
a.
b.
c.

This Old Covenant type and shadow was fulfilled in the New Covenant through the ordinance of Holy Communion.

21. What was the physical state of the Israelites when they left Egypt? (Psalm 105:37)

22. What did the Lord tell Israel after they crossed the Red Sea? (Exodus 15:26)

_____

_____

23. When Jesus died on the cross, what did He die for besides our sins, and what promise do we have? (Matthew 8:17, Isaiah 53:4-5, 1 Peter 2:24)

a. _____

b. _____

c. _____

d. _____

Every time we take Holy Communion, we have the privilege of partaking of all the blessings of forgiveness from sin, salvation, deliverance, and healing, as well as the peace, joy, and the Presence of God that are part of the Atonement.

The Covenant

24. Who is our High Priest under the New Covenant? (Hebrews 10:21)

_____

25. The book of Hebrews teaches us that Jesus is not a priest after the order of Aaron. What High Priestly order is Jesus from? (Hebrews 5:5-6)

_____

26. The Scriptures tell us that Melchizedek was a priest of God Most High. He met Abram (Abraham) and blessed him after he had defeated four kings. What did Melchizedek offer Abram that was a foreshadowing of Jesus and the New Covenant?
(Genesis 14:18) _____

27. Melchizedek recognized God's blessing on Abraham's life. He called God the Possessor of Heaven and Earth. What blessing did God give Abraham and his descendants? (Romans 4:13-16) _____

28. Who does God's promise to Abraham belong to today? (Galatians 3:29)

_____

The bread and the wine in both the Old and New Covenant is the Covenantal sign and declaration of God's Covenant with Abraham and those who belong to Christ. The earth belongs not to the wicked, but to the righteous, to those who are of Christ, who are Abraham's seed and heirs according to the promise. Every time we take the Lord's Supper we are proclaiming God's covenant with us to take charge of the earth and make disciples of all nations.

29. What do we proclaim when we partake of the Lord's Supper? (1 Corinthians 11:26)

_____

In the midst of universal idolatry, Jesus sent His disciples out to preach the Gospel. Daily, the early church broke bread from house to house, proclaiming the Lord's death and His redemption of the earth, salvation, and forgiveness of sin in His name. By taking the Lord's Supper, the early church was proclaiming that, by covenant, every nation belonged to Christ.

Every day they partook of His Holy Supper. Every day they prayed the prayer that Jesus taught them to pray: "Thy kingdom come, Thy will be done on earth as it is in heaven." Idolatry supported by ancient blood covenants with spiritual principalities and the pagan Roman Empire with its cult worship of Caesar as god eventually came crashing down and was swept into the ash bin of history. The Church of Jesus Christ arose on its ruins.

The redemption of the earth and the salvation of humanity is still going on today. As we partake of Jesus' body and blood, the same great power is released today as it was then. As we partake in faith, all the enemies of Christ will eventually be made His footstool, and His kingdom of righteousness, peace, and joy in the Holy Spirit will continue to be established on the ruins of all the false ideologies of man until it fills the entire earth.

30. What prophetic promise do we have of this from the prophet Daniel? (Daniel 2:44)

_____

_____

Priesthood of Every Believer

31. What has Jesus made us to be through His blood? (Revelation 1:5-6)

_____

32. Who is waiting for us within the veil, and what is He called? (Hebrews 6:19-20)
a. _____
b. _____

According to the New Covenant, Jesus has established the priesthood of every believer. As our High Priest and Elder Brother, Jesus waits within the veil and invites those who have been born of His Spirit and have become a New Creation to follow Him into that Holy Presence that is within - just beyond the rent veil. As a "Forerunner," He has gone in before us and beckons us to follow Him in and join Him there. This is the fourth dimension - the realm of the Spirit.

As a priest of God, you may partake of the Lord's Supper in the privacy of your own devotions as well as in a small or large gathering of believers. Every believer as a New Covenant priest may consecrate the elements of the bread and the wine (or grape-juice) as Christ's body and blood, and then partake of them in faith.

33. The privilege of experiencing the Presence of God, of abiding and dwelling in His Presence, is the great blessing of the New Covenant. What does Paul call the Communion cup? (1 Corinthians 10:16) _____

The Message Bible renders 1 Corinthians 10:16:

> I assume I'm addressing believers now who are mature. Draw your own conclusions: When we drink the cup of blessing, aren't we taking into ourselves the blood, the very life, of Christ? And isn't it the same with the loaf of bread we break and eat? Don't we take into ourselves the body, the very life, of Christ? Because there is one loaf, our many-ness becomes one-ness—Christ doesn't become fragmented in us. Rather, we become unified in Him. We don't reduce Christ to what we are; He raises us to what He is. That's basically what happened even in old Israel—those who ate the sacrifices offered on God's altar entered into God's action at the altar.

34. What does taking Communion together as a church do for the church members corporately and for each member personally? (1 Corinthians 10:16 answer from, *The Message Bible* quoted above).

a._____

b._____

35. The Communion cup is meant to be a blessing to every believer. However, what does Paul say happens when we drink the wine and eat the bread in an unworthy manner? (1 Corinthians 11:29-30)

a._____

b._____

c._____

36. What should be our attitude when we partake of the Lord's Supper? (1 Corinthians 11: 27, 31) _____

The believers at Corinth had turned the Lord's Supper into a drunken and glutinous party, which was similar to the way they worshiped idols. Paul asks, "Don't you have homes to eat and drink in?" (1 Corinthians 11:20-21). Paul wants them to partake of the Lord's Supper, but he wants them to do it with a repentant heart, reverently, and in the fear of God.

So we see that it is important to ask the Holy Spirit to search our heart, ask for forgiveness for any sin, and make a full surrender of self to the Lord. If we will do this and judge ourselves, we will not be judged, our sins will be forgiven, and we will be blessed.

John Wesley explained about the New Covenant meal, "This is the food of our souls. If we desire the pardon of our sins, if we wish for strength to believe, to love and obey God, then we should not neglect any opportunity of receiving the Lord's Supper."

Receiving a Revelation of Jesus

After the crucifixion of Jesus, two of His disciples left Jerusalem and were walking on the road to Emmaus, which was a village seven miles from Jerusalem. Suddenly, Jesus walked up along side them, but they didn't know it was Jesus. He asked them why they were sad. They told Him about the crucifixion of Jesus, of how they had believed He was the Messiah, and how all their hopes had been dashed. When Jesus began explaining the Scriptures to them and the meaning of what had just happened, they invited Him to come to their home and stay with them, still thinking that He was a stranger.

37. What happened? (Luke 24:13-35 answer from v 31, 35) _____

_____

Jesus was recognized in the breaking of the bread. If you want a greater revelation of Jesus, take the Lord's Supper daily or as often as you can and ask the Holy Spirit to give you a revelation of Jesus.

Down through the ages in Christian liturgy, the Lord's table has been called the *Marriage Supper of the Lamb*. It is the Supper that leads us to a deep union and intimacy with our Lord and Savior, Jesus Christ.

38. What words of invitation do we have from Jesus? (Revelation 3:20, 19:9; Revelation 22:14-17)

a. _____

_____

b. _____

_____

c. _____

_____

Memory Verse: John 6:56

_____

_____

_____

And Can It Be

- Charles Wesley, 1738

Long my imprisoned spirit lay,
Fast bound in sin and nature's night;
Thine eye diffused a quickening ray—
I woke, the dungeon flamed with light;
My chains fell off, my heart was free,
I rose, went forth, and followed Thee.

No condemnation now I dread;
Jesus, and all in Him, is mine;
Alive in Him, my living Head,
And clothed in righteousness divine,
Bold I approach the eternal throne,
And claim the crown, through Christ my own.

Worship with Enfield Hymn Sessions- *And Can It Be* <http://goo.gl/3I6WL2>

Watch the *Last Supper* from the *Passion of the Christ* <http://goo.gl/2MqRf6>

Watch the *Last Supper* from The *Visual Bible* <http://goo.gl/LVVlDc>

Worship with Travis Cottrel, *In Christ Alone* <http://goo.gl/g8QixM>

Worship with Stuart Townend. *Behold the Lamb Communion Hymn*
<http://goo.gl/RKf924>

Worship with this great hymn of the church, *Jesus Paid it All with* Kristian Stanfill
<http://goo.gl/rH1Nlj>

Worship with Sandy Patti, *Holy Ground* <http://alturl.com/8tvpz>

Study 8: How to Develop Deep and Abiding Fellowship with Jesus

> I serve a risen Savior, He's in the world today;
> I know that He is living, whatever men may say;
> I see His hand of mercy, I hear His voice of cheer;
> And just the time I need Him, He's always near.
>
> He lives, He lives, Christ Jesus lives today!
> He walks with me and talks with me along life's narrow way.
> He lives, He lives, salvation to impart!
> You ask me how I know He lives? He lives within my heart.
>
> from *He Lives*
>
> *- Alfred H. Ackley, 1887-1960*

When Jesus walked the earth with His twelve disciples, the thought that He was leaving to go back to the Father was unbearable to them. Having become so accustomed to walking in unbroken fellowship with the Living God, it was among their deepest sorrows to contemplate going back to life like it used to be before they knew Him.

1. What did Jesus tell His disciples when He was leaving them to go back to the Father? (John 16: 7-8) _____

_____

2. What did Jesus promise His disciples in order to comfort them after His departure? (John 14:16-20) _____

_____

_____

_____

_____

Through the power and presence of the Holy Spirit in their lives, Jesus explained to His disciples that it was better for Him to go away. They only knew Jesus face to face, friend to friend. When the Holy Spirit came, they would experience Christ's Presence in their hearts in an intimate way. After Pentecost, Jesus' very Presence would live within their hearts! It is to this intimate fellowship with Christ Jesus that His disciples in every age are called.

3. For what three reasons did Jesus choose His disciples? (Mark 3:14)

a.

b.

c.

To Know Jesus is Eternal Life

4. As Christians and partakers of the New Covenant, we have been called to inherit eternal life. What did Jesus say eternal life was all about? (John 17:3)

5. The Apostle Paul understood this. What did he proclaim in his letter to the Philippians? (3:8-11)

6. In one of Paul's great apostolic prayers, what did he request for the church? (Ephesians 1:15-23)

a.

b.

c.

d.

e.

If your heart's desire is to know God and to experience the depths of Jesus Christ, pray Ephesians 1:15-23 daily. Marvelous benefits will follow.

In the latter part of the seventeenth century, Jeanne Guyon wrote in *Experiencing the Depths of Jesus Christ*:

> If a new convert were introduced to real prayer and to a true inward experience of Christ as soon as he became converted, you would see countless numbers of converts go on to become true disciples.... The new Christian should be led to God. How? By learning to turn within to Jesus Christ and by giving the Lord his whole heart.
>
> If you are one of those in charge of new believers, lead them to a real inner knowledge of Jesus Christ. Oh, what a difference there would be in the lives of those new Christians! Consider the results! We would see the simple farmer, as he plowed his field, spend his days in the blessing of the Presence of God. The shepherd, while watching his flocks, would have the same

abandoned love for the Lord which marked the early Christians. The factory worker, while laboring with his outward man, would be renewed with strength in his inner man. You would see each of these people put away every kind of sin from his life; all would become spiritual men and women with hearts set on knowing and experiencing Jesus Christ.

For a new Christian - for all of us in fact - the heart is all important if we are to go forward in Christ. Once the heart has been gained by God, everything else will eventually take care of itself. This is why He requires the heart above all else.

Dear reader, it is by the Lord gaining your heart, and no other way, that all your sins can be put away. If the heart could be gained, Jesus Christ would reign in peace, and the whole church would be renewed. In fact, we are discussing the very thing that caused the early church to lose their life and beauty. It was the loss of a deep, inner, spiritual relationship to Christ. Conversely, the church could soon be restored if this inner relationship were recovered!

The simplest can know Him, and in the deepest way, with no help from rituals or forms or theological instruction! When it pleases Him, He turns factory workers into Prophets! No, He has not turned man away from the inner temple of prayer. The reverse! He has thrown wide open those gates so that all may come in!" (Mme. Guyon, *Experiencing the Depths of Jesus Christ,* Auburn, ME: Seed Sowers, 1975, pp. 117-124.)

The greatest doctrine of the Bible is that God can be known in personal experience.

7. How did John explain the Gospel that he and the other disciples preached? (1 John 1:1-3)

---

8. What did John see as the purpose for preaching the Gospel? (1 John 1:3)

John preached from a continual fellowship with Jesus. He wanted others to share this same fellowship.

Andrew Murray wrote in 1898:

The great lack of our religion is - we need more of God. We accept salvation as His gift, and we do not know that the only object of salvation, its chief blessing, is to fit us for, and bring us back to, that close intercourse with God for which we were created, and in which our glory in eternity will be found. That only is a true and good religious life, which brings us every day nearer to this God, which makes us give up everything to have more of Him. (Andrew Murray, *The Two Covenants,* Fort Washington, PA: Christian Literature Crusade, 1974, pp. 8-9)

Seeking to Know Him with Your Whole Heart

9. What promise did God give Israel through Jeremiah the prophet? (Jeremiah 29:13)

A.W. Tozer explains, "A spiritual kingdom lies all about us, enclosing us, embracing us, altogether within the reach of our inner selves, waiting for us to recognize it. God Himself is here waiting on our response to His Presence. This eternal world will come alive to us the moment we begin to reckon upon its reality." (A.W. Tozer, *The Pursuit of God*, Camp Hill, PA: Christian Pub., Inc., 1982, p. 52.)

10. How did the psalmist describe his pursuit of God? (Psalm 42:1-2)

11. Read Psalm 84. In this psalmist's pursuit of God, how does he compare the blessing of knowing God to seeking other things? (Psalm 84: 10)

A.W. Tozer continues:

The moment the Spirit has quickened us to life in regeneration, our whole being senses its kinship to God and leaps up in joyous recognition. That is the heavenly birth without which we cannot see the kingdom of God. A birth is not an end, but a beginning. Now begins the glorious pursuit, the heart's happy exploration of the infinite riches of the Godhead.

To have found God and still to pursue Him is the soul's paradox of love, justified in happy experience by the children of the burning heart. Come near to the holy men and women of the past and you will soon feel the heat of their desire after God. *(The Pursuit of God*, pp. 14-15)

12. Jesus' life was marked by His desire to seek the Father. What was Jesus in the habit of doing? (Matthew 14:23; Mark 1:35; Luke 6:12; Luke 9:28)

Jesus was always withdrawing from the multitudes to a lonely place to be alone with His Father. Sometimes He would rise up before sunrise and go out to pray. Other times He would stay up and pray late into the night. It was always in lonely places and in lonely hours while others slept that He found His closest fellowship with His Father. Jesus' relationship to His Father was one of the greatest examples He left for us to follow.

13. What did Jesus say was the directive behind everything He did and said? (John 5:19:-20, 30; 8:26, 28-29)

As Jesus waited in the Father's Presence for Divine direction and enabling, so must we. The blessings of the New Covenant cannot be experienced apart from a personal ongoing relationship with the Living God. We cannot live and walk in the power of the new life unless we are guided by the Holy Spirit every day and hour. This kind of guidance cannot be known apart from spending time in the Father's Presence, acquainting ourselves with His voice, His will, and His nature.

Worship in Spirit and in Truth

14. When Jesus spoke to the woman at the well, what did He explain to her about true worship? (John 4:19-24)_____

The early church was not caught up in external forms and programs, but in the Presence of Christ. They understood that true Christianity was a worship of the heart. They came together to enjoy the Presence of their Risen Lord, to worship Him, to adore Him, to hear inspired messages from Him. Jesus Himself had prom
ised them, "Wherever two or more are gathered together in My name there am I in the midst of them." (Matthew 18:20)

Throughout church history, the church program has often been substituted for experiencing the Presence of God. The most popular church is many times the one that can present the best program that interests the public. Christians make the mistake of accepting the substitution of the program for the Presence. They also make a mistake when they count on attending that program for their spiritual growth and omit spending time with the Lord in their daily lives. The result will be the deadening of their spiritual life.

15. Isaiah began his ministry during the reign of King Uzziah. What indictment did God have against Israel? (Isaiah 1:1-3) _____

The *Amplified Version* of the Bible says it this way: "Israel does not know or recognize Me."
16. Why had Israel become corrupt and wicked? (Isaiah 1:4)

    a. _____
    b. _____
    c. _____

17. Although Isaiah had been prophesying during the reign of King Uzziah, in the year King Uzziah died, Isaiah had a revelation of God. What five things happened when Isaiah had this encounter with God? (Isaiah 6:5-8)

a. _____

b. _____

c. _____

d. _____

e. _____

Even though Isaiah prophesied in the name of the Lord, sin was present in his life, as well as in Israel, because a deep knowledge of God was lacking.

Beholding His Glory

18. What will happen to us as we spend time beholding Him? (2 Corinthians 3:18)

_____

The *Phillips Translation* records: "We are transfigured in ever-increasing splendor into His own image, and the transformation comes from the Lord Who is the Spirit."

19. Who did Jesus say were the ones who truly love Him? (John 14:21)

_____

20. What were Jesus' commandments? (Matt. 22:37-40; John 13:34-35; 15:12,17)

_____

_____

_____

21. What will Jesus do for the one who has His commandments and keeps them? (John 14:21_____

_____

Other translations say, "I will manifest Myself to him, reveal Myself and make Myself real to him, disclose Myself to him." Disclose means "to open up, to bring to light, to lay open, to view, to reveal by word, to tell, to disclose the secret thought of the heart." Jesus promised to those who really love Him to reveal the secret counsels of God's heart. He promised that He would show them His power and His glory and would reveal Himself to them. Of the twelve disciples that followed Jesus, there were three, Peter, James and John, who were His closest friends. Because of this deep friendship, Jesus took Peter, James, and John up to a high mountain to show them His glory.

22. What did they see and hear? (Matthew 17:1-5) _____

_____

We know that these three disciples loved Jesus because He disclosed Himself to them. Were Peter, James, and John more special to Jesus than his other disciples? Did Jesus love them more? No. Then why did Jesus single them out? Because these three men were always walking as closely to Jesus as they could possibly get. They followed Jesus everywhere. Jesus revealed Himself to them because they showed by their actions that they loved Him more.

Revealing His Heart

23. On the evening before His crucifixion, Jesus took His disciples to the Garden of Gethsemane to pray with Him. What did He do? (Mark 14:32-33)

24. What did Jesus tell them? (Mark 14:33-34)

To these men, His closest friends, Jesus began to show His grief and distress. Jesus wanted only those who loved Him deeply to be near Him in His greatest sorrow. After Jesus' arrest in the garden, most of His disciples ran away and hid because they were afraid for their lives. Only John followed Jesus to the cross. In such a time of crisis only those who loved Jesus the most stayed by Him.

Of the twelve disciples who followed Jesus, it was John who showed that He loved Jesus most of all. John, along with Mary the mother of Jesus, His mother's sister, and Mary Magdalene were the only people who dared to stand at the foot of the cross. To so identify with a crucified man could mean certain death.

25. What did Jesus say was the greatest demonstration of love? (John 15: 13)

John and the three Marys showed the greater love for their Master. They did not care about their own lives. They loved Jesus intensely and did not want to abandon Him at the hour of His suffering. The rest of the disciples, however, showed by their actions that they cared more about themselves than they did about Jesus. At the crucifixion, the others stood at a distance with the crowds, because they feared that they too might be arrested.

Jesus was greatly moved by the affection and devotion of these four people. When Jesus saw His mother and John, the disciple whom He loved, standing nearby, He said to His mother, "Woman, behold your son!" Then He said to John, "Behold, your mother!" From that hour John took her into his own house. It is only to one who is deeply loved and trusted that a man will commit his most treasured possession.

The Disciple Whom Jesus Loved

When John wrote his account about the life of Jesus, of all those who wrote the gospels, he revealed the deepest understanding of who Jesus really was. It is John's gospel that reveals Jesus' Deity, as God in human flesh. In his gospel, John always speaks of himself as being the disciple whom Jesus loved. John was confident of Jesus' love for him. Of the remaining disciples who had personally walked with Jesus, John was the only one who did not die a martyr's death. When John stood at the foot of the cross, he had already shown that he was ready to lay down his life for the sake of Christ.

It was also to John that Jesus entrusted the book of Revelation. It was to John that Jesus revealed the secret counsels of His heart. In the book of the Revelation, the capstone of Bible prophecy, Jesus revealed to John the history of the church, the glorious triumph of good over evil, and the final victory and glory of Christ's coming kingdom. He instructed John to tell this to all the churches.

26. What will God do for those who fear Him? (Psalm 25:14) _____

_____

Mary Magdalene, one of the women who had stood by Jesus at the foot of the cross, went to Jesus' tomb early on the first day of the week. When she arrived at the tomb, she found that the stone had been rolled away and that Jesus' body was gone. She ran to get Peter and John. When the men came to the tomb and saw that the body of Jesus was gone, they returned to their own home.

27. What did Mary do? (John 20:10-13) _____

28. What happened? (John 20:14-18)_____

_____

Mary Magdalene was the first person Jesus revealed Himself to after the resurrection. Mary alone had remained at His tomb, deeply grieved, seeking to find His body. As a result of Mary's love for Him, Jesus chose her as the first to behold His glory. Jesus was irresistibly moved by the strength of her love for Him. Mary was Jesus' first messenger. He first sent Mary with the word to His disciples of His victory over death. Most of the disciples were in hiding because they feared for their lives. When Mary brought word to the disciples that Jesus was risen from the dead, the only disciples who ran to the tomb to see if this was true were John and Peter. John writes about himself that when he saw that the body was gone, he believed. This tells us that John received a revelation of who Jesus was. Both men returned home.

Peter, James, John, and Mary were all lovers of God. It was not that God loved them more than the others or had favorites upon whom He bestowed special blessings. But the reason that Jesus came close to them and revealed Himself to them in ways which He had not done for others was because they loved Him more than other people did. Such has been the testimony of numerous saints in all ages. The choice to love Jesus more and seek Him more belongs to each one of us. We are the only ones who can limit the depth of our relationship with Him.

Memory Verse: John 14:21

I Come to The Garden Alone

- C. Austin Miles, 1912

-

I come to the garden alone,
While the dew is still on the roses,
And the voice I hear falling on my ear,
The Son of God discloses.
And He walks with me and He talks with me,
And He tells me I am His own,
And the joy we share as we tarry there,
None other has ever known.

Worship with Eden's Edge, *Be Thou My Vision,* <http://goo.gl/LIAtIq>

Worship with Selah, *O the Deep, Deep Love of Jesus* <http://goo.gl/g2DNss>

Worship with Michael W. Smith, *Draw Me Close to You* <http://goo.gl/2J1JYr>

Worship with Selah, *Turn Your Eyes on Jesus* <http://goo.gl/o4m8bm>

Worship with Selah, *Wonderful, Merciful Savior* <http://goo.gl/uUY7SK>

Worship with JoAnn McFatter, *Saphire Sea,* <http://goo.gl/kGQ98h>

Worship with Julie True, *Heaven's Embrace* <http://goo.gl/kGQ98h>

Study 9: The Power and Authority of God's Word

The Bible is the greatest storehouse of Truth in the world. It is the record of God's interaction with man since the beginning of time. The Bible is a copy of historical records and original biographies which are thousands of years old that tell of men and women who walked and talked with God. If you want to know about God's existence, about His plan for you, and about how you can know Him, no greater source can be found than the Bible.

How does the Bible compare as an accurate historical record in Western Literature? Consider this list of the number of the oldest manuscripts in existence today.

Manuscript	Number	Oldest Manuscript in Existence
Dialogues of Plato	7	1200 Years after the Death of Plato
Homer's Iliad	643	500 Years after the Death of Homer
Julius Caesar's Gallic Wars	10	1000 Years after the Death of Caesar
Pliny's History	7	750 Years after the Death of Pliny

Have you ever heard anyone question the credibility of Pliny or Julius Caesar or Plato?

New Testament	24,000	25 Years after the Death and Resurrection of Jesus.

The New Testament was written by eyewitnesses who listened to Jesus' teachings for over three years and saw Him after He rose from the dead.

Of these 24,000 Manuscripts:

    5,000 Copies are in Greek

  10,000 Copies are in Latin

   9,000 Copies are in Ethiopian, Slavic, Armenian, Aramaic, and various languages.

Their accuracy? When you compare these manuscripts of the New Testament, they all say the same thing. The manuscripts of the New Testament are the most accurate, authentic manuscripts in the possession of mankind today. All of Western Civilization that has been good and helpful to the human race was built from the Light and Truth of the Bible. The

United States was founded by Christians who made the Bible the cornerstone of our Republic and believed that all men should be guided by the light of its Truth. Our Founders modeled their free form of self-government after Moses' representative government in the wilderness. In early America, the Bible was the main textbook in our schools. The Founders held the view that the Bible was crucial in maintaining individual freedom, good government, and our free Republic.

There is something in the Bible that is so powerful that it has been banned by those who have threatened the rights of men down through the centuries. It is historical fact that wherever governments, tyrants, dictators, or false religious leaders are determined to keep people in bondage and force them to believe what the state wants them to believe, there is a war against the Bible. There is obviously something in the Bible they don't want people to know.

What Do They Hate about the Bible?

Have you ever wondered exactly what there is in the Bible that makes oppressors of men so afraid? Let's consider the recent example of communist nations who based their national life on the political theory of Karl Marx coupled with the Darwinian theory of evolution. Marx and Darwin were both atheists who rejected the idea of God as Creator and Law Giver and exalted the theory of man as God. Marx's theory wreaked havoc in the 20th century. Historically, every Marxist government has made it a crime for people to own a Bible. It was so in the former Soviet Union and in China. Why? Because everything about Marx's political theory is opposed to God's Truth as it is revealed in the Bible.

By the 1970s, almost one-third of the world had fallen to Marxist communism. Western civilization did not escape the icy fingers of Marx and Darwin that reached out from the grave to rule the minds of men. In the early part of the 20th century, the United States had its own group of men and women who were enamored with Marxism and devoted to Darwinism who called themselves Progressives. Headed by John Dewey, these educators and politicians wanted to change the direction of our nation from a Christian Republic and make it a secular, socialist state. To accomplish this, they decided to use the public schools. Dewey and his friends presented a document called the *Humanist Manifesto,* in which they stated that one of their goals to improve the education of children was to remove the Bible and the Christian religion from the public classroom so that children could become more enlightened and progressive.

Dewey had such an influence that he became known as the Father of American Education. It is important to understand this because this philosophy succeeded in shaping our public schools and universities and changing our national life. For this reason, many Christians hold Marxist ideas that are in direct opposition to the truth of the Bible, and they don't even know it. In fact, Christians often view the Bible through the dark glasses of Marxist theory.

Let's separate the precious from the vile and make a comparison between what Karl Marx taught that is still being propagated today and what the Bible teaches. Marxist theory teaches that the end justifies the means. The Bible says, *No!* God gives us a standard of right and wrong. Wrong can never produce right. If the root is bad, so is the fruit. Marxist theory teaches the redistribution of wealth - take from those who have and give it to those who have not. The Bible says, *No!* People have a right to private ownership of property which is as sacred as the laws of God. People have a right to keep the fruit of their labor. The eighth and tenth Commandments are: "Do not steal. Do not covet what belongs to your neighbor." It is *your work* that should be rewarded. The Bible teaches that laziness will result in poverty.

The Bible teaches us to care about people. God wants us to prosper and tells us to help others in need out of our surplus. The Bible teaches this is to be a freewill offering, not something taken by force or coercion. Marxism teaches the opposite and raises its citizens to be wards of the state who are to depend upon the state to meet all their needs. The Bible says, *No!* You are to look to God as your Savior and Provider. The Bible tells us not to trust in man or look to man to meet our needs, but to "seek the kingdom of God first and His righteousness and everything we need will be given to us."

Marxism teaches that rights and privileges are granted and regulated by the state. The Bible says, *No!* The rights of life and liberty are given by God. He is the Author of all Liberty, and He has come to proclaim Liberty to all the earth's captives. The Bible says that you are God's free man and woman and that you are to "Stand up in the liberty with which Christ has made you free and don't be entangled in the yoke of bondage." Marxist socialism teaches people to wait for direction and guidance from the state - do not act without being told or without consulting an expert. The Bible says, *No!* When you lack wisdom, ask God and He will give you the wisdom you need.

Marxism teaches that the group action is more important than the individual effort - wait for the group to act, make sure everything you do is in agreement with the group. The Bible says, *No!* The believer is to act immediately in obedience to the Voice of God's Spirit within, even if it means standing alone. The Bible teaches that when it comes to the time of choosing, "We must obey God and not man." Individual salvation is what counts. The Bible says that it is the *individual* in fellowship with God who can change the world. God calls the *individual* to be His disciple and gives each person his or her special mission. The *individual* has a personal responsibility for himself and his or her actions. *Individuals* are required by God to not be lazy, but to be good stewards of everything God has given them, and to multiply their gifts and talents by putting them to good use.

Marxism teaches that there is no God - the state or the individual is God. The Bible says, *No!* There is One God to Whom all people owe allegiance and to Whom each person must answer. Marxism teaches that history is moving people to a socialist state where everyone is equal in property and wealth, where there is no distinction, and everyone is entitled to the same wages, privileges, and recognition, regardless of whether they are diligent and industrious, or thoughtless and lazy. The Bible says, *No!* The Bible makes a distinction in reward between a life poorly spent and a life well-lived, not only in this world but in the world to come. The Bible teaches that there is a distinction between those who are faithful and those who are unfaithful. The Bible teaches that the curse of poverty is in the earth and gives us the remedy of how to escape it - let each person turn to God and receive His blessing. He is the one who "opens His hand and satisfies the desire of every living creature." Each person will live a blessed or cursed life on this earth depending on whether that person obeys God's commands and loves God or not.

The Bible also teaches that in the world to come all things will not be equal. Each person who has received Jesus as their Savior will be rewarded for their work, their good deeds, their obedience to God's commands, and their faithful service to Christ. Each person will reap what they have sown. Those who have loved Jesus and have followed Him will enter into the joys of heaven and life everlasting. Jesus warned in a visitation to John, His apostle, on the Isle of Patmos: "Cowards who turn away from Me, and unbelievers, and the corrupt, and murderers, and the immoral, and those who practice witchcraft, and idol worshipers, and all liars - their doom is in the lake that burns with fire and sulfur. This is the second death." (Revelation 21:8) Marx teaches that communism is the great pinnacle toward which all history is moving. The Bible says, *No!* All of history is moving toward the day when "the kingdoms of this world will become the kingdoms of our God and of His Christ and He shall reign forever."

The War against the Bible

The 20th and 21st century aren't the first centuries to oppose the Bible. Down through history, there has been a war against the Bible. Christians have been imprisoned, burned at the stake, beheaded, and persecuted for daring to publish the Bible or preach from its pages. During the Protestant Reformation in the 16th century, Europe burst into flames over efforts to translate the Bible from the archaic language of Latin into the language of the people. More Christians were executed over attempting to publish and preach the Bible than those who were thrown to the lions by Caesar and his cohorts in the church's infancy. It is estimated that 50 million people died during the Protestant Reformation for seeking to worship God according to the dictates of their heart and conscience. (David Plaisted, *Estimates of the Number Killed by the Papacy,* <www.cs.unc.edu/~plaisted/estimates.doc>)

Why the resistance to the Bible? The Bible was scarce and few of the church leaders had ever read it, consequently Europe was controlled by the Roman Catholic Church that in those days taught the traditions of man for the commandments of God. Many of these traditions were contradicted by the Bible. Those who taught biblical truth that was contrary to tradition were persecuted, hunted down, imprisoned, and killed like common criminals. In the 1500s, the printing press was invented, and in spite of this great persecution, the first large book printed was the Bible. Most people of that era could not read or write, but when the Bible was made available to the masses, people all over Europe put forth every effort to learn to read, so they could read God's Holy Word for themselves. When they read the Bible, they realized that many things they believed about God were incorrect.

In the midst of this persecution over preaching, publishing, and reading the Bible, Martin Luther, 16th century reformer and Father of the Protestant Reformation, doctor of Theology, penned:

> The Bible is the proper book for men. There the Truth is distinguished from error far more clearly than anywhere else, and one finds something new in it every day. For twenty-eight years, since I became a doctor, I have now constantly read and preached the Bible; and yet I have not exhausted it. There I began to understand that the righteousness of God by which the righteous live is a gift of God, and is received namely by faith...There I felt that I was altogether born again and had entered the gates of paradise itself through open gates. There a totally other face of the entire Scripture showed itself to me...the work of God, what God does in us, the power of God, with which He makes us strong, the wisdom of God, with which He makes us wise, the strength of God, the salvation of God, and the glory of God.

> You should diligently learn the Word of God and by no means imagine that you know it. Let him who is able to read, take a psalm in the morning, or some other chapter of Scripture, and study it for a while. This is what I do. When I get up in the morning, I pray and recite the Ten Commandments, the Creed, and the Lord's Prayer with the children, adding any one of the Psalms. I do this only to keep myself well acquainted with these matters, and I do not want to let the mildew of the notion grow that I know them well enough. The devil is a greater rascal than you think he is. His definite design is to get you tired of the Word and in this way to draw you away from it. This is his aim." (LW 34:33, WA 32, 64f).

While Martin Luther was not correct in everything he said and did, in particular his persecution of the Jews, he championed a great deal of truth for every believer for which we should be forever grateful. Luther recovered and propagated the truth that all those who believe are saved through faith in the shed blood of Jesus Christ alone. He also championed the concepts of the priesthood of every believer and the right of every individual - even a plowboy - to read and understand the Bible for himself. Luther translated the Bible into German.

William Tyndale was burned at the stake for working to translate the Bible into English. Nonetheless, this translated Bible was smuggled into England. Because of Tyndale's sacrificial work, English-speaking people were able to read the Bible in their mother tongue. Having read the Scriptures for themselves, many saw that the state church of England was little better than the church of Rome and equally persecuted nonconformists. Finally, in the 17th century, the Pilgrims and Puritans set sail for the shores of North America to start the world over again and to establish a nation where freedom to worship God would be the heritage of all.

We should never forget that our nation was founded by Christians who fled the tyranny of the Old World, seeking religious freedom and the right to read, preach, and practice the teaching of the Bible. Through the sacrifice of these great Christians, we live in a nation where everyone is free to read, believe, and own as many Bibles as they want. Our Founding Fathers viewed the truths of the Bible as the cornerstone and foundation of all our liberty and were insistent that the Bible be read in our nation's schools. In the 18th century, the first book printed in the USA was a Bible published for our schools by our national Congress. Congress believed that the teachings of the Bible showed people right from wrong and taught them love for their fellow man. They believed that the Bible elevated our thoughts, softened our manners, and taught our individual responsibility to our Creator.

George Washington, the Father of Our Country and the first President of the United States wrote, "It is impossible to govern the world without God and the Bible." Noah Webster, author of the *American Dictionary of the English Language* and one of the framers of the U.S. Constitution, said, "All the misery that men suffer come from neglecting the precepts of the Bible." Patrick Henry, noted for his work for American Independence, spoke these immortal words about resisting the oppression of the British King, "I know not what course others may take, but as for me, give me liberty or give me death!" He also said, "The Bible is a book worth more than all the other books that were ever penned." In the 19th century, Abraham Lincoln wrote, "The Bible is the best book ever given to men."

This was our national faith until an attack began to overturn it in the beginning of the 20th century. As mentioned earlier, the warfare against the Bible that was going on in the Marxist nations moved front and center to the United States. Humanist educators were convinced that the Bible had to be eliminated from the American classroom at all costs. False teaching worked its way into the churches. Doubt was cast on the Bible's accuracy and importance. Christians were taught to focus on their own spiritual life. They withdrew from the culture that was opposed to God. They were told, "Politics are dirty; stay out of them."

As a result, Christians in North America began to withdraw their stewardship over the public arena. Christians lagged behind in statesmanship and civic and cultural leadership.

They became focused on their own personal lives, their pietistic devotional life, and heaven. Some even believed that as things got worse - which was a certainty if the Christians give up leadership - it was a sure sign that Jesus was coming soon and everyone should be glad about it. Christians were lulled to sleep and no longer tried to disciple our nation and teach it to obey Christ's teaching of love and life. The devil and evil men had a field day. While Christians were sleeping, by the early 1970s, the secular humanist educators realized their dream, and the Bible became a banned book in American public schools. Not a single Christian showed up at the Supreme Court to interpose an objection when the liberty to read the Bible in our public schools had its hearing. Soon it became illegal to offer public prayer in the classroom to the God Who made us. Following this, the Ten Commandments were taken down from the classroom walls. As one educator commented: "If children read these commandments, they will think they have to obey them, and this will just not do!"

What philosophy did the Progressives put in the place of biblical truth? The theories of Darwin and Marx. As Darwinists, they viewed people as descended from the monkey, and as Marxists, they went to war against the power of the individual and truth itself. They believed that there were no moral absolutes because there is no Divine Creator or Absolute Law Giver. Since there was no God to answer to, there was no such thing as the devil or heaven and hell. They taught that all truth is relative. My truth may not be your truth. Truth is evolving and ever changing. Since there are no moral absolutes, people are free to be whomever they want to be and do whatever they want to do. Whatever a person needs to do to further what he or she thinks is best is totally permissible, if it is for a good end.

Up until the 1970s, the greatest offenses in the public classroom were chewing gum, talking in class, throwing paper wads, or being in the hallway when the study bell rang. Now our children have become the victims of sexually transmitted diseases and teen pregnancy. Sexual deviancy is applauded and encouraged. Students have to pass through metal detectors to enter the public classroom where they often become the victims of drug peddling, theft, murder, and other sordid crimes. And to add insult to injury, many students graduate without basic reading and math skills. Should we be surprised at the rising tide of evil living and mass murders in our nation? To all this ideology the Bible says, *No!* The Bible teaches that each person is created in the image of God. Each person owes God their obedience and allegiance. Each person has been put here to be a part of God's plan, and each person must answer to God for the way they live their lives and use their talents.

Because of this false teaching, we have lost a large portion of the liberty and religious freedom that our Founders worked so tirelessly to win. We must work to gain it back, and yes, we can succeed because the Truth is on our side. We can take courage from the center of Marxist thought, the former Soviet Union. In the 1990s, the tide began to turn in Soviet Russia against Marx that would relegate Marxism to the dustbin of history. As Marxism proved to be an abject failure, a great spiritual awakening broke out in these former atheistic nations, and the Bible rose once again from the dead. Where the Bible had been a forbidden book, the Bible is now required reading in the public classroom. These former Marxist nations learned that there is something valuable within the pages of the Bible after all. How is that for the power of the Bible to conquer and prevail! Eighteenth century writer, William Cullen Bryant, said it this way:

> Truth crushed to the earth will rise again.
>
> The eternal years of God are hers;
>
> But Error, wounded, writhes in pain,
>
> And dies among his worshippers.

In the public arena in the United States today, the war is still raging against the Bible as humanists continue to question its accuracy and promote the idea that the Bible is contradictory, archaic, boring, and irrelevant. The cosmic battle continues between the Truth and the Lie - between "God said!" and Satan's probing question, "Did God really say?" The only way we can be captured by the devil's lies is to *not know* what God has said. What a great blessing that God's words have been recorded for us in the Bible by men who knew Him. And best of all, in the privacy of our own homes, we still have the privilege of freely learning from its pages every day.

Jesus upheld the truth of Scripture and quoted from it throughout His ministry. Jesus reminds us, "You shall know the Truth, and the Truth shall make you free!" The Bible has the power to transform our way of thinking, to set us free from the law of sin and death, and to purge us from socialist Marxist dogma that has infected our way of thinking. The Bible is a place we can encounter the Living Christ as He breathes His transforming Word into our hearts through the revelation of the Holy Spirit. The greatest crime we can commit against ourselves and our spiritual progress and the progress of Christ's kingdom in this world is to let the Bible sit and gather dust on our library shelf.

1. How were the Scriptures originally given? (2 Timothy 3: 16; 2 Peter 1:20-21)

a. _____

b. _____

2. What profit are the Scriptures to the believer? (2 Timothy 3:16)

a. _____

b. _____

c. _____

d. _____

3. As newborn babies, having committed ourselves to the Lordship of Jesus, what are we exhorted to do? (1 Peter 2:2; 2 Timothy 2:15)

a. _____

b. _____

4. As we drink the milk of the Word, what will happen? (1 Peter 2:2)

_____

The Lordship of God's Word

5. What name is given to Jesus? (John 1:1)_____

   In submitting to the Lordship of Jesus, we must also submit to the absolute authority of the written Word of God. God's written Word contains God's thoughts, opinions, ideas and personality. God's Word is His expressed will to man.

6. What did Jesus say about this? (Luke 6:46) _____

_____

   No matter what our opinions, objections, or reasoning might be, they must be brought into submission to God's Word. God's Word is the absolute and final authority over our life.

7. In light of this, what must we do with any thought, reasoning, or imagination that would exalt itself above God's Word? (2 Corinthians 10:5) _____

_____

_____

8. What did Jesus say was the spiritual "food" of the believer? (Matthew 4:4)

_____

Ignorance of God's Word

9. What has the god of this world done? (2 Corinthians 4:4) _____

_____

   After coming out from a world filled with carnality and sin, we find that our minds have been warped and molded by sin and the things of this world.

10. How is our mind transformed? (Romans 12:2; Ephesians 5:26-27) _____

_____

11. Under the New Covenant what did Jesus promise He would do? (Hebrews 10:16)

_____

12. As a result of the washing of the water of the Word, what will we be? (Ephesians 5:27; 2 Corinthians 3:18)

a. _____

b. _____

c. _____

13. What can exclude us from the life of God? (Ephesians 4:17-18)_____

14. Why do God's people perish? (Hosea 4:6) _____
_____

15. What will happen if we reject the knowledge of God's Word and forget His law? (Hosea 4:6)_____

From these Scriptures we learn that "for lack of knowledge the people perish." It is Satan's will to keep people blinded to the Word of God and to the life and light that is in it. Ignorance of God's Word can exclude us from the life of God and consequently keep us bound to sin, darkness, misery, and the power of the wicked one.

The Bible, God's Greatest Gift of Blessing

The Bible is God's greatest gift to humanity. From its pages, God Himself directs us in the way we should go. From it, we receive wisdom and understanding, so we are no longer slaves of the evil one, but sons of God, who share the inheritance of the saints in light.

16. What does the Psalmist David say about the guidance that comes from God's Word? (Psalm 119:105)_____

17. What does David say about the wisdom that comes from God's Word? (Psalm 119: 98-100) a. _____

b. _____

c. _____

18. How can young believers keep their way pure and free from sin? (Psalm 119:9-11)
_____

19. What two other things does meditation in God's Word do for you? (Psalm 119:45-46)

a._____

b. _____

20. Describe David's love for God's Word. (Psalm 119:103) _____
_____

21. When Jeremiah fed on God's Word, what did it become to him? (Jeremiah 15:16)
_____

22. How much did Job esteem God's words? (Job 23:12) _____
_____

23. As we trust in God's Word, what assurance do we have? (Psalm 119:89, 160; Numbers 23:19; Matthew 24:35)

a.

b.

c.

d.

Importance of Meditating on God's Word

24. How can you obtain life and health for your body through God's Word? (Proverbs 4:20-22)

a.

b.

c.

d.

This passage tells us how to meditate on God's Word. Meditation is more than a casual reading of the Scriptures. It is to deeply ponder Scripture with a prayer that God will reveal something to me or speak to my heart from the passage.

25. What are the blessings for those who *meditate* on God's Word day and night? (Psalm 1:1-3)a.

b.

c.

d.

26. What conditions did the Lord set for Joshua so that he might be successful and inherit the Promised Land? (Joshua 1:8)

a.

b.

c.

27. What orders did the Israelites have concerning the Word of God? (Deuteronomy 11:18-21)

a.

b.

c.

d.

e.

f.

28. As you love the Lord with all your heart and walk in His ways, what promise does God give you? (Deuteronomy 11:21-25)

a. _____

b. _____

c. _____

d. _____

Because we are heirs of salvation, joint-heirs with Christ, and are descendants of Abraham through our faith in Jesus Christ, God extends these promises to us in our spiritual promised land.

The Sword of the Spirit

29. In the spiritual armor of the Christian, what is the Word of God called? (Ephesians 6:17)_____

30. Give a description of this "sword." (Hebrews 4:12-13)

a. _____

b. _____

c. _____

d. _____

As we dwell in the Word of God, its edge cuts away all things that are offensive and evil from our lives. The Word in our mouth pierces the hearts of those who hear us and brings conviction of sin.

31. How did Jesus answer the devil when He was tempted? (Matthew 4:4, 7, 10)

_____

32. How can you prove your love to Jesus? (John 14:23)_____

Becoming a Doer of God's Word

33. Describe the wise man and his house. (Matthew 7:24-25) _____

_____

_____

34. Describe the foolish man and his house. (Matthew 7:26-27) _____

_____

_____

35. Whom did Jesus call His mother and His brothers? (Luke 8:20) _____

_____

36. Write down four things that result in the life of a believer who hears the Word of God and does it. (Acts 20:32; 2 Peter 1:4)

a. _____

b. _____

c. _____

d. _____

Memory Verses: Hebrews 4:12-13

_____

_____

_____

_____

_____

from **This Present Crisis**

- James Russell Lowell (1819-1891)

Careless seems the great Avenger;
    History's pages but record
One death-grapple in the darkness
    Between old systems and the Word;

Truth forever on the scaffold,
    Wrong forever on the throne,
Yet that scaffold sways the future,
    And, behind the dim unknown,
Standeth God within the shadow,
    Keeping watch above His own.

Worship with Michael Card, *How Firm a Foundation* <http://goo.gl/6BVlGt>

Worship with Steve Green, A *Mighty Fortress is Our God* - <http://goo.gl/1o1kj7>

Study 10: Praise, Worship, and Prayer

1. What is the Lord worthy to receive? (2 Samuel 22:4)

2. God has called us to be His people. For what has He formed us? (Isaiah 43:21)

3. Who should praise the Lord? (Psalm 150:6)

4. How often should we praise the Lord? (Psalm 34:1-3)

5. How can we honor the Lord? (Psalm 50:23)

The Many Ways to Praise the Lord

6. What are three ways to praise the Lord? (Psalm 47:1; Psalm 98:4)

a.

b.

c.

7. What type of instruments were used in praising the Lord? (Psalm 150:3-5)

a.   e.

b.   f.

c.   g.

d.

8. What other ways can we praise the Lord? (Psalm 149:1-3)

a.

b.

9. What is to be found in the mouth of the godly ones? (Psalm 149:6)

The Power of Praise

10. What power is there in praise when it is coupled with the two-edged sword, which is the Word of God? (Psalm 149:8-9) _____

_____

11. When Jehoshaphat went out to battle, he sent forth the praisers before the armies of Israel. What happened? (2 Chronicles 20:17-23) _____

_____

12. What actually happens when we begin to praise the Lord? (Psalm 22:3) _____

_____

The Fallen Tabernacle of David

13. In the last days, what is God going to restore? (Acts 15:16-18)

_____

14. When did the *last days* begin? (Acts 2:17-18) _____

We have been in the last days for two thousand years since the day of Pentecost and the outpouring of the Holy Spirit.

15. Where is the tabernacle of God to be? (Revelation 21:3) _____

16. What was the one thing that characterized the tabernacle of David? (1 Chronicles 15:16, 22, 24; 1 Chronicles 16:4-6,37-42) _____

_____

God Himself was enthroned upon these praises. The Hebrew *Midrash* tells that the Divine motivation in creation was that God desired a dwelling place. God instructed Israel to build the Tabernacle "so I can dwell in them." Under the Old Covenant, the nation of Israel was "the sanctuary of God."

Under the New Covenant, God has completed His work of making a sanctuary so He can dwell in our midst. The blood washed heart of a redeemed man, woman, or child is now His dwelling place and the throne of God in the earth. He raises up redeemed people in whom He can tabernacle, so that all mankind might seek the Lord. If you are redeemed, then your heart is God's throne. The *tabernacle of David* is not some building or place that is going to be erected. Individually, as a believer, you are the dwelling place of God, your heart is His tabernacle, His sanctuary. Your body is His temple. In addition, we are all being built together corporately as a dwelling of God in the Spirit.

Your heart is to be continually filled with His praises. Your life is to be a 24/7 worship unto Him. The Jewish *Midrash* states that God's ultimate purpose in tabernacling among men is to enable His people to draw down the blessing so that all the world will be blessed and God's kingdom will fill all the earth.

17. What did Paul teach about God's temple today? (1 Corinthians 3:16)

_____

His tabernacle (your life) is noticed because of the praise, thanksgiving, music and songs that go forth in the worship of the Lord. It is in this tabernacle that His Spirit will dwell.

18. In fact, what kind of people is the Father seeking? (John 4:23-24)_____

_____

The Holy Spirit has been given to us to teach us how to worship in spirit and in truth.

19. How should we worship the Lord? (Psalm 2:11) _____

_____

20. What is one way to show this reverence? (Psalm 5:7) _____

21. When the king ordered the Levites to praise and worship the Lord, how did they do it? (2 Chronicles 29:30)

a. _____
b. _____

22. In what way should we worship the Lord? (1 Chronicles 16:29)_____

_____

This is referring to the quality of "holiness." We are to worship the Lord in the "beauty of holiness," without a divided heart, in total dedication to Jesus.

Prayer

23. What three things did Jesus tell His disciples about prayer? (John 16:24)

a. _____
b. _____
c. _____

24. What did Jesus say for us not to do when we pray? (Matthew 6:7)

_____

25. Why do some people use meaningless repetitions? (Matthew 6:7)

_____

_____

26. What does your Father know? (Matthew 6:8)

_____

Hinderances to Answered Prayer

27. When we stand praying, what must we do if we expect to receive forgiveness from God? (Mark 11:25) _____

28. How should we pray and what assurance do we have that our prayer will be answered? When we pray and ask for something, what should we believe? (1 John 5:14-15; Mark 11:24)

a. _____

b. _____

c. _____

29. As a result, what will happen? (Mark 11:24)

_____

30. What are two reasons that a person does not receive things from God? (James 4:2-3)

a. _____

b. _____

31. What three things can hinder our prayers? (Psalm 66:18; James 1:6-7; 1 Peter 3:7)

a. _____

b. _____

c. _____

The Type of Person God Hears

32. What type of person does God hear? (John 9:31)

a. _____

b. _____

33. When the answer to a prayer seems to be slow in coming, what does Jesus tell us that we ought to do? (Luke 18:1) _____

34. Jesus gave a parable about a widow and an unrighteous judge. What happened? (Luke 18:2-5) _____

_____

35. What did Jesus say about God in comparison to this unrighteous judge? (Luke 18:6-8)

_____

36. Therefore, what should we have? (Luke 18:8) _____

_____

God's Promises

37. What promise does Jesus give us? (Matthew 7:7-8)

a. _____

b. _____

c. _____

38. What will the Father give? (Matthew 7:11) _____

Notice that *we* must do the asking, the seeking and the knocking. We must ask God for something. We should believe that He hears us, and we should thank Him that the answer is on its way.

39. In what does the Lord delight? (Proverbs 15:8)_____

40. What does the Lord hate? (Proverbs 15:8) _____

41. What privilege do those who abide in Jesus and allow His words to dwell in them have? (John 15:7) _____

Daily Disciplines in Prayer

42. What should a Christian do instead of worrying? (Philippians 4:6)_____

43. How should we begin each day? (Psalm 5:3) _____

Although we can pray in our hearts all day long, if do not have a regular time of prayer we will miss out on a lot of God's blessings because we never get around to asking for them.

44. What gives us the privilege of entering the holy Presence of God? (Hebrews 10:19)

_____

45. How does the Spirit of the Lord help with our prayers? (Romans 8:26-27)

_____

46. When we are trying to overcome satanic forces, what must we sometimes join with in prayer? (Mark 9:29) _____

47. What does Jesus promise will happen if two or more agree on anything for which they are praying? (Matthew 18:19) _____

48. Who should we especially pray for? (1 Timothy 2:2) _____

49. Why should we pray for these people? (1 Timothy 2:2)

a. _____

b. _____

50. How should we pray, and what should we avoid? (1 Timothy 2:8)

a. _____

b. _____

51. How often should we pray? (Ephesians 6:18; 1 Thessalonians. 5:17)

_____

Memory Verses: Philippians 4:6-7

_____

_____

_____

Sweet Hour of Prayer

William Walford, 1845

Sweet hour of prayer! Sweet hour of prayer!
That calls me from a world of care,
And bids me at my Father's throne
Make all my wants and wishes known.
In seasons of distress and grief,
My soul has often found relief,
And oft escaped the tempter's snare,
By thy return, sweet hour of prayer!

Sweet hour of prayer! Sweet hour of prayer!
The joys I feel, the bliss I share,
To Him whose truth and faithfulness
Engage the waiting soul to bless.
And since He bids me seek His face,
Believe His Word and trust His grace,
I'll cast on Him my every care,
And wait for thee, sweet hour of prayer.

Worship with Wintley Phipps, *Amazing Grace* <https://youtu.be/qNuQbJst4Lk>

Worship, *You Are My All in All* <https://youtu.be/xDZZ0-F5EKk>

Worship with Andrea Bocelli, *The Lord's Prayer* <https://youtu.be/qTv6d7NEhEw>

Worship with Chris Rice, *Come Thou Fount of Every Blessing* <http://goo.gl/NlT5xx>

Worship with Paul Wilbur, *Worthy,* <http://goo.gl/cm0h3D>

Worship with the Maranatha Singers, *He is Exalted on High,* <https://youtu.be/Ic1UBwVHGGU>

Study 11: What is God's Provision for Healing?

1. Why did pain, sickness, and death first come to man? (Genesis 3:16-19)

_____

By turning away from God in disobedience, man lost the blessing and protection of God and came under a curse and the power of the devil.

2. Who oppresses men with sickness? (Acts 10:38; Luke 13:11, 16) _____

God's Promises of Physical Healing

3. What was God's promise under the Old Covenant for those who obeyed Him? (Exodus 15:26)_____

4. In Isaiah 53, we find a prophecy about the Messiah. What did Isaiah prophesy that Jesus would do through His atoning death to provide for physical healing? (Isaiah 53:4-5)_____

_____

5. What does the apostle Peter say about this provision for healing? (1 Peter 2:24)

_____

6. Why was Jesus manifested? (1 John 3:8) _____

_____

7. What does God promise to do for those who serve Him? (Exodus 23:25)

a. _____

b. _____

8. What did David say that the Lord did for him? (Psalm 103:3)

a. _____

b. _____

9. How many of God's promises may we claim through faith in Jesus? (2 Corinthians 1:19-20)_____

Some Causes for Sickness and Disease

10. According to the Scriptures, what is one thing that can make people physically ill? (Deuteronomy 7:15)

11. Who else is a candidate for sickness? (Deuteronomy 28:58-59)

12. What kind of sickness will come upon those who disobey God's Word and refuse to fear Him? (Deuteronomy 28:58-61)

a.

b.

c.

d.

Those who turn from following the Lord put themselves under the Lordship of Satan. Therefore, they are at the mercy of the enemy of their souls and out from under God's protective covering.

13. What does God desire for us? (Deuteronomy 30:19)

Scriptural Conditions for Receiving God's Blessing

14. What are the conditions for receiving the blessing rather than the curse? (Deuteronomy 30:20)

a.

b.

c.

15. What promise do those who trust in the Lord and make Him their refuge have? (Psalm 91:9-10)

a.

b.

16. What does God promise for those who return to Him from a life of sin and disobedience? (Jeremiah 33:6)

a.

b.

Consequently, you see that as you turn from sin to serve the Living God, God desires not only to save you from sin, but also from sickness. Jesus came to redeem you completely from the hand of the enemy.

17. For what purpose was Jesus anointed with the Holy Spirit? (Acts 10:38)_____

Jesus Heals the Sick

18. Of all those who came to Jesus, how many did He heal? (Matthew 8:16; 12:15; 14:35-36)_____

19. How many kinds of sicknesses did Jesus heal? (Matthew 4:23-24; 9:35)

20. When Jesus did not heal many people, what was the reason? (Matthew 13:58; Mark 6:5-6) _____

21. In two accounts of healing given in Matthew, what did both the leper and the centurion recognize about Jesus; and what did they both have? (Matthew 8:2, 8)

a. _____

b. _____

22. What does God send to heal us? (Psalm 107:20) _____

23. The Roman soldier, a centurion, demonstrated this principle. What did he say to Jesus? (Matthew 8:8-9) _____

24. What did Jesus say about the centurion, and what did this man receive? (Matthew 8: 10, 13)

a. _____

b. _____

25. What did Jesus look for in those who came to Him for healing? (Matthew 9:28-29; Mark 2:5; 9:23)_____

It is this simple childlike faith of accepting God's Word as truth that moves the heart of God.

26. How did Peter explain the healing of the lame man? (Acts 3:16)

Jesus' Command to Heal the Sick

27. Peter healed the lame man through faith in the name of Jesus. Peter was simply being obedient to Jesus. What had Jesus commanded his disciples to do? (Matthew 10:8)

a. _____

b. _____

c. _____

d. _____

28. What did Jesus say a person who believed in Him would be able to do? (John 14: 12)

a. _____

b. _____

29. In what name are the sick healed, and what is one method of healing? (Mark 16:18)

a. _____

b. _____

30. According to Jesus' words, should we expect people prayed for in this manner to be healed? (Mark 16:17-18) _____

31. What are the elders of the church to do for a sick Christian? (James 5:14)

a. _____

b. _____

32. What will the Lord do? (James 5:15)

a. _____

b. _____

33. What kind of prayer will heal the sick? (James 5:15)

_____

Hindrances to Healing

34. What could be one reason that this Christian is sick? (James 5:15)

_____

Sin is not always the reason that people are sick. Poor diet, lack of rest, stress, and other environmental factors can also cause us to be sick. The Old Covenant is not silent about dietary laws and health laws that God gave Israel to practice. Washing your hands before eating, disposing and burying human waste outside the city, and the types of food that are good and nutritious were all part of God's health and wellness plan for Israel. Our body is God's temple, and it is important that you familiarize yourself with principles of healthy eating. However, because sin opens the door to sickness, it is important to understand what God's Word teaches about this.

35. What did David say happened to him when he hid his iniquity and did not confess his sin? (Psalm 32:3-5) _____

36. What type of man was King Hezekiah? (2 Kings 20:1-3) _____

37. When Hezekiah prayed to the Lord for healing, what happened? (2 Kings 20:5-6)_____

38. What type of man was King Asa? (2 Chronicles 15:16-17; 16:7-10)_____

_____

39. Because Asa had not trusted in God and had imprisoned God's prophet, what happened? (2 Chronicles 16:12)_____

40. What did Asa fail to do, and as a result, what happened? (2 Chronicles 16:12-13)_____

_____

Getting Rid of Fear, Worry, Stress, and Anxiety

Fear, worry, stress, and anxiety are also root causes of many diseases. To be alive is to be in stressful situations. The only stress-free environment is the graveyard. How then do we deal with these issues in our life? The New Testament diagnoses this problem and offers the remedy.

41. What did Jesus say about the certainty of tribulation? (John 16:33)

_____

42. What had Jesus spoken to His disciples that was to be the source of their peace? (John 16: 23-24, Phillipians 4:6-7)_____

43. If you are trusting in Jesus' Word and His promise to answer your prayers, what will be the evidence in your life besides peace? (John 16:33) _____

_____

44. What did Jesus say those who love Him will do? (John 14:21)

_____

45. What did Jesus command us to do about worry, what does He tell us to seek, and what promise does He give? (Matthew 6:25-34)

a._____

b._____

c._____

If we love Jesus, then we will want to keep His commandment and will not worry. Just as we would not think of breaking God's commandments to steal, kill, or commit adultery, we should not *worry* for the same reason - *to worry* is to break God's commandment.

46. What is the kingdom of God that we are to seek? (Romans 14:17)

_____

47. What does Paul remind us to do, and what promise do we have? (Philippians 4:6-7)

a._____

b._____

c. _____

48. Is fear of the future, or of the unknown, or of calamity from God? What has God given us? (2 Timothy 1:7)_____

49. How can we get rid of fear? (1 John 4:18, Psalm 27:1-6)_____

_____

50. What does Peter teach as the way to get rid of care and worry? (1 Peter 5:6-7)

_____

51. What does Peter explain you are doing when you cast all your care on the Lord? (1 Peter 5:6) _____

52. Why are some Christians not healed? (James 4:2b) _____

_____

53. All those who desired healing from Jesus did one thing. What was it? (Mark 10:46-50; Matthew 9:27)_____

54. Therefore, what does Jesus exhort us to do? (John 16:24; Matthew 21:22)

_____

55. The fourth chapter of Malachi speaks of the last days (church age). What will be prevalent among those who fear God's name? (Malachi 4:2)

_____

Memory Verses: Isaiah 53:5; Matthew 8:17

_____

_____

_____

Watch Jesus Heal the Blind Man from the movie _Jesus of Nazareth_ <http://goo.gl/XoS7Wq>

Worship with Michael W. Smith, _Healing Rain_ <http://goo.gl/ZqiZi5>

Worship with Julie True, _Healing in Your Presence_ <https://youtu.be/fVjV8lEjR4E>

Study 12: What is God's Plan for Inner Healing and Deliverance?

1. In what condition do most people come to the Lord? (Isaiah. 1:5-6; Psalm 38:3-8, 18)

_____

_____

The Lord has not left the condition of those who come to Him unanswered.

2. As we follow the Lord, what will He do for us? (Psalm 23:3a)

a. _____

b. What are the three parts of man? (1 Thessalonians 5:23)_____

3. What did Paul teach the early church about their body? (1 Corinthians 3:16)

_____

The Hebrew Temple is a type and shadow - an allegory of our physical body, which under the New Covenant has now become the Temple of God (Hebrews 8:5). The Hebrew Temple was divided into three parts - the Outer Court, the Inner Court, and the Holy of Holies. The Outer Court corresponds to our *physical body*, the Inner Court corresponds to our *soul*, and the Holy of Holies corresponds to our *spirit*.

The Temple of God

Outer Court - *Body*, Inner Court - *Soul*, Holy of Holies - *Spirit*

Spirit - The Holy of Holies
Ark of the Covenant

Body - Outer Court
Altar of Sacrifice
Bronze Laver

Taste, Touch, Sight
Hearing, Smell

Soul - Inner Court
Lamp-Stand,
Table of Show-Bread
Altar of Incense

Mind, Emotions, Will

Spirit of Man - The Holy of Holies

The Ark of the Covenant - The *Holy Of Holies* in the Hebrew Temple corresponds to the spirit of man in the new temple (my body) under the New Covenant. In the Holy of Holies was the Ark of the Covenant. On top of the Ark, overshadowed by the cherubim with outspread wings, was the *Mercy Seat*. Here *the blood of atonement* was *sprinkled on the Mercy Seat* for the forgiveness of sins. Here the *Shekhinah Glory* of God rested. A veil hung before the Holy of Holies signifying that there was not a way that fallen humanity could approach the glory of God's Presence. God's Holy Presence could only be approached by the High Priest once a year, and he had to bring blood for the atonement of sin. When Jesus made the last and perfect offering for our sin on the cross, the veil was ripped in half from top to bottom, signifying that those who accepted Jesus' sacrifice could now enter in to the holiest of all. Now, *Jesus* comes into my heart as my High Priest, He brings His blood and washes my heart. When I am immersed in the Holy Spirit, the *Shekhinah Glory, the Presence of the Holy Spirit,* takes up residence in my blood-washed heart. Under the New Covenant, the center of my being is now God's Holy dwelling place, the Holy of Holies, the sanctuary of God's Spirit.

Before I was saved and immersed in the Holy Spirit, my spirit was dead in trespasses and sin - in the pride of self. Now God's Spirit has made my spirit alive again and responsive to His Holy Spirit. God's Holy Spirit mingles with my spirit, and I become one with God.

4. What does Paul teach has happened to the person who has been joined to the Lord?
a.(1 Corinthians 6: 17)_____

The spirit of man can be divided into three parts: *conscience, intuition,* and *fellowship.*

The conscience is the door of my spirit. It is that which tells me right from wrong and by which I feel guilt. Sin makes my conscience dull and not sensitive to the Spirit of God by searing it with a hot iron. My conscience tells me I am not right with God. The conscience is the door which I open to let God's Spirit enter my spirit. The conscience must be informed by the Word of God of what is right and wrong. If I have been told it is wrong to wear a watch, every time I wear a wrist watch I will feel guilty.

b. What has God promised to do for our conscience? (Hebrews 9:14)_____
_____

Now that my conscience has been cleansed from dead works, I am now free to be led by the Holy Spirit and convicted by the Holy Spirit if I do something that does not please God.

The intuition is the knower, I use my intuition to perceive or sense things or circumstances. Here the spiritual gifts of wisdom, knowledge, and discernment activate my intuition for powerful revelation and inner knowing.

The fellowship area of my spirit is that which is made to have fellowship with God. It is impossible to fellowship with God without honesty or openness. Here I meet with God and worship Him in spirit and in truth. Here I also commune with true believers.

Soul - The Inner Court

The *soul* is my mental and emotional realm. It is the seat of my personality—my intellect and my thoughts (mind), my emotions, and my will. It is with my mind that I understand facts, think, etc. I may know a set of facts, but when God enlightens my mind, then "I truly understand." The Bible explains, "There is a spirit within man, but the inspiration of the Almighty gives the understanding" (Job 32:8).This mental and emotional realm can be likened to the *Inner Court* of the Hebrew Temple. In the Inner Court were three items of furniture - the *Table of Show-bread*, the *Lamp-stand*, and the *Altar of Incense* (Hebrews 9:2).

Table of Show-bread - This table held were twelve loafs of bread laid out fresh daily before the Lord Lord - one loaf for each of the twelve tribes of Israel. The number *twelve* also represents *Divine government*. The *bread* represents *my will,* which I willingly lay before the Lord to do His bidding. Jesus said, "I have food to eat you don't know about. My food is to do God's will and finish His work" (John 4:32,34). This bread was also known as *The Bread of His Presence.* The 12 loafs mean that I have *surrendered my will to God's will and to His Divine government.* As I daily spend time meditating in His Presence waiting and willing to follow the leading of His Spirit, I will experience His Presence and direction in all that I do.

Lamp-stand - The *Inner Court* was not lit by the natural sun, but by the Lamp-stand. The *Lamp-stand* corresponds to *my intellect* by which I understand what the will of the Lord is. The *Lamp-stand* was fueled by *oil*, in the same way, *my intellect is illumined by spiritual light from the anointing oil of the Holy Spirit within.* When my mind is transformed by the Word of God and illumined by the Holy Spirit, my thoughts become God's thoughts. With my mind I "take every thought captive to the obedience of Messiah." In the New Covenant the veil has been removed and my entire being is saturated, illumined by the light of Shekhinah, the Holy Spirit - God's marvelous presence out-raying from the sanctuary of my heart.

Altar of Incense - This altar was used by the priests to burn incense before the Lord. The Altar of Incense corresponds *to my emotions* and the *incense represents praise, worship, and prayer* that I am offering to God. Of the twenty-four elders it is said: "Each one had a harp, and they held gold bowls filled with *incense, which are the prayers of God's people*" (Revelation 5:8). It is with my emotions that I sense God's Presence, with my emotions I pour out my worship, praise, and thanksgiving to Him. With my emotions I pray for myself and others. My emotions are moved with God's compassion to love God back and to extend God's love to others. I don't put my emotions into doubt and unbelief and into things that contradict God's Word and promises by letting fear, worry, and doubt dominate me. Instead, I align my emotions with God's Word. I take a stand in my emotions trusting in God's Word and obeying Him, and with my emotions I offer thanksgiving to God and let joy fill my heart as I declare His Word into my circumstances.

Body - The Outer Court

The body represents the *Outer Court* in the temple. It is that part of me which deals with the physical realm. It is dominated by the five senses and is the vehicle I use to communicate to the outside world. In the Hebrew temple, it was here multitudes of people brought animals and offerings to sacrifice to the Lord. Here the priest dealt with the people of Israel and helped them to be reconciled to God.

Altar of Sacrifice - This altar which corresponds to the *shed blood of Jesus for the forgiveness of sins.* Here the sins I have committed are cleansed. Here I offer my body to God, to serve Him.

Brazen Laver - This washbasin was used by the priests to wash their hands before they could go into the Inner Court to serve the Lord by offering up incense (praise, worship and prayer) and to trim the lamps (receiving revelation). The Bronze Washbasin corresponds to *immersion in water.* In the New Covenant, my body is totally immersed in the water, I am burying my old nature, and God is cutting off my sinful nature to prepare me for fellowship with God. This is the New Covenant's spiritual mark in my flesh of my covenant with God. The washbasin also represents "the washing of the water of the Word" (Ephesians 5:26). The washbasin was made of *Bronze. Bronze* represents judgment. Immersion and the washing of God's Word and water baptism judges sin in my life, washes me, and transforms me.

A New Creation

When I come to the Lord, my sin of rejecting Him is forgiven. I am born again; I receive a new life and a new heart, and I am taken into Christ's kingdom. Paul explains the new birth and the new creation life to the church in Corinth: "All those who are in Christ are new creatures, old things have passed away, all things have become new" (2 Corinthians 5:17). We are made partakers of the Divine nature. Regenerating grace creates a new world in my soul and spirit; *all things are new.* I have received the Spirit of God and operate now from a new spirit. When I am really born-again, my motives are changed from being self-centered to God centered. As a new person, I act from new principles, by new standards, with new ends, in new company, and from a new nature - all this has been given to me by My Heavenly Father, through Christ Jesus my Lord.

I was once dead in trespasses and sin. Can a dead man raise himself to new life? No! Paul asks, "Who shall deliver me from the shackles of this body of sin and death?" Then he answers his own question: "Thank God, Jesus will!" (Romans 7:24-25) And now, as I continue to look into His glory, His sanctifying Spirit reforms my mind and emotions, transforming them to correspond with my glorious new nature.

5. From what have we been made free? (Romans 8:2)

_____

    I no longer have two natures - a sin nature and a new nature. I have died to my old way of living life under the lashes of the great taskmaster "self." I have buried the old sin-loving nature in the waters of baptism. While my very nature has been made new, there are areas in my soul - in my mind and emotions - that have been damaged by sin. These areas are in need of restoration, transformation, and renewal by the Spirit of God. As I behold Christ's glory through worship and meditation on His Word, the Spirit of God works to transform and renew my mind and my emotions into the image of Christ. As I look into the Word of God, I discover the great provision for inner healing and deliverance and freedom that are mine through Christ Jesus our Lord.

Transformation by His Spirit

6. What are two things Paul tells us we must do before we can experience this transformation? (Romans 12:1-2)

a._____

b._____

    Paul exhorts us to be transformed by renewing our mind, by letting God "change the way we think" so we can understand what the will of the Lord is (NLT).

7. What is one way this transformation of the mind takes place? (Ephesians 5:26)

_____

    This renewing of the mind takes place "by the washing of the water of the Word." Through daily reading and meditating on the Scripture and the words that Jesus has spoken to my heart, my mind is bathed and cleansed - "washed" - by the Word of God. As we meet God in His Word, the inner healing, restoration of the soul, and the deliverance from anything that holds us captive begins to take place. The splendor of His glory that lives within us through the Holy Spirit begins to flow out. Besides empowering us to be His witness, God has also provided the anointing and ministry of the Holy Spirit for our personal renewal. Jesus proclaimed what the anointing of the Holy Spirit has come to do.

8. What was Jesus anointed to do? (Isaiah 61:1, Luke 4:16-20)

a._____

b._____

c._____

d. _____

In this passage, we find the basis for the ministry of inner healing and deliverance for the body of Christ. The Spirit of the Lord anoints us for this ministry, just as Jesus was anointed. We are enabled to receive this ministry for ourselves and bring this ministry to others. As we study this passage carefully, we find that there are three main areas involved in this ministry of restoration. They are as follows:

1. **Healing of the memories** - "Binding up the broken hearted, setting at liberty those who are bruised."

2. **Deliverance** - "Proclaiming deliverance to captives, the opening of prison to those who are bound."

3. **Breaking and renouncing of curses,** which are passed down from generation to generation - "Raising up the former devastations, repairing the desolations of many generations."

A Glorious Church

9. What does Jesus want the church and every member of the body of Christ to become? (Ephesians 5:26-27) _____

We see a prophetic type of this inner working of God's Spirit in the offering up the *Fellowship Offering* in the Old Covenant. This offering was a burnt sacrifice. It was not for the atoning of sins, but was offered to purify those believers who desired fellowship with God. This was not a compulsory offering, but a freewill offering.

10. The fellowship offering prepared people for fellowship with God.
a. What did the priests do with the "inner parts" of this offering in the Old Covenant? (Leviticus 1:9) _____

b. Jesus is the High Priest of our confession - He is the Great Shepherd. How does he wash the inner parts of our mind and the thoughts of our hearts? (Ephesians 5:26)

_____

11. What does the Lord desire in the innermost parts of our heart? (Psalm 51:6-7)

_____

12. How can we help others overcome their hurts? (James 5:16)

_____

Jesus has now become the Great Shepherd, and we are the sheep of his pasture. In our prayer time, we can receive inner healing directly from Him. As members of the body of

Christ, we can also pray for each other. If God has given us an anointing to help pastor His people, we may also help people in this.

13. What does God desire to have proclaimed in the church? (Isaiah 61:2)

_____

The favorable year of the Lord is a reference to the Old Covenant *year of Jubilee.* In this time of Jubilee in Israel, everything was returned to its rightful owner; each man received back his inheritance. Jesus has proclaimed the year of Jubilee in perpetuity (forever, for all ages to come) to His blood-bought church so that every person might receive back what the enemy has destroyed and taken from them.

14. What prophetic exhortation does Isaiah give to the church? (Isaiah 52: 1-2)

a._____

b._____

c._____

Part 1 - Inner Healing - Healing of the Memories

The brain has one billion cubicles for storage of information and memories. People who are mentally healthy bury unpleasant events, but they will go through their lives reacting to certain situations and not realizing why. In the back of their mind is buried a memory that is distasteful, which brings the reaction and often the reason for reacting the way that they do.

When we find ourselves reacting to situations or to people in an unbiblical way, we need to ask the Lord to show us the root of this reaction. When He does, we can pray and ask Him to heal us, ask Him to help us forgive those who have hurt us, and give up our bitterness.

1. What does the Lord desire to do for these wounds? (Isaiah 1:6)_____

_____

2. Song of Solomon has long been understood by Jewish sages to represent God's love for Israel. Under the New Covenant, Song of Solomon can be understood as an allegory of the love between Christ and the church. What is the Lord's name compared to? (Song of Solomon 1:3)_____

3. If any hurts or bruises are hidden in our memory, but still affecting us, how can we know them? (Daniel 2:22)_____

4. If we pray and ask God to reveal what is hidden there, what will He do? (Daniel 2:23)

_____

5. What spiritual gift is vital to this ministry? (1 Corinthians 12:8) _____

6. What are two ways we can receive healing? (James 5:16)

a. _____

b. _____

7. To receive this healing, what must we be willing to do? (Ephesians 4:32)

_____

8. What provision did Jesus make for this inner healing of broken hearts in the atonement? (Isaiah 53:4)_____

Any provision in the atonement must be appropriated by faith. Jesus died for the sins of the world; yet each person must individually appropriate that forgiveness by faith, or he cannot be saved. Jesus bore our sicknesses, and "by His stripes we are healed." Yet, we must appropriate this healing by faith in order to be healed. Likewise, Jesus "bore our griefs and carried our sorrows." Jesus wants to give us deep, inner joy for mourning and heaviness. The Lord has provided a ministry through which we may receive this inner healing. This too must be received by faith.

9. What three things does the Spirit of the Lord anoint us to do for others? (Isaiah 61: 1-2; Luke 4:18)

a. _____

b. _____

c. _____

10. What will the Lord give to replace the mourning and heaviness? (Isaiah 61:3)

a. _____

b. _____

c. _____

11. What promise of this inner healing do we have from the Lord? (Isaiah 57:18)

_____

We have this promise, "The One who breaks open the way will go up before them; they will break through the gate and go out. Their King will pass through before them, the Lord at their head." Micah 2:13

Part 2 - Deliverance

1. On the cross, what provision did Jesus make for deliverance? (Hebrews 2:14)

_____

2. What did Jesus say to do with demons? (Mark 3:14-15)

_____

3. By what authority are demons cast out? (Mark 16: 17)

4. How can a person be captured by a demonic force and be held in bondage? (Proverbs 5:22)_____

When a person comes to the Lord out of a life of sin, sorrow, and wickedness, these cords need to be loosed so the captive can go free.

5. Sometimes a believer can remain in bondage after he has been saved. Why is this possible? (Proverbs 5:23)_____

Because of lack of instruction and ignorance, many children of God are held in bondage. Because a person has sinned in an area so many times, he can be brought into captivity. According to this Scripture, iniquities *capture* the wicked, and he will be *held* with the *cords of his sins.*

Jesus said that He came to set the *captives* free. This is the expressed will of God. In order for a person to be released from this captivity, these *cords of sin* must be confessed and cleansed in the blood of Jesus.

6. What warning do we have in Isaiah? (Isaiah 5:18)

_____

7. What are the "cords" by which we drag this unconfessed sin around? (Isaiah 5:18)_____

8. Why does the unrenewed mind stay corrupted? (Ephesians 4:22) _____

_____

Confession of Sin

9. What does the Lord say about those who try to hide and conceal their transgressions? (Proverbs 28:13) _____

_____

10. What are we exhorted to do? (Proverbs 28:13)_____

11. We see this practiced by the early church. What happened? (Acts 19:18-19)

_____

_____

We must be honest and truthful about the hidden things in our lives. As we confess our faults to the Lord and to those who are ministering to us, these cords will be broken; we will be set free from captivity. The following diagram illustrates *the cords of sin,* which *hold* a person *captive to a demonic force:*

SPIRIT OF LUST **SPIRIT OF REJECTION**

DEMONIC FORCE →

ROOTS →

Seeing of Evil

Pornography

Fantasy

Self - Gratification

Unholy Affections

← DEMONIC FORCE

ROOTS →

Inner Healing Must Be Ministered Here

Rejection by Mother Before Birth

Belittled by Father

Rejected by Friends

Rejection by Boyfriends

Laughed at by School Teacher

Specific sins that have been committed must be confessed to God and forsaken as the Spirit of the Lord reveals them to us. To be delivered from a demonic force that has its roots in hurts and wounds, we must forgive from our heart those who have inflicted hurt or pain upon us. The key to this deliverance is first, get the roots out by confession and forgiveness, and next, cast out the demonic spirit that is involved. If all the roots have been removed, there is no reason why the person will not be delivered. It is only the debris of unconfessed sin and the harboring of unforgiveness that gives the demonic spirit legal right to hold on.

12. Jesus describes this concept using a parable. What does Jesus say we are to do first? Second? (Luke 11:20-22)

a. _____

b. _____

We take away the strong man's *armor* on which he has relied by breaking or removing the roots or cords of unconfessed sin.

13. What did Jesus say that the casting out of demons signifies? (Luke 11:20)

_____

14. What are three other reasons that a person can be held captive to a demonic force? (2 Peter 2:19; Matthew 18:32-35; Deuteronomy 5:9)

a. _____

b. _____

c. _____

In many cases, because of the sins and iniquities of their fathers or mothers or ancestors, children are born with a demonic hold in their life in certain areas. A parent who has an extremely violent spirit of anger can pass it down to his children who also may have a terrible time with anger. Children who were unwanted can be born with a spirit of rejection. Those whose parents have been involved in sexual immorality can be born with various spirits of lust. Lust is often indiscriminate and can be directed toward the same or opposite sex. Many people who are born with spirits of lust find themselves lustfully attracted to the same sex and think they are born a homosexual or lesbian. Nothing could be farther from the truth. It is simply a demon that needs to be cast out, a curse to be broken. Sadly, many people are counseled by worldly wise men that God made them this way. Sadly they believe they are doomed to a life with the same sex. They try to reconcile themselves to this perversion and try the best they can to have their condition accepted as normal so they will feel better about themselves. Really all that is needed is inner healing, forgiveness, breaking of curses and casting out of demons.

Harboring Unforgiveness

15. What happens to those who harbor unforgiveness? (Matthew 18:34-35)

_____

16. What must the believer do in order to get released from the "tormentors"? (Matthew 18:34-35) _____

17. If you do *not* forgive others, what will God do for you? (Matthew 6:14-15)

_____

18. As we confess these things, what happens? (Ephesians 4:22-24)

a._____

b._____

c._____

19. What are three characteristics of the new self? (Ephesians 4:24)

a._____

b._____

c._____

20. What two things are a sure sign of demonic activity? (James 3:14-16)

a._____

b._____

21. What else can bring demonic activity? (Hebrews 12:15)

_____

All bitterness must be confessed and forsaken. If you find this hard ask Jesus to help you and He will.

22. What are two ways that we can determine what is holding a person in bondage?

a. (Hebrews 4:12-13; Proverbs 11:9)

_____

b. (Daniel 2:21-23; Psalm 13:3-4; 18:28; 1 Corinthians 4:5)

As we study the Bible, we discover keys that unlock the doors of those who have been imprisoned. *Ignorance* of the Word of God can keep a person bound. Knowledge of the Bible, coupled with the supernatural revelation of the Spirit, will bring detection of these forces.

23. What two revelation gifts of the Spirit are vital for this ministry? (1 Corinthians 12:8, 10)

a. _____

b. _____

24. What has the Spirit of the Lord anointed us for in the area of deliverance? (Isaiah 61:1)

a. _____

b. _____

Section 3 - Breaking of Curses

1. What provision did Jesus make for us in the atonement? (Galatians 3:13)

_____

2. Why did He become a curse for us? Who is under the curse? (Galatians 3:14, 1 Cor. 16:22)

a. _____

b. _____

3. What is the "blessing of Abraham"? (Romans 4:6-8)

a. _____

b. _____

c. _____

When Adam sinned, the curse came upon the earth. God offered Israel freedom from this curse if they would obey Him. Through His atoning work on the cross, Jesus provided for a final deliverance from the curse that is in the earth. We must appropriate this provision by faith just as we do healing, forgiveness of sins, deliverance and so on.

4. What did the Lord set before Israel? (Deuteronomy 30:15, 19)

a. _____

b. _____

5. Why did the Lord say the curse would come upon Israel? (Deuteronomy 30:17-18)

_____

We see that deliverance from this curse was only provided as Israel was faithful to God.

6. Upon whom did the Lord say that this iniquity and curse would come? (Exodus 20:5)

_____

7. What did the Lord promise to those who keep His commandments? (Exodus 20:6)

_____

8. What are some other sins that God names that will bring curses upon your family? (Deuteronomy 27:15-26; 28:45)

a. _____ g. _____

b. _____ h. _____

c. _____ i. _____

d. _____ j. _____

e. _____ k. _____

f. _____ l. _____

9. What will be the effects of these curses on future generations? (Deuteronomy 28:46)

_____

For those who have hated God and turned from Him or sinned in the ways mentioned previously, curses have been passed down upon them from generation to generation. Because of this many children of God live under these curses unknowingly.

10. How are we alienated from the life of God and His blessings? (Ephesians 4:17-18)

_____

Through the knowledge of the Word and by faith in the finished work Christ, we can appropriate deliverance from these curses. Through the blood of Jesus, the power of these curses can be broken. As we examine the Scriptures, we find a list of these curses in Deuteronomy. These curses are not just reserved for disobedient Israel - the curse is in the earth because of sin. When people walk away from God's goodness and refuse to acknowledge Him, they are left to their own devices. There is nothing to protect them from the curse of sin. As we take a look at these curses, we can quickly discern when a person is suffering from them.

11. List some of the curses of poverty. (Deuteronomy 28:16-20, 29, 33)

a. _____

b. _____

c. _____

d. _____

e. _____

f. _____

g. _____

h. _____

i. _____

j. _____

12. What physical infirmities may be the sign that a curse is present? (Deuteronomy 28:27, 35, 58-61)

a._____   e._____

b._____   f._____

c._____   g._____

d._____   h._____

Notice that the majority of these illnesses are incurable.

13. What mental problems are the result of curses? (Deuteronomy 28:28, 34, 65-67)

a._____

b._____

c._____

d._____

e._____

14. What curses do the following verses speak about? (Deuteronomy 28:36, 43, 49-50)

_____

15. What curse is mentioned in verse 30? (Deuteronomy 28:30)

_____

16. What is the curse mentioned in the following verse, and what are the effects? (Deuteronomy 23:2) _____

_____

The effects of this curse can usually be detected in those Christians who never *feel fully accepted by the believers.*

17. If you do serve the Lord, but do it with complaining and murmuring, what will happen? (Deuteronomy 28:47-48)_____

_____

By revelation of the Spirit, causes for these curses can be discerned, and the sin and effects of these curses will be removed from the believer and his descendants forever.

18. What does the Spirit of the Lord restore? (Isaiah 61:4)

a._____

b._____

c._____

19. In this aspect of inner healing, deliverance, and liberation from curses, what has the Lord become to us? (Hosea 11:4) _____

Although these promises were first given to Israel, they come down to us through faith in

Jesus Christ. We have been grafted into the Israel of God. As we diligently listen to God and obey His voice, God promises not only individual blessings, but national blessings.

20. What great blessings will come upon us and overtake us? (Deuteronomy 28:1-14)

1) _____

2) _____

3) _____

4) _____

5) _____

6) _____

7) _____

8) _____

9) _____

10) _____

11) _____

12) _____

21. As a result of Christ's deliverance, what will be recognized about us and our descendants? (Isaiah 61:9)_____

22. Having received this ministry as part of our redemption rights in Jesus, what will happen in your soul and why? (Isaiah 61:10) _____

_____

Memory Verses: Isaiah 61:1-2a

_____

_____

_____

Worship with Randy Rothwell, *Lord Prepare Me to Be a Sanctuary*
<http://goo.gl/6Fzaj6>

Worship with Jason Upton, *Under the Shadow of Your Wings* <http://goo.gl/CtpbgS>

Worship with Jason Upton, *Faith* <http://goo.gl/OJEaOO>

Watch Jesus cast out a demon, *Jesus of Nazareth* <http://goo.gl/APuehA>

Worship, *Songs of Deliverance* <http://goo.gl/vyd0Hz>

Love Divine All Loves Excelling

- Charles Wesley, 1747

Love divine, all loves excelling, joy of heaven, to earth come down;
Fix in us thy humble dwelling; all thy faithful mercies crown!
Jesus thou art all compassion, pure, unbounded love thou art;
Visit us with thy salvation; enter every trembling heart.

Breathe, O breathe thy loving Spirit into every troubled breast!
Let us all in thee inherit; let us find that second rest.
Take away our bent to sinning; Alpha and Omega be;
End of faith, as its beginning, set our hearts at liberty.

Come, Almighty to deliver, let us all thy life receive;
Suddenly return and never, nevermore thy temples leave.
Thee we would be always blessing, serve thee as thy hosts above,
Pray and praise thee without ceasing, glory in thy perfect love.

Finish, then, thy new creation; pure and spotless let us be.
Let us see thy great salvation perfectly restored in thee;
Changed from glory into glory, till in heaven we take our place,
Till we cast our crowns before thee, lost in wonder, love, and praise.

Worship with this historic hymn of the church - *Love Divine All Loves Excelling* <http://goo.gl/zBaM1D>

Watch Jesus proclaim His mission to bring deliverance to the captives from *The Bible MiniSeries* <https://youtu.be/Bh9w6TgUkaU>

Worship *Yeshua Is the Light* (Note: *Yeshua:* Hebrew for *Jesus, Hashem-* Hebrew for *"The Name" referring to God*) <https://youtu.be/zG4gh95tfYQ>

Worship with Paul Wilbur, *The Shout of El-Shaddi* (Note: *El Shaddai* - Hebrew for *God Almighty*) <http://goo.gl/gMck5M>

Worship with the Maranatha Singers, *Create in Me a Clean Heart*, <https://youtu.be/OYZibL9w2U8?list=PL46C040F76F22B191>

Prayer Against Generational Curses <https://youtu.be/GHeV3rpg-wM>

Study 13: What is My New Life in Christ Like?
The Sermon on the Mount

As the Savior of the world, and the Second Adam from above, Jesus came to start the human race over again. To do this, He calls all those who believe in Him to be born again and promises to give each believer a new heart fashioned after His own. From fiery Mt. Sinai under the Old Covenant, the Lord spoke as the Great Lawgiver and gave the Ten Commandments of blessing to govern Israel and the human race in all their outward behavior because of their hearts of stone. Under the New Covenant from a mountain in Israel, God spoke again as the Great Lawgiver- this time He was veiled in human flesh in the person of Jesus Christ. As the God of love, Jesus emptied Himself of His eternal glory to visit humankind to declare His Father's will. Jesus sat down among His followers and gave them a new set of laws, the laws of Spirit and Life, for the new heart.

1. Under the Old Covenant, God's law was written on tablets of stone (symbol of the heart of stone). Under the New Covenant, where would these new laws be written and how would they be written? (Hebrews 8:10) _____

_____

By His Spirit, Jesus writes these new laws on our hearts and minds as the way of His kingdom. Jesus' Sermon on the Mount is the New Covenant standard and the commandments He gives for the new heart are just as binding as the Ten Commandments given on Mt. Sinai. Jesus' words are not optional. As His followers, we are to use His standard as the way to measure and judge all our thoughts and behavior. The principles Jesus gave show us the new way to live under the New Covenant. Any behavior that is not in agreement with these spiritual principles is behavior from habits formed from our old way of thinking and acting from the old stony heart. These old ways are sinful and must be forsaken and rejected as our mind is renewed and we embrace the new heart.

2. What are nine heart attitudes that bring us into a place to be blessed by God, and what are those blessings? (Matthew 5:1-12)

1) Attitude _____

   Blessing _____

2) Attitude _____

Blessing _____

3) Attitude_____

   Blessing _____

4) Attitude_____

   Blessing _____

5) Attitude_____

   Blessing _____

6) Attitude_____

   Blessing _____

7) Attitude_____

   Blessing _____

8) Attitude_____

   Blessing _____

9) Attitude_____

   Blessing _____

3. a. If you lust in your heart, of what are you guilty? (Matthew 5:28)_____

b. If you are angry with your brother, what are you guilty of? (Matthew 5:22)

Importance of Your Words

4. Are you to make a vow or an oath, and what is your statement to be? (Matthew 5:33-37)

5. What is anything beyond that? (Matthew 5:37) _____

  We should always speak the truth. To swear that what we are saying is true implies that we are sometimes lying.

6. What will happen to us for speaking careless words? (Matthew 12:36)

7. How will we be justified, and how will we be condemned? (Matthew 12:37)_____

8. What does the mouth speak? (Matthew 12:34-35)

Attitude in Persecution

9. What should your attitude be toward one who mistreats or slaps you? (Matthew 5:39)

10. How did Jesus demonstrate this principle? (Matthew 26:51-52; 27:12; 29-30;1 Peter 2:21-23) _____

11. What is to be our attitude when we are persecuted for righteousness' sake? (Matthew 5:10-12)_____

12. What did Jesus say our attitude toward our enemies should be? (Matthew 5:44-47)

_____

13. How does God set this example? (Matthew 5:45)

_____

14. Therefore, what are we to be? (Luke 6:36)_____

15. If you love only those who love you, do good to you, and lend to you is that any credit to you? (Luke 6:32) _____

16. What are you to do ? What should be your attitude? What is your reward? Who shall you be? (Luke 6:33)a._____

b. _____

c._____ d. _____

Judging Others

17. What are three attitudes that Jesus condemned, and how did He measure each offense? (Matthew 5:22)   The Offense   The Guilt

a._____   a._____

b._____   b._____

c._____   c._____

18. If you judge others in this way, what will happen? (Matthew 7:1-2)

_____

19. By what standard will you be judged? (Matthew 7:1-2)

_____

20. In light of this, what are we exhorted to do? (Luke 6:37)

a. _____

b. _____

c. _____

21. If you are presenting your offering to God and remember that your *brother* has something against *you,* what are you to do? (Matthew 5:23-24)

_____

Outward or Inward Religion

22. Of what are you to beware? (Matthew 6:1) _____

23. What should your attitude be in giving to the Lord, and what will the Lord do for you? (Matthew 6:4) a. _____

b. _____

24. If you do not forgive others, then what attitude does the Father take toward you? (Matthew 6:14-15) _____

25. How often are you to forgive others? (Matthew 18:21-22) _____

26. How are we to treat others? (Matthew 7:12; Luke 6:31) _____

27. What should be your attitude toward giving to others? (Luke 6:29-30, 34-35)

a. _____

b. _____

c. _____

28. What are we to beware of and be on guard against? (Luke 12:15) _____

Faithfulness and Humility

29. What did Jesus say about faithfulness? (Luke 16:10) _____

30. What did Jesus say about unfaithfulness? (Luke 16:10) _____

31. What attitude will God honor? (Luke 18:10-14) _____

32. What will happen to those who try to exalt themselves? (Luke 18:14) _____

33. If you want to be great in the kingdom of God, what attitude should you always have? (Matthew 20:25-27) _____

34. What example did Jesus set in this area? (Matthew 20:28) _____

35. When invited as a guest, should you try to take the best seat? What attitude should you have? (Luke 14:8-11) _____

36. When you have a luncheon or dinner, whom should you invite? (Luke 14:12-14) _____

Walking in Love

37. What is the greatest sign of love? (John 15: 13) Lay down life

117

38. What did Jesus say for us to do if we love Him? (John 21:15-17)

Feed His Sheep; Feed His Lamb; Feed His

39. What six things are we to do for others? (Matthew 25:35-40)

a. *Drink the thirsty*

b. *Take the stranger in*

c. *Feed the Hungry*

d. *Cloth the naked*

e. *Visit the Sick*

f. *Visit Prisoner*

40. What does John exhort us to do? (1 John 3:16-18)

41. Read this passage and answer the questions below: (1 Peter1:13-23 NLT)

13 So think clearly and exercise self-control. 14a So you must live as God's obedient children. b Don't slip back into your old ways of living to satisfy your own desires.15 But now you must be holy in everything you do, just as God who chose you is holy.17a And remember that the heavenly Father to whom you pray has no favorites. He will judge or reward you according to what you do. b So you must live in reverent fear of Him during your time as "foreigners in the land."18 For you know that God paid a ransom to save you from the empty life you inherited from your ancestors. And the ransom He paid was not mere gold or silver. 19 It was the precious blood of Christ, the sinless, spotless Lamb of God. 21 Through Christ you have come to trust in God. 22 You were cleansed from your sins when you obeyed the truth, so now you must show sincere love to each other as brothers and sisters. Love each other deeply with all your heart.23 you have been born again, but not to a life that will quickly end. Your new life will last forever because it comes from the eternal, living word of God.

a. What 3 things are we to do? (vs13-14a) *Think clearly, exercise Control, obey God*

b. What conduct should we have and why? (vs 14b 15) *Don't Backslide, be Holy*

c. How will we be judged or rewarded? (17a) *According to what we do*

d. What should be our attitude toward God? (17b) *Live in Reverent fear*

e. What ransom did God pay for our salvation? (vs18-19) *His blood; Sinless life*

f. What should we treat fellow believers? (22) *Love one the other*

Memory Verses: Luke 6:47-48

Watch Jesus give *The Sermon on the Mount* from *The Visual Bible* <http://goo.gl/Vj9LWw>

Worship, *Shine Jesus Shine* <http://goo.gl/IOTKCm>

Worship with Jason Upton, *We Are One in the Spirit* <http://goo.gl/6QO2Fy>

Study 14: God's Perfect Choice

As we love God with all of our heart, mind, soul and strength, God has promised in His Word, "No good thing will He withhold from those who walk uprightly" (Psalm 84:11b). The Bible also tells us, "He who finds a wife finds a good thing, and obtains favor from the Lord" (Proverbs 18:22). Marriage is God's idea. Marriage between a man and a woman is God's good thing. When God put Adam and Eve together in the garden, He pronounced it "very good." Because marriage is God's plan, He has given us specific guidelines in His Word to help us choose a perfect mate. God has also set down certain parameters to guide single adults in their conduct with one another. Of course, this directive on trusting God for a mate does not apply to those who are already married. When married people come to know the Lord, it is God's will for you to walk together into God's great love. He takes you where you are, puts you on the road of righteousness, and reveals His plans to use your lives together for His glory. He can fill your hearts with His love for one another.

On a deeper level, this study has a message for every believer regardless of marital status. The Bible tells us that Jesus is the Heavenly Bridegroom who came to earth to seek a Bride. In the words of the old hymn "From heaven He came and sought Her to be His holy Bride. With His own blood He bought her and for her life He died." Paul taught that marriage points to this deeper revelation - a spiritual mystery - "the union of Christ with His church." Paul taught that the person who is joined to the Lord has entered into a spiritual marriage - "the person who is joined to the Lord is one spirit with Him." (1 Corinthians 6:17)

1. What is God's plan; what is His good thing? (Genesis 2:18-25)

_____

2. Who chose the mate for Adam? (Genesis 2:22)

_____

Consider the story of Isaac and Rebekah; their story is another example of God choosing a mate for those who serve Him. In the story of Isaac, we can find in Isaac a type of all those who have been born again according to God's promise. We see this reflected in Galatians 4:28, "And you brethren, like Isaac are children of promise." Abraham, a type of the heavenly Father, sent out his servant to bring home a wife for his son.

3. According to the Scripture, who did Abraham and his servant believe would choose a wife

for Isaac? (Genesis 24:12-27; note v. 14)

God used a person to find Issac's wife, but Abraham and his servant were seeking God's direction and leading. They were not frantically seeking for a wife for Isaac in their own strength and effort.

4. What type of girl was Rebekah? (Genesis 24:16)

---

5. God had chosen Rebekah for Isaac. What was Rebekah's attitude toward God's choice for her life? (Genesis 24:58) _____

6. What was Isaac doing when God brought Rebekah to him? (Genesis 24:63)_____

7. Did Rebekah and Isaac spend a lot of time dating and getting to know one another after God brought them together? (Genesis 24:64-67) _____

8. What was Isaac's attitude toward God's choice for his life? (Genesis 24:67)

The Spirit of Holiness

9. In our male and female relationships, how should we treat others? (1 Thessalonians 4:1-6) *In Sanctification And Honor ; Abstain from Sexual Immorality*

As heirs of the New Covenant, God calls us to be led by the Spirit in our male-female relationships, to walk holy and blameless before Him, "to keep clear of all sexual sin...to treat each other with holiness and honor, not in lustful passion as the pagans do."

10. If we are disobedient to these rules for moral purity, who are we disobeying? (1 Thessalonians 4:8) *God*

The early church fathers called the Holy Spirit the "Spirit of Holiness." To live in a way that is contrary to Scriptural teaching because we live in the "modern era" is to oppose God's own holiness and the Holy Spirit that He has given you. Dating relationships are often based upon fleshly or worldly desires, rather than upon a Divine leading by the Holy Spirit. We cannot obtain perfection or righteousness by the flesh, nor can we obtain that deep love relationship with our future mate by efforts of the flesh.(Galatians 3:3).

11. What promise do we have from God? (Psalm 37:4)
Delight thyself in the LORD, + He will give you the desires of thine heart

We are assured that as we delight in the Lord, He will give us the desires of our hearts. Instead of searching for a mate through dating and trying different people out to find the perfect person, seek the Lord first and trust Him to bring your mate into your life. Then, led by God's Spirit, you will not make decisions to satisfy the lusts of the flesh, but will glorify

God through that one relationship, which is God's "best" for you.

Avoiding Worldly Thinking

12. We must be careful that we do not use worldly methods to search for our life partner. What attitudes are in the world that are not from God? (1 John 2: 16)

a. _Lust of the flesh_

b. _Lust of the eyes_

c. _Pride of life_

13. As we seek to do God's will in everything, including our choice of a mate, what assurance of stability do we have? (1 John 2:17) _He that do the Will of God Abides frenm_

Relationships based on the lust of the flesh and of the eyes can only bring hurt. Dating relationships are too often based on these principles. Those involved in the worldly way of dating usually wind up with a broken heart somewhere along the way. Consequently, lives filled with brokenness, hurt, emotional scars, and rejection are what the majority of young people bring into a marriage relationship. We may enjoy going out with those people who are going to make us "look good" in the eyes of others or with those who appeal to our flesh, but we need only to look at the results of the worldly dating system to see who the author of it is. One out of every two marriages end in divorce. Premarital pregnancies, sexually transmitted diseases, and abortions plague our nation.

14. As Christians, how does God call us to conduct ourselves in our relationships with members of the opposite sex? (1 Timothy 4:12; 1 Corinthians 6:18-20; 1 Thessalonians 4:3-5)

a. _Keep Faith in God Be examples of the believers..._

b. _Flee Fornication_

c. _Flee Sexual immorality_

d. _Reject Lust of Concupiscence_

Undistracted Devotion to the Lord

15. With what are the unmarried to be concerned? (1 Corinthians 7:32; Matthew 6:32,33)

16. As Christians, what are we exhorted to do? (Romans 12:1,2; Titus 2:12-15)

It is clear that we are called to conduct our relationships with the opposite sex in a different way from the world. We are called to be motivated by the Spirit's leading, not by the lust of the flesh. We are instructed to conduct ourselves in a pure and holy fashion, fleeing from "youthful lust." How are we to do that? Avoid getting into situations that could stir up worldly lusts. Treat each member of the opposite sex as your very own brother or sister.

Fear says, "I am afraid if I trust God to pick out my mate, he or she will be someone my heart does not desire - some very weird person." Since Satan always wants to present God as One who gives us a "raw deal," it is obvious who inspired these doubts.

17. What does the Scripture say? (Matthew 7:9-11)

_____

The Blessings of Trusting in God

18. As we trust in God for His choice for our mate, of what can we be assured? (Psalm 37:4,5,7; Proverbs 18:22; Psalm 84: 11; Proverbs 19: 14)

a._____

b._____

c._____

d._____

19. What should be the basis in our choice for a mate? (1 John 2: 7)

_____

God's Word teaches us to walk by faith, not sight. If your choice is based on human wisdom alone can you be certain that person is the right one for you? God in His infinite wisdom knows what you need. The mate He has for you will complete your life at every level. You will add your strengths to one another. Why not join the thousands of young people who have seen the truth of this message and are now walking in the great liberty of spirit that this truth brings with it. As you commit this area of your life to Him, you will know the great blessing of being free from concern and from divided interests; as a result, you will be able to give undistracted devotion to the Lord. He will bring His perfect will to pass in your life as you trust in Him. Remember, marriage is God's idea. Build your marriage on the perfect will of God - it will have a real promise of enduring. "Present your bodies to God as a living sacrifice and don't be conformed to this world but be transformed by changing the way you think so you can learn what the will of God is." Dare to believe God for His perfect choice. "Seek the kingdom of God first and His righteousness." You can be assured that the promise which follows this commitment will also come true, "all these things will be added to you."

20. What was Paul convinced of? (2 Timothy 1:12)_____

_____

Memory Verse: Psalm 37:4

_____

_____

Worship, *Tis' So Sweet to Trust in Jesus* <http://goo.gl/xRROjy>

Worship with Andre Bocelli and Celine Dion, *The Prayer,* <https://youtu.be/cjNfkbQr5zc>

Study 15: What is Commitment
To the Body of Christ?

1. How did Jesus say all men would know that we are His disciples? (John 13:35)

_____

2. What kind of love did Jesus say that this is? (John 13:34)

_____

3. How does John define that love? (1 John 3:16; 15:13)

_____

The Many Expressions of Love

4. List how this love expresses itself:

a. (1 Peter 4:8)_____

b. (Galatians 5:15) _____

c. (Philippians 2:3-4)_____

d. (1 Corinthians 12:26; Romans 15:1)_____

_____

e. (Matthew 5:44) _____

f. (James 5:16; 1 Corinthians 12:25)_____

_____

g. (1 John 3:17-18) _____

_____

5. What are we to be diligent to preserve? (Ephesians 4:3)

Unity of the Spirit + the Bond of Peace

When we cause division by backbiting and devouring others, we tear down each other and disrupt the work of God. This is one of Satan's main devices to try to destroy or hinder God's purposes.

6. Why does Satan try to cause division? (Luke 11:17)

He tries to make it fall

It is Satan's desire to divide and destroy God's kingdom.

7. Therefore, if you know that anyone has anything against you, what are you to do? (Matthew 5:23-24) Go be Reconciled with that one

8. What attitude should we have? (Ephesians 4:32) Forgiving Spirit, tender-hearted, Kind

9. Into what are we, as children of God, baptized? (1 Corinthians 12:13) Into One Body; Into One Spirit

A Many-Membered Body

10. What is the body of Christ? (1 Corinthians 12:14) One body, many parts

11. Is it God's will for us to walk alone in our service for Him? (1 Corinthians 12:15-21) No; because each member has a function Needed by the body

12. Where has God placed each individual member? (1 Corinthians 12:18) As God pleases (Wills)

13. If you are an "eye" seeing things in the Spirit, or an "ear" hearing the direction in which the Spirit of God says to go, can you function properly on your own? (1 Corinthians 12:21) No, We Need the function provided by other Members

An eye sitting by itself on a table, detached from the rest of the physical body, cannot function. It is no good to itself or to anyone else. It is also not very pleasant to look at. Yet, an eye connected to the physical body in its proper place is a great asset to the body because it gives light and sight to the whole body. The eye is also a very lovely thing to look at when it remains where God has designed it to be. An eye apart from the body is dead and can do nothing. So it is in the spiritual body of Christ. A member of the body separate and apart from the other members cannot function properly. Yet, that member, when attached to the rest of the body, performs its function and blesses the entire body by being useful in the work of God. Each member receives its supply from the head of the body, who is Jesus.

14. Why is the manifestation of the Spirit, or the gifts and operations of the Spirit, given to each individual believer? (1 Corinthians 12:7) For the profit of All (the body)

15. How is the body fitted and held together? (Ephesians 4:16) Knit + held together by that which each part provides

16. In order for the joints to fit and hold the body of Christ together, in what type of "working" order must each individual part be? (Ephesians 4:16)

17. As each joint is supplying that which it has to give, what will happen? (Ephesians 4: 16)

The growth and edifying of the body

18. Into what are we individually and corporately being built? (1 Peter 2:5; Ephesians 2:21-22) *Into a holy temple; a spiritual house*

Jesus is Building His Church

19. What is Jesus building, and what promise do we have from Him? (Matthew 16: 18)

20. For whom is Jesus coming? (Ephesians 5:25-27)

Jesus is coming for a glorious church without spot or wrinkle - a church that is walking together in unity and love, not only in local expressions of the Body of Christ, but also universally.

21. What ministries has God appointed to operate in the church? (1 Corinthians 12:28)

a._____ e. _____
b._____ f. _____
c._____ g. _____
d._____ h. _____

22. How is the manifold wisdom of God going to be revealed? (Ephesians 3:10)

23. What does Jesus call Himself? (John 15:5)

24. What does He call the members of His body? (John 15:5)

It is interesting that Jesus did not call Himself a tree; He called Himself a *vine*. A tree has a main trunk with the branches directly connected and branching off from the main trunk. A vine, however, has no main trunk. It is composed of many interconnected branches. Each branch receives its life from the other by drinking the life-giving sap that flows from its roots. Jesus speaks of Himself as the Vine - *the whole thing*—and speaks of us as branches of it. The branches are inseparable from the vine. If you chop off the branches of a tree, the trunk remains. If you cut all the branches from the vine, nothing remains.

25. In order to bear fruit, what must we do? (John 15:5-6)

_____

As we have discussed, the body of Jesus, which is His church, is not a building with a steeple on top, but a living, active organism. The word for *church* in the Greek is *ecclesia*, which means *called out ones*. Those who make up the church according to the New Testament definition are true believers of Jesus, who have repented and turned from the ways of the world and sin. As they are joined together in a local expression of Christ in the earth, they bring forth fruit.

26. Describe the unity of the early church. (Acts 2:40-47)_____

_____

_____

_____

How the Church in Jerusalem Lived Together in Community

In Jerusalem, the early church held all things in common. It is important to understand that just because the early church did this in Jerusalem, this is not the Bible's sanction of government-mandated socialism and the Marxist idea of redistribution of wealth. In fact, Jesus presents the opposite idea.

For a government, or anyone else for that matter, to take your hard-earned money away from you to redistribute to others is the same thing as stealing and slavery. The sharing of goods in Jerusalem was a freewill offering. When Ananias and Sapphira sold their property and agreed to deceive the apostles and keep some of the proceeds back for themselves, they fell dead at the apostles feet, not for withholding the proceeds, but because they agreed to lie and tried to deceive the Holy Spirit.

27. What did Peter tell them about their property? (Acts 5:1-11 answer from verse 4)

_____

The New Living Translation states it this way: "The property was yours to sell or not sell, as you wished. And after selling it, the money was yours to give away. How could you do a thing like this? You weren't lying to us but to God." Peter emphasized to Ananias and Sapphira that their property was theirs to keep or theirs to freely give. The confiscation of wealth through higher taxes and redistribution of wealth by government entities is not the same thing that the early church was practicing. It is not an example of Christian government. Redistribution of wealth by the state through force is not a Christian idea. It is theft.

This communal situation practiced in Jerusalem was not necessarily practiced in the other churches outside of Jerusalem. If this was to be the continual practice of the church then the apostles would have taught all churches throughout Asia and Europe to do this.

The church in Jerusalem felt led of the Lord to do this. Here are two probable reasons - they had an earnest desire to help the needy believers among them, and they also had a prophetic word from Jesus that the Temple in Jerusalem would be destroyed in their lifetime (Matthew 24:2, Luke 23: 28-30, Mark 13:30). James, the head of the church in Jerusalem, refers to this soon coming judgment and destruction of Jerusalem, and the plight of those who were still trusting in their riches. (James 5:1-9) When Roman soldiers were on their way to destroy Jerusalem in 70 AD, it is a matter of historic record that the Christians were warned by God and escaped before the slaughter. There was nothing that held the Christians back from leaving Jerusalem immediately since they had already sold all their property and possessions.

God's Warning about Oppressive Government

28. Israel demanded a king so they could be like every other nation. God warned them that the king would oppress them. How does God describe oppressive government? (1 Samuel 8:7-9, 14-17)

_____

_____

_____

_____

In history, there have been two types of governments that have stolen from their people. There have been kings and dictators who have stolen from their citizens to enrich their own pockets, and there have been governments that have stolen from the wealth of the more industrious members of society to redistribute their wealth to the less industrious people who lived in lack. Both are illegitimate forms of government based on stealing.

Private property rights are as sacred as the laws of God and are based in the Ten Commandments. God forbids stealing and coveting anything that belongs to your neighbor. Wealth confiscated by the government in more taxes on everything and higher taxes on wage earners is theft and oppressive government. Inevitably, the money is misspent and wasted with bureaucracy and fraud. Historically, the nations which have tried to provide cradle-to-the-grave security were atheistic nations who attempted to avoid personal responsibility and make the state God. In the end, everyone became equal in poverty with no surplus left to give. The former Soviet Union ended in bankruptcy and ditched the Marxist socialism they practiced as a failure. They embraced personal responsibility instead of government planning. China is moving away from redistribution as a failed system of economics toward free enterprise. The Chinese people say that what helped them the most was not Mao's social revolution that made everyone equal in poverty. What really helped them economically as a nation was when their leaders opened the nation up for free enterprise.

The Biblical Method of Helping the Poor

Then how are the poor to be helped? Jesus said that the poor will always be with us. Why? Poverty is part of the curse in the earth. Poverty can result in being ignorant of God's blessings. Peter reminds us that Jesus has given promises to the church and that we are to "make every effort to apply the benefits of these promises to your life" (2 Peter 1:5). Poverty often can be the plight of those who are disobedient to God, and as a result, they are not members of God's family and cannot enjoy the covenant of blessing. According to the Bible, we know that it is not God's will for His children to live under poverty. At the same time, under the Old Covenant, the Israelites were instructed to help the poor among them with very specific offerings, especially for the widow and the orphan. The whole development of philanthropic organizations and charities in the modern era in Western civilization is historically a biblical idea that was birthed during the eighteenth and nineteenth centuries through the First and Second Great Awakenings and the Wesley revivals as people sought to live out Jesus' commandment to "love your neighbor as yourself."

The teaching of the Old Testament tells of God's covenant promise of prosperity for His people. In the teaching of the New Testament, Jesus' parable of the talents and the rewards given to the faithful stewards who used their money wisely and multiplied it, reveals a God who prospers His obedient servants. Both Old and New Covenants show that poverty and lack is the consequence of being lazy and idle.

29. What is the immutable law of the universe, ordained by God? (Galatians 6:7, Proverbs 6:10-11, 2 Thessalonians 3:10)

a._____

b._____

c._____

Prosperity is God's idea for His people. God gives His people creative ideas to lead them into prosperity. From our overflow, Christians are to reach out to first help members of the household of faith. Then we are to reach out and help others, not just by feeding the hungry, but by preaching the Gospel to them, which has the power to "lift the beggar from the dunghill and cause him to inherit the throne of glory."

Memory Verses: Ephesians 4:11-12

Worship with Twila Paris, *How Beautiful is the Body of Christ* <https://youtu.be/kJM0hFvz_64>

Worship with Russ Taff, *We will Stand* <https://youtu.be/AwcK1FEQ-i4>

Study 16: What is God's Government and Order for the Church?

God is a God of order, structure, form, and organization. The Scripture calls the Holy Spirit *rivers* of living water. A natural river without a channel is a flood. While floods help to fertilize fields, they can be very destructive. However, a river flowing inside its channel provides great benefit for the world. The force and power of the river eventually cuts its own channel over land and rock. When the Holy Spirit was poured out, the mighty rivers of God flowing through the early church eventually cut a governmental form, as the church endeavored to comply with Jesus' teaching and the leadership of the Holy Spirit. That governmental form is outlined in the Bible in the teachings of Jesus and the writing of the apostles.

1. What types of ministries are set in the body of Christ to watch over and instruct the saints? (Ephesians 4:11)

a._____   d._____

b._____   e._____

c._____

2. What are their responsibilities? (Ephesians 4:12)

a._____

b._____

3. How long will their ministries be in operation in the church? (Ephesians 4:13)_____

_____

4. As a result of these ministries, what will happen? (Ephesians 4:14-15)

_____

_____

Oversight of the Elders

5. What office of oversight has God appointed for the local church? (Acts 14:21-23)

_____

6. What are the responsibilities of the elders? (Acts 20:28; Hebrews 13:17)

a.

b.

c.

d.

7. As watchmen of the flock of God, what are the elders to do? (Ezekiel 33:2-7)

8. If the watchman fails to warn the people, whose fault is it, and who is held accountable? (Ezekiel 33:5-7)

9. If the people under the oversight of an elder refuse to take warning from their elder, who is responsible? (Ezekiel 33:4-5)

10. In light of this, what are the members of the body exhorted to do? (Hebrews 13:17; 1 Peter 5:5)

a.

b.

Proper Attitude of Overseers

11. Jesus taught that the attitude of those who are appointed as overseers in the church must be different from the attitude of the heathen. Contrast the proper attitude with the improper attitude. (Matthew 20: 25-28)

12. What attitude does Peter instruct those who have been placed in church government to have? (1 Peter 5:1-3)

13. Jesus contrasts the attitude of the scribes and Pharisees who were the overseers of the Old Covenant with what He desired the attitude of the overseers of the New Covenant to be. Compare these attitudes. (Matthew 23: 1-12)

The priesthood of every believer is one of the central features of the New Covenant. Any title or attitude that would cause anyone to first seek spiritual guidance from men, rather than from God, tends to make Christians dependent on people and usurps the place that should be given in each person's life for the personal guidance and direction of the Holy Spirit.

14. After we believe that we have received guidance from the Holy Spirit, what should we do? (Deuteronomy 17:6; Proverbs 11:14) _____

_____

15. What should our attitude be toward those who are teaching us and leading us in the ways of God? (Hebrews 13:7)_____

16. In Jesus' parable of the Good Shepherd, what did the shepherd do when he realized one of his sheep had strayed away? (Matthew 18: 12-14) _____

_____

Guarding the flock is not the attitude that all truth must come from the overseers. Jesus told His disciples that their is to be no hierarchy in the church. *The Message Bible* records Paul's directions to the Corinthian church this way: "We're not in charge of how you live out the faith, looking over your shoulders, suspiciously critical. We're partners, working alongside you, joyfully expectant. I know that you stand by your own faith, not by ours." (2 Corinthians 1:24) The Holy Spirit is given to each member of the body to lead each individual member into all truth. There was no fear for the ninety-nine who were safely in the fold. Guarding the flock is watching diligently lest any member should stumble in sin.

An Example of What it Means to Guard the Flock

This parable is illustrated in a story about the Apostle John in *Fox's Book of Martyrs*. After John returned from exile on Patmos, he went to a certain city. The Apostle John was already an old man. There he won a young man to the Lord and committed his care to the bishop of the church, asking him to take spiritual oversight of the young man. The bishop took him to his home, baptized him, and nourished him. However, after a while, he relaxed his care of the boy. The young man, now having more liberty, fell in with his old friends who were hardened in sin. He began attending their riotous banquets. They began to rob and steal. The young man became like a wild, unbroken horse without a bridle. He left the way of salvation and went with the band of thieves committing murder and other wicked crimes.

When the Apostle John returned later, he asked the bishop to present his charge. The bishop thought he meant some money. John said, "The young man, the soul of our brother I committed to your custody, I do require." When John learned what had happened he said, "A fine keeper of his brother's soul have I left here!" He then asked for a horse and guide so he could be taken to the highway where the gang of robbers lay in watch.

John was overtaken by the thieves, dismounted and said, "Take me to your captain." The men led John through the woods. As soon as the backslidden young man saw John, he was stricken with shame and began to run. But John, forgetting his age, began to run after him saying, "My son, do not fear, there is still hope for your salvation. I will answer to Christ for you, and if need be, I will die for you as Christ has died for us. Believe me, Christ has sent me."

The young man stopped, began to weep bitterly, dropped his weapons, and embraced John, weeping in repentance. John brought him back to the church, and after praying for him daily with fasting and prayer, restored him to the church and left him as proof of regeneration and a future trophy of the resurrection.

Church Discipline

17. After teaching the parable of the lost sheep, Jesus applied the principle to those going astray within the church. What should you do if you know a member of the church is caught up in a sin? (Matthew 18: 15-17)

a. _____

b. _____

c. _____

d. _____

If a person is asked to leave the fellowship because of unrepentant sin, Jesus said let him be as a sinner and a Gentile. How would we treat a sinner? We should pray for his salvation, seek to persuade him to return to Christ, and show him the love of God. In this way, the unrepentant person realizes his spiritual state and isn't deceived into thinking that he is right with God.

18. How should an accusation be brought against an elder? (1 Timothy 5:19)

_____

19. If a person is caught in a sin and desires to be restored, how should he be treated and what should be our attitude? (Galatians 6:1)

a. _____

b._____

20. We see this principle of church discipline practiced by the early church. What did Paul say that letting evil and sin remain in the church does? (1 Corinthians 5: 1-6)

_____

21. What are we exhorted to do? (1 Corinthians 5: 7) _____

_____

22. With whom are we *not* to associate? (1 Corinthians 5: 10-11)_____

_____

_____

23. How did Paul tell Timothy to treat elders, young men, older women, and young women in the church? (1 Timothy 5:1-2,17)

Elders _____

Young Men _____

Older Women _____

Young Women _____

24. Whom are we to judge, and whom does God judge? (1 Corinthians 5:12-13)

a. _____

b. _____

25. What are we to do with those "brothers" who refuse to repent of their wickedness? (1 Corinthians 5:13) _____

26. The body of Christ is spoken of in the Scriptures as a human physical body with many parts. In this passage, Jesus tells us to be ruthless against sin and not to tolerate it. What does Jesus tell us to do with infected members of the physical body that we can apply to the body of Christ? (Matthew 5:29-30)

_____

_____

The point here is not that Jesus wants us to literally gouge out our eyes or chop off our hands if they cause us to stumble into sin. He wants us to have a ruthless attitude against sin in our life and refuse to make excuses for it, or tolerate it. Peter explains, "But now you must be holy in everything you do, just as God - who chose you to be His children - is holy. For He himself has said, 'You must be holy because I am holy' "(1 Peter 1:15-16).

We see this same principle practiced among the Israelites at the time of the conquest of Canaan. God had forbidden Israel to take any spoil from the city of Jericho. In Joshua, chapter 7, we find that some Israelites acted unfaithfully to this command and took some of the things that were under the ban.

Sin in the Camp

Read Joshua, chapter 7, before you answer the following question.

27. What happened to the Israelites when they went up against Ai? (Joshua 7:4-5)

_____

28. What reason did God give Joshua for this defeat? (Joshua 7: 11)

_____

We find that the sin in the camp caused the whole assembly of Israel to be defeated before their enemies. So it is in the church.

29. God promised to be with Israel if they complied to certain conditions. What were those conditions? (Joshua 7:12)

_____

_____

30. What did God tell Israel to do? (Joshua 7:15)

_____

If sin and rebellion are allowed to remain in the church fellowship, the whole body is in danger of being infected, and the church will be defeated before her enemies.

God Disciplines His Children

31. If we are under correction and discipline, of what is this a sign? (Hebrews 12:5-8)_____

32. Why does the Lord discipline us? (Hebrews 12:10)

a. _____

b._____

33. What kind of feeling do we have when we are under discipline? (Hebrews 12:11)

_____

34. For those who have been trained by it, what does discipline yield? (Hebrews 12:11)

_____

The Government of God

35. Because of the number of Israelites, how did Moses divide the people to be governed? (Deuteronomy 1:9-15)_____

Paul teaches that the things that happened to the Israelites happened for our example. Their example of the governing of the people is a good one to follow. Therefore, the local body should be divided into smaller groups for more personal pastoring, discipleship, and counseling.

36. What problem did Moses run into that caused him to make this decision? (Exodus 18:13-18) _____

37. What were the qualifications for those who were chosen to shepherd, lead and judge the people? (Exodus 18:19-21; Deuteronomy 1:13)

a._____   e._____

b._____   f._____

c._____   g._____

d._____

38. What were their responsibilities? (Exodus 18:22)_____

_____

39. What disputes did Moses judge? (Exodus 18:22,26)_____

_____

40. How are these judgments supposed to be made? (Deuteronomy 1: 17; Isaiah 11:3-4)

a._____

b._____

c._____

41. What are the sixteen qualifications for a bishop, overseer, or elder in the New Testament? (1 Timothy 3:1-7)

1)_____

2)_____

3)_____

4)_____

5)_____

6)_____

7)_____

8)_____

9)_____

10)_____

11)_____

12)_____

13)_____

14)_____

15)_____

16)_____

42. What are the qualifications of a deacon? (1 Timothy 3:8-12)

1)_____

2)_____

3)_____

4)_____

5)_____

6)_____

7)_____

8)_____

9)_____

43. What are the qualifications of those who would be a servant of the Lord who instructs others? (2 Timothy 2:24-25)

1)_____

2)_____

3)_____

4)_____

5)_____

44. In dividing the church for more effective counseling and discipleship, who should be in charge of counseling the women? (Titus 2:3-5)_____

The older women are to counsel the younger women on personal issues - in a church dominated by young people that would be those who are older in the Lord. Likewise, the men are to personally counsel men. Any cases that are too difficult, or cannot be settled, must be brought before the elders for judgment and further discernment.

This study covers the basic order, authority, and discipline for the church. If a local body of believers follows this order, it will be strong in the Lord. Each member will be personally connected with other members of the body, and each member will have his or her needs met. The body of Christ will be a holy place where Jesus can dwell in great power and glory. The church will rise up in victory and be able to instruct entire nations in Christ's teaching.

Memory Verse: Hebrews 13:17

The Church's One Foundation - *Samuel Wesley, 1866*

The Church's One Foundation is Jesus Christ her Lord;

She is His New creation by water and the Word,

From heaven He came and sought her to be His holy bride,

With His own blood He bought her and for her life He died.

Worship with this great hymn of the church: *The Church's One Foundation,*
<http://goo.gl/ASCJ0h>

Worship with the Maranatha Singers, *Lord Make Me a Servant,*
<https://goo.gl/clpnzu>

Study 17: What is God's Plan for Prosperity And Giving?

Financial prosperity is part of God's Covenantal promise under both the Old and New Covenants. Poverty is part of the curse that comes on those who are disobedient to God. However, those who are ignorant of God's great blessings can also experience financial lack. Jesus came to lift the curse from the earth. Living in financial lack and limitation is not the will of God. Jesus proclaimed that He came "that we might have life and have it abundantly, that it might be full and meaningful" (John 10:10). According to the Scripture, it is God's will that we have more than enough for our needs and an abundance to share and give to others. God isn't poor. He wants to give good things to His sons and daughters. He wants us to be just like Him.

To the Corinthian church, Paul explained, "Jesus became poor so He could make the many rich" (2 Cor. 8:9). Paul reminded the church at Philippi, "And this same God who takes care of me will supply all your needs from His glorious riches, which have been given to us in Christ Jesus" (Phil. 4:19). The Bible is full of promises for financial prosperity which is your Divine heritage as the child of God. As we look at the promises in God's Word, we will see the great blessings that the Lord has stored up for those who will believe and obey Him.

1. What are two basic prosperity principles?

a. (Malachi 3:8-12) _____

b. (Matthew 6:25-33) _____

2. How does a man rob God? (Malachi 3:8)_____

_____

3. What is the tithe? (Nehemiah 10:38)_____

_____

4. Besides one-tenth of their wages, what else did Israel pay tithes on? (Leviticus 27:30, 32)

a. _____

b. _____

c. _____

d. _____

While most people today are not farmers and don't have agricultural products or farm animals to make a tithe on, we can understand this Scripture still refers to a tenth of all our increase. This is what we owe God. It is not a gift. The tenth part belongs to Him. In addition to the tithe, God also asked Israel to give contributions and offerings.

5. How is a contribution determined? (Exodus 25:2; Exodus 35:5)

_____

6. What happens if we fail to pay the tithe and give contributions? (Malachi 3:9)

_____

Who Receives Our Tithe

7. Where do we put our tithe, and to whom is it given? (Malachi 3:10; Nehemiah 10:38)

_____

8. For what is the tithe used? (Malachi 3:10; Numbers 18:21, 24)

_____

Therefore, we see that the tithe is used to supply the needs of the ministry and the needs of those who minister to you.

9. Do the ministers pay tithes? (Numbers 18:26) _____

God's Blessing Released through Tithing

10. As we give God the part of our income that belongs to Him, what will He do for us? (Malachi 3:10) _____

11. What will the Lord rebuke for us? (Malachi 3:11) _____

12. How did Abraham give his tithe to God? (Genesis 14:18-20)

_____

13. Although Melchizedek, the Priest of God, received the tithe, who ultimately receives the tithe we give on earth? (Hebrews 7:8)

_____

14. When Abraham gave God a tenth of all, what did God do for him? (Genesis 13:2; 24:1,35) _____

So according to the Word of God, when we give our tithes on earth to support Christian ministry, and those who minister to us, God receives them to our account in heaven, and He is the one who blesses our giving and our lives.

15. As we honor the Lord with our produce and with the first-fruits of our wealth, what will happen? (Proverbs 3:9-10) _____

Jacob's Covenant with God for Provision

16. What three things did Jacob desire for the Lord to do for him? (Genesis 28:20)

a. _____

b. _____

c. _____

17. What did Jacob promise to give God in return? (Genesis 28:22)

_____

18. God blessed Jacob with great riches. Describe the gift that he gave to his brother Esau? (Genesis 32:13-15) _____

_____

_____

When God delivered Israel from Egyptian slavery, God caused the Egyptians to give the Israelites gold, silver, beautiful tapestries, and all kinds of riches.

19. God told Moses to take up an offering from the children of Israel for the construction of the tabernacle. What did they have to give? What type of offering was this? (Exodus 25:1-2)_____

20. What did the Lord tell Moses to take up in the offering? (Exodus 25:3-8)

_____

_____

_____

21. What happened when Moses took up the offering? Summarize (Exodus 35:20-29; 36:5-7)_____

_____

_____

22. Under the Old Covenant, what promise of prosperity is given to those who love God and keep His commandments? (Deuteronomy 28:8-12)

a. _____

b. _____

c. _____

d. _____

e. _____

Under Old Covenant blessing, the great men of the Bible prospered with riches and the great bounty of the Lord. Israel became a nation of the extremely wealthy. Lack and want came to Israel when they despised God's law and turned away from His covenant.

23. What was the condition for God's blessing? (Deuteronomy 28:9,13)

_____

24. Why are people under that curse of poverty, and what is that curse? (Deuteronomy 28:15, 47-48)

a. _____

b. _____

Under the Old Covenant, God continually showed Himself as Israel's Provider. Every day in the wilderness, they were fed with manna that fell from heaven. Their clothes and shoes never wore out. God brought three million quail into the camp when they were hungry for meat, and He brought water out of a rock so they could drink. He ultimately led them into a land flowing with milk and honey that He had promised to His servant Abraham.

25. Describe the Promised Land. (Deuteronomy 8:7-9)_____

_____

_____

As long as Israel loved God and kept His commandments, the whole nation was blessed with prosperity and joy.

26. Are the promises of financial blessing for Abraham and Israel only? Who are they for? (Galatians 3:28-29)_____

Memory Verses: Malachi 3:10-11

_____

_____

_____

_____

_____

_____

Worship with Keith Green *The Lord is My Shepherd* <http://goo.gl/c8fhci>

Worship with Maurice Skylar *Jehovah Jireh, My Provider,* <http://goo.gl/vrd0xW>

Study 18: The New Covenant and Prosperity Economics

Under the New Covenant, we have a better covenant and better promises. When Jesus was born, He was given rich gifts by the Magi. His first miracle produced the finest wine. His seamless robe that He wore was so valuable that Roman soldiers gambled for it at the foot of the cross. He told His disciples where to catch fish, and there were so many fish their boats began to sink. He multiplied the bread from a few loaves and fed the five thousand. He sent His disciples out to preach without any financial provision. When they returned, they came back and reported that they "lacked nothing." He sent Peter out to pay the taxes and told him to go catch a fish, open the fish's mouth, and the money would be in it.

Jesus taught and demonstrated prosperity economics. In His parable about the lost son, Jesus reinforced the Old Covenant teaching of the financial rewards of living inside God's covenant and the dire financial results that followed those who gave themselves over to a life of sin.

1. What happened to the son who turned against God's covenant and went and indulged in drunkenness and riotous living? (Luke 15:11-17)

_____

2. What financial blessing awaited the wayward son when he returned to his father's house? (Luke 15:17-24) _____

_____

Over the years, controversy and misunderstanding have arisen over Jesus' statement: "Blessed are the poor in spirit for theirs is the kingdom of heaven." This does not mean that there is a blessing in being poor. A person who is "poor in spirit" is a person who is humble and recognizes his deep spiritual need for salvation and God's blessing. It is only when we recognize our need that God can come to our aid. And we have this promise from Jesus, that if we recognize our spiritual poverty and our need for Him, the kingdom of heaven will be ours.

Some people believe that poverty is a virtue, however, according to Scripture, poverty is not spiritual. Poverty drives people to despair, to depression, to drink, to prostitution. It fills jails with people who steal or push drugs for a living. It is a miserable state of affairs. During the history of the church in the medieval ages, because the Word of God was not readily available to people, a doctrine that it was a Christian virtue to be poor in the necessities of life began to be widely taught and believed. To keep the people under control, the medieval church in conjunction with rich feudal lords taught the people that the poorer you were, the more you were spiritual and blessed by God. Unsuspecting millions came to believe that this was a spiritual truth. Feudal lords who counted on the lower classes to do all their work for them supported a church who offered "poverty and penance" as a way of salvation.

This was a convenient teaching for those in authority who wanted to keep the people subservient to the state, who exploited the poor, and kept the wealth for themselves. When the Bible was distributed to the masses during the Reformation, these ideas began to be proven false in the light of God's Word. People began to gain a new understanding of God's teaching on wealth and poverty, and eventually the biblical teaching on prosperity economics gave birth to a new economic system.

The Law of Sowing and Reaping

Jesus reinforced the Old Covenant idea of giving and the spiritual law of sowing and reaping.

3. Who taught Israel about prosperity under the Old Covenant? (Isaiah 48:17)

---

4. When we give, what did Jesus teach will be given back to us? (Luke 6:38)

---

5. In what measure or proportion will it be given back to us? (Luke 6:38)

---

6. What is the law of sowing and reaping? (2 Corinthians 9:6)

---

7. What attitude should be avoided in giving? (2 Corinthians 9:7)

---

8. What kind of giver does God love? (2 Corinthians 9:7)

---

9. What is God able to do? (2 Corinthians 9:8)

a.

b.

10. What will the Lord supply? (2 Corinthians 9:10)

a._____

b._____

Hoarding and Greed

Therefore, as we give bountifully, the Lord will supply us with an extra amount - not to hoard - but to use and give out to meet the needs of others.

11. What are we exhorted to be on guard against? (Luke 12:15)

_____

12. Of what does life not consist? (Luke 12: 15)

_____

13. What type of man was the farmer who hoarded his crops for himself, and what was his end result? (Luke 12:16-20)_____

14. Who is this parable about? (Luke 12:21)_____

15. What is a grievous evil? (Ecclesiastes 5:13) _____

16. What can choke out the Word? (Matthew 13:22) _____

Surplus versus Sacrificial Giving

17. What two types of givers are there? (Luke 21:1-4)

a. _____

b. _____

18. Which person did Jesus say gave the most? (Luke 21: 1-3)

_____

19. As riches increase, what must we be careful not to do? (Psalm 62:10)

_____

20. Where will your heart be? (Matthew 6:21)_____

21. What are we exhorted to do? (Matthew 6: 19-20) _____

22. What is the root of all evil? (1 Timothy 6: 10) _____

23. God wants us to have prosperity. However if we set our hearts on riches and long for them and focus our lives on obtaining them, what can happen? (1 Timothy 6:9-10)

a. _____

b. _____

c. _____

24. What will happen to the generous man? (Proverbs 11:25)

_____

25. As we give bountifully, what will happen? (2 Corinthians 9:11-12)

a. _____

b. _____

c. _____

Economics of Personal Responsibility

Jesus taught the importance of personal responsibility and stewardship. In His parable of the talents, Jesus told about a rich landowner who distributed talents (money) to his servants according to their ability. He then asked them to do business with the money until he returned.

Read Matthew 25:14-30, then answer the questions below:

26. What did the man who was given five talents do with his money, and what was his master's response? (Matthew 25:15-16, 20-21 KJV)

a. _____

b. _____

27. What did the man who was given two talents do with his money, and what was his master's response? (Matthew 25:17, 22-23 KJV)

a._____

b._____

28. What did the man who was given one talent do with his money, what was his master's response, and what was the servant's punishment? (Matthew 25:18,24-30 KJV)

a._____

b._____

c._____

29. Did the master re-distribute the wealth and take some of the money from the man who had ten talents and give it to the man with one? What did the master do? (Matthew 25:28-30)

_____

30. What moral did Jesus draw from this story? (Matthew 25:29)

From this parable of the stewards, we can see that government planning and redistribution of wealth is not God's idea for helping the poor. In the King James Bible, the preeminent English Bible for centuries, the word for *money* was translated as *talent*. In fact, Jesus' *parable of the talents* became so ingrained in the thoughts of the English speaking world that the word *talent,* which originally was money, came to stand for *all the gifts and abilities that God has given to the individual.*

Basis of America's Economic Model

The Founders of the United States, steeped in the knowledge of the Bible, developed a new kind of economics for the world based on the teachings of Jesus. The Founders believed that it was God's will that men and women prosper and keep the fruit of their increase. They believed that they were to use all their gifts, talents (abilities), and money that they had been given for the glory of God. They developed a cultural climate of freedom and small government that made it possible for people to keep the fruit of their labor so they could use it to create their future.

The Bible teaches that we should give to the poor and help lift them up. We should not just give them fish, but teach them "how" to fish. This is to be by freewill offerings, not by government-mandated theft. Modern-day philanthropic organizations and charities were initially Christian ideas that were birthed out of the Second Great Awakening.

31. When we have a feast, who should we invite and what will be our reward? (Luke 14:12-14) _____

_____

The greatest thing that we can ultimately do for the poor is preach the Gospel to them and show them how to enter into God's covenant for blessing and prosperity. It is a matter of historical record that wherever the Gospel is preached and people embrace it, prosperity will eventually follow for the individual, society, and nation.

32. What is God able to do? (1 Samuel 2:8) _____

_____

33. What does the Old Covenant teach about poverty and personal responsibility? Look up the following verses in the book of Proverbs:

a.(6:10-11) _____

b.(13:18) _____

c.(21:5) _____

d.(22:16) _____

e.(23:20-21) _____

f.(28:19-20) _____

g.(28:22) _____

h.(28:27) _____

34. What did Paul teach about personal responsibility and what promise do we have?" (Galatians 6:7-9) _____

_____

35. If people are lazy, what does Paul teach? (2 Thessalonians 3:10)

_____

Seeking God's Kingdom First and His Righteousness

36. What three things are we exhorted not to be anxious about? (Matthew 6:25)

a. _____

b. _____

c. _____

37. Who eagerly seeks these things? (Matthew 6:32) _____

38. If the Gentiles or unbelievers are seeking these things, what should the believer be seeking? (Matthew 6:33) _____

39. As a result, what will happen? (Matthew 6:33) _____

_____

40. Therefore, since we have been raised up with Christ, what should we keep seeking and on what should we focus our minds? (Colossians 3: 1-2) _____

_____

41. One day Peter asked Jesus, "We have left all to follow you, what will we have?"
What was Jesus' promise? (Mark 10:28-30) _____

_____

_____

42. What was John's desire for the church? (3 John 1:2) _____

_____

43. What was the secret of Joseph's success even in slavery and prison? (Genesis 39:2-4)

_____

44. What will happen to the man who fears the Lord? (Psalm 25:12-13)

45. What type of man was Job? (Job 1:1)_____

46. After Job's trial, describe the blessings that God gave Job. (Job 42:12-16)

47. What did Solomon ask God, and what did God give him? (2 Chronicles 1:7-12)

a._____

b._____

48. What will the Lord give to those who walk uprightly? (Psalm 84:11)

49. What will God give to those who fear Him and seek Him? (Psalm 34:9-10)

50. Describe the person who prospers in everything that he does. (Psalm 1:1-3)

a._____

b._____

c._____

d._____

e._____

51. What did David write about God's provision? (Psalm 23, summarize)

Memory Verse: Luke 6:38

Worship with Robin Mark, *Here is Love* <https://youtu.be/v8YOPj5TnUM>
(This hymn is known as the love song of the Welsh Revival 1905, where the Modern day outpouring of the Baptism of the Holy Spirit began.)

Worship - *Seek Ye First the Kingdom of God* <http://goo.gl/25USqZ>

Study 19: What is the Great Commission?

The Psalmist David foretold, "The king proclaims the Lord's decree, 'Ask of Me and I will give you the nations for your inheritance, the uttermost parts of the earth for your possession'" (Psalm 2:7). When Jesus died on the cross, arose from the dead, and ascended into heaven, He took His redeeming blood and sprinkled it on the Mercy Seat in heaven, and according to His Father's promise, He surely proclaimed, "Mine! I claim every nation!" After His resurrection, Jesus appeared to His disciples on a mountain in Galilee where He had told them to meet Him and commissioned them saying, "I have been given all authority in heaven and on earth. Go make disciples of all nations, baptize them...and teach them to obey everything I have taught you. And I will be with you to the end of the age!" (Matt. 28:16-20 NAS and NLT)

To oppose Jesus and to fight against His eternal decree to make disciples of all nations is to be on the wrong side of history. The Creator of the earth has redeemed every nation and claimed them for His own. Who can ultimately stop Him and keep Him from realizing His purpose. It is just a matter of time before "all the earth will worship Him and sing praises to His name."

The Apostle John in exile on the Isle of Patmos received the confirmation from his angelic visitor. As the trumpet sounded, John heard voices in heaven call out, "The kingdoms of this world have become the kingdoms of our God and of His Christ and He will reign forever!" (Revelation 11:15). In time and in history, this is God's divine project in every nation. This is the pinnacle toward which all of history is moving.

To accomplish this task, Jesus commissioned all His followers to tell the whole world about the Great News of the Gospel and teach the whole world to observe His commandments in every age for all time to come. Not only that, He promised always to be working with us to accomplish this great endeavor.

1. When Jesus called His disciples to forsake all and follow Him, what promise did He give them? (Matthew 4:19)_____

2. What did Jesus preach? (Matthew 4:17; Mark 1:14-15) _____
_____

3. What was the "Great Commission" that Jesus gave to His disciples? (Luke 24:47-48; Matthew 28:18-20)

a. _____

b. _____

c. _____

d. _____

4. What signs did Jesus promise would follow the preaching of the Gospel? (Mark 16:15-20)

a. _____

b. _____

c. _____

d. _____

e. _____

5. Give some of the signs that followed Paul. (Acts 28:1-10; 19:6) _____
_____

6. What did Paul say was necessary for the Good News of the Gospel to be made known to all people? (Romans 10:14-15) _____
_____

7. What did the disciples preach? (Acts 4:2; 17:18) _____
_____

8. What was Paul told to do? (Acts 9: 15-16; 22:15) _____
_____

9. What did Paul continue to do from the day that he came to know Jesus? (Acts 26:22)
_____

Anointed to be a Witness

10. What power has Jesus given to all those who have received the Holy Spirit? (Acts 1:8) _____

11. What does a wise Christian do? (Proverbs 11:30) _____

12. What does Paul say that he did in preaching the Gospel and why? (1 Corinthians 9:19-23) (Summarize) _____
_____

13. When the Pharisees questioned the man born blind, what did he answer from his own experience? (John 9:25-33)

14. What happened as a result of his testimony? (John 9:34)

Persecution for the Gospel

15. What will be three areas of conflict as a result of our testimony? (Matthew 10: 17-18, 36)

a.

b.

c.

16. When we are asked to give our witness and defense for the Gospel, what did Jesus promise us? (Matthew 10:19)

17. Who actually will be speaking through us? (Matthew 10:20)

18. What did Jesus tell His disciples about being afraid of persecution? (Matthew 10:28-30)

19. When Stephen was questioned by the synagogue leaders about Jesus, what happened? (Acts 6:10)

20. What two things should we talk about and make known to other people? (1 Chronicles 16:8, 9)

a.

b.

21. When people opposed Paul's testimony at Corinth, what did God tell him? (Acts 18:9)

22. What does the fear of man bring? (Proverbs 29:25)

23. When we are persecuted for righteousness' sake, what did Jesus say that we should do and why? (Matthew 5:10-12)

24. When some of the apostles were thrown in prison for preaching the Gospel in the temple, an angel came and let them out. What did the angel tell them? (Acts 5:19-20)

It is interesting to note that the angel told them to go right back to the temple where they were first arrested and thrown in prison and preach again.

25. When questioned about this, what did Peter say? (Acts 5:25-29)_____

Standing Strong in the Face of Opposition

26. What instruction did Paul give Timothy concerning the preaching of the Gospel?
(2 Timothy 1:8) _____

27. If we confess Him before men, what will He do for us? (Matthew 10:32)_____

28. If we deny Him before men, what will He do to us? (Matthew 10:33) _____

29. What did Jesus tell the disciples to preach? (Matthew 10:27)

a. _____

b. _____

30. What did the Lord tell Jeremiah that those who preach in His name should do, and what will be the results? (Jeremiah 23:18, 21-22) _____

31. What is God's Word like? (Jeremiah 23:29) _____

It is not our job to try to convict people of sin or convince them of the Gospel. It is just our job to speak to people the words that God wants them to hear. The Word of God, the power of Truth, has the power in itself to accomplish what God sends it to do.

32. Who will convict the world of sin, righteousness, and judgment? (John 16:7-11) _____

33. Why did Paul say he was free from the blood of all men at Ephesus? (Acts 20:26-27) _____

34. What was Paul's attitude toward his own life and the ministry that God had given him? (Acts 20:22-24) _____

35. What was Paul able to say before his execution? (2 Timothy 4:6-8)

a._____

b._____

c._____

d._____

Rewards for the Faithful

36. What reward is laid up for all faithful witnesses? (2 Timothy 4:8)

_____

37. What will happen to those who turn many to righteousness? (Daniel 12:3)

_____

38. When we turn a sinner from the error of his way, what else will we be doing? (James 5:20)

a. _____

b. _____

39. What will happen to those who sow the Word of God in tears? (Psalm 126:5-6)

a. _____

b. _____

40. What did Jesus say happens in heaven when one sinner repents? (Luke 15:7,10)_____

Laborers for the Harvest

41. How did Jesus feel when He beheld the multitudes and why? (Matthew 9:36)

_____

42. What did Jesus say about the harvest and the workers? (Matthew 9:37)

_____

43. For what did the Lord tell us to pray? (Matthew 9:38)

_____

44. Who are those who are blessed by God? (Isaiah 32:20) (The ox and donkey are animals that work in the harvest fields, and in allegory, represent the ministers and laborers of the gospel).

a._____

b._____

45. What does Jesus say to those who put off evangelizing the lost to some future date? (John 4:35) _____

46. What does the Word say about sowing and reaping, planting and watering? (John 4:37; 1 Corinthians 3:6-7) _____

_____

47. How will each be rewarded? (1 Corinthians 3:8)_____

_____

48. What example did David set forth in this area? (1 Samuel 30:22-24)

49. Into what are those who go out to reap sometimes entering? (John 4:38)

50. Therefore, what should he who sows and he who reaps do? (John 4:36)

51. How will you overcome the enemy? (Revelation 12:11)

a.

b.

c.

Spectacular miracles, signs, and wonders followed the apostles and those who witnessed about Jesus wherever they went.

52. What happened to Paul in Antioch? (Acts 14:19-20)

53. What does Paul remind the believers to do? (Acts 14:22)

54. When Paul was in Philippi, he cast a demon of fortune telling out of a slave girl. What happened to him there? (Acts 16:19-40) Summarize.

The Jews had stirred up intense persecution against Paul and had him arrested requesting his death. The mobs were so violent that the soldiers had to lift Paul over their shoulders to whisk him away from the crowd. They took Paul inside to question him. When they ordered him to be whipped, Paul revealed that he was a Roman citizen and demanded to be taken to Rome for trial.

Because Paul was born as a Roman citizen, he was of higher rank than the arresting officer. The Roman commander held him in custody but treated Paul with respect. Paul's nephew learned of a plot that forty Jews had devised to kill Paul. When the commander learned of this secret plot, he had Paul taken out of the city under guard.

55. Describe the military guard that took Paul from the city to protect him against the Jews. (Acts 23:23-24)

All the apostles, except one, sealed their testimony of Jesus in their blood. Peter died upon a cross upside down. James was dragged behind a horse until his brains were dashed out on the ground. Others were beheaded and were fed to the lions. John was boiled in oil. When that didn't work, they exiled him to a desert island to work as an old man in the stone quarries. John was so filled with the life of God, he survived and was finally released and returned to preach the Gospel at Ephesus. Through these twelve men and all those who followed Jesus and their converts, the Gospel of the Kingdom was preached throughout the known world. Multitudes came into the kingdom of God, and they all continued to spread the Word. Today most of us have freedom to preach the Gospel unhindered. Think how the world would be changed if we would dedicate our lives to preach the Gospel regardless of our arena of service.

56. What should be our attitude? (2 Timothy 2:3) _____

57. What should we avoid? (2 Timothy 2:4)_____

58. Besides a soldier, to what two things does Paul compare us? (2 Timothy 2:5-6)
a. _____ b. _____

59. What should we do and why? (2 Timothy 2:10)

_____

60. How will you know where to fish for men, and what will be the eventual result? (Luke 5:4-10)_____

_____

Memory Verse: Acts 20:24

_____

_____

_____

Worship - *Thank You for Giving to the Lord* <https://youtu.be/Kkn5iMB840g>

Watch Jesus raising Lazarus from the dead <https://youtu.be/vPormnnx1aw>

Watch Jesus preach to the Woman at the Well, *The Visual Bible*
<https://youtu.be/NzC5yCHvSSY>

Watch Jesus commissioning His disciples *The Visual Bible* <http://goo.gl/nM65GF>

Worship, *Worthy is the Lamb* <http://goo.gl/kQrwhW>

Watch Africa responding to the Great Commission <https://youtu.be/MBtBHZtdU78>

Study 20: What is the Second Coming of Jesus, The Resurrection of the Dead and the Eternal Judgment?

1. When Jesus was taken up into heaven, what promise did the angels give concerning Him? (Acts 1:9-11) _____

2. When the Lord descends from heaven with a shout, what will happen? (1 Thessalonians 4:16-17)

a._____

b._____

3. For those who are alive and remain until the coming of the Lord, what type of change will take place in them when He appears? (1 Corinthians 15:41-44, 51-53)

_____

4. Over what will this be a victory? (1 Corinthians 15:54-55) _____

5. a. How long must Jesus reign in heaven before His return? (1 Corinthians 15:25)

_____

b. Hebrews emphasizes this truth. Although all things have been put under His feet in heaven, what is Jesus waiting for on earth? (Ephesians 1:21-22; Hebrews 9:13)

_____

Jesus is the head of the church, and we are His body here on the earth. "Heaven is His throne and earth is His footstool" (Acts 7:49). As followers of Jesus Christ, we are His feet on the earth. It is through preaching the Gospel and obeying the Gospel that we put all His enemies under our feet and His.

6. What is the last enemy to be destroyed? (1 Corinthians 15:26) _____

Changed into His Image

7. We have learned that the saints will receive a resurrection body when Jesus appears. What other change takes place in us meanwhile? (2 Corinthians 3: 18)

_____

8. How does this transformation into the likeness and image of Jesus take place? (2 Corinthians 3: 18) _____

As we behold God's glory with the eyes of our spirit in daily fellowship with Jesus through praise, worship, and prayer, through taking the Lord's Supper and meditating on God's Word, we become more and more like Him. The final consummation of this transformation will take place at the return of the Lord when death is swallowed up in victory.

9. Jesus was a Lamb without spot or wrinkle. What kind of church does He intend us to be? (Ephesians 5:25-27)

a._____

b._____

c._____

10. How will this cleansing be accomplished in the church? (Ephesians 5:26)

_____

11. To what are we predestined? (Romans 8:29)

_____

12. What does it mean to be conformed to the image of Jesus? (Ephesians 4:24)

_____

The Righteous Acts of the Saints

13. What is said about the bride of Christ in Revelation? (Revelation 19:7)

_____

14. What is the fine linen with which she is clothed? (Revelation 19:8)

_____

James explains the righteous acts of the saints and tells us that faith without works is dead.

15. What examples does James give of righteous acts? (James 2:15-26)

a. (15-17) _____

b. (21-23) _____

c. (25) _____

Works that are the result of our faith and obedience to God's direction show themselves in deeds of compassion for others, especially for fellow believers.

16. What did Jesus point out as righteous acts? (Matthew 25:31-36)

a. (35)_____ d. (36) _____

b. (35)_____   e. (36) _____

c. (35)_____   f. (36) _____

Purity of Heart and Life

17. What does everyone who has the "hope" of being transformed into the image of Jesus do before He returns? (1 John 3:2-3)_____

18. How are we to live in this present age? (Titus 2:12)

a. _____

b. _____

19. In agreement with Jesus' high priestly prayer, what must be seen in the church by the world as a witness and testimony of Jesus? (John 17:18,21-23)

a. _____

b. _____

c. _____

d. _____

Jesus was a Lamb without spot or wrinkle, anointed with the Holy Spirit and power, healing the sick and destroying the works of the devil. Jesus manifested the nature of God before the world. Before the end comes, Jesus will return, not for a weak defeated and sickly church hiding out in the wilderness, but for a victorious and holy bride anointed with the Holy Spirit and power, who goes around doing good and healing all oppressed by the devil just as Jesus did.

The victorious church, washed in the water of the Word, is glorious and holy within and without. She goes forth in the power of the Holy Spirit, healing the sick, raising the dead, casting out demons, setting the captives free. She is a conquering church. She is mighty and powerful in the earth as she endeavors to go forth and disciple the nations, teaching them the ways of the Lord.

20. Jesus was perfectly led by the Spirit of God. What are some of the things that characterized His life? These are the characteristics that should be seen in our lives as we are led by His Spirit and as we are transformed into His image by the power of His Spirit working in us. (John 5:19-20, 30; 12:45-50; 18:38)

a. (5:19)_____

b. (5:20)_____

c. (5:30)_____

d. (5:30)_____

e. (12:49-50)_____

f. (12:45) _____

g. (18:38)_____

The Eternal Judgment

21. At the Great White Throne Judgment at the end of days, when the dead are judged, who is thrown into the lake of fire along with the devil and his angels? (Read Revelation 20:11-15, 21:8)

a._____

b._____ f._____

c._____ g._____

d._____ h._____

e._____ i._____

According to John who are those categorized with the liars? (1 John 22:2)

j. _____

Who will not be able to inherit the kingdom of God? (1 Corinthians 6: 9-10)

k._____ n._____ q._____ t._____

l._____ o._____ r. _____

m._____ p._____ s. _____

22. The members of the church at Sardis were involved with evil deeds. What did the Lord say that He would do for those who overcame this evil and repented and turned back to Him? (Rev. 3:2-6, answer from v5)_____

23. How can you know that you are a child of God? (1 John 5:1-3)

a. _____

b. _____

c. _____

24. How do you overcome the evil of this world? (1 John 5: 4-5)

a. _____

b. _____

c. _____

25. How can you know you have eternal life? (1 John 5:9-13)

a. _____

b. _____

c. _____

Being Alert and Ready

26. What attitude does Jesus exhort us to have concerning His coming? (Luke 12:35-40)_____

_____

27. Jesus gives a parable about four types of servants and their rewards at the Master's return. Describe them and their rewards. (Luke 12:42-48)

Faithful Servant: _____

Reward: _____

Drunken Servant: _____

Reward:_____

Lazy Servant: _____

Reward:_____

Ignorant Servant:_____

Reward:_____

28. Jesus told another parable of ten virgins. Five were wise and five were foolish. Who went in to the marriage feast? (Matthew 25:1-13)_____

Everyone there was a virgin (signifying those undefiled by the world) and all were waiting for the bridegroom. Five let their light go out. They represent foolish believers who did not tend to the fires of their heart in spending time and fellowship with the Lord. They quit growing spiritually and did not continue in obedient acts of faith and charity. Salvation, Baptism in Water and the Holy Spirit, and sanctification are not to be our final resting place. These experiences are just the doorway to new life in Christ and the adventure of the Spirit that lies ahead.

29. What did Jesus say that His followers were to do? What were people to see? (Matthew 5:14-16)

a._____

b._____

30. How will the day of the Lord come to the unrighteous? (1 Thessalonians 5:2-3)_____

31. How will the day of the Lord come to the righteous? (1 Thessalonians 5:4-8)_____

32. What promise do we have from the Lord? (Amos 3:7)

_____

Memory Verses: 1 John 3:2-3

_____

_____

_____

_____

We Shall Behold Him

- Dottie Rambo

The sky shall unfold, preparing His entrance;
The stars shall applaud Him with thunders of praise.
The sweet light in His eyes shall enhance those awaiting;
And we shall behold Him then face to face.

O we shall behold Him, we shall behold Him
Face to face in all of His glory
O we shall behold Him, yes we shall behold Him
Face to face, our Savior and Lord

The angel shall sound,
The shout of His coming,
The sleeping shall rise from their slumbering place.
And those who remain,
Shall be changed in a moment,
And we shall behold Him then face to face.

We shall behold Him, o yes we shall behold Him
Face to face in all of His glory
We shall behold Him, face to face
Our Savior and Lord
We shall behold Him, our Savior and Lord
Savior and Lord!

Worship with Sandi Patti, *We Shall Behold Him* <https://youtu.be/KZ3H3lg9NZM>

Worship with Keith Green, *The Easter Song* <http://goo.gl/YYFyja>

Worship with Michael English, *I Bowed on My Knees and Cried Holy*
<https://youtu.be/ouvfpmgP7D0>

Worship with the Gaithers, *The King is Coming* <https://youtu.be/hBNhNffsNMo>

Study 21: The End of the Old Age
The Beginning of the New

1. Peter preached to the Jewish people on the day of Pentecost (Shavuot) and explained that the Holy Spirit had been poured out. What day did Peter say had begun? (Acts 2:16-17)

_____

Peter told the Jewish people on Pentecost that the *last days* had begun. When Peter preached his first sermon after the outpouring of the Holy Spirit, four thousand years of the recorded history of the world had passed. The Jewish people had now entered into the last days of temple worship. Peter explained that these were the last days foretold by the prophet Joel when the Holy Spirit would be poured out on all people.

During the Mosaic Age under Old Covenant law, no one but the High Priest could enter the Holiest of All where the Shekinah glory hovered over the Mercy Seat. The High Priest could only go in once a year and had to bring blood.

2. What did Jesus do for the human race? (Hebrews 10:19-20)_____

_____

The veil of the temple had been rent from the top down, torn by an angel's hand, on the day Jesus was crucified. The way had been opened into the Hoy of Holies through Jesus' blood. Now all believers were invited to receive the very Presence of God into their blood-washed hearts. The Holy Spirit had moved out of the Jewish temple made with hands to take up His home in the hearts of believing people everywhere.

3. What did Peter say about this stunning event of salvation and the outpouring of the Holy Spirit that had just changed human history forever? (1 Peter 1: 10-12)

_____

_____

_____

A new era of human history began on that day that was not possible before the death and resurrection of Jesus. Since that day, for 2,000 years the Holy Spirit has been establishing the kingdom of God in the hearts of believers through the preaching the Good News of redemption through Jesus' atoning blood. During this current period of history through the preaching of the Gospel and the outpouring of the Holy Spirit, God will sum up the entire world in Jesus, and "the kingdoms of this world will become the kingdom of our God and of His Christ." Everyday we should eagerly greet our glorious Lord in our hearts. We should anticipate with joy the blessed hope of His glorious appearing. We are to follow the Lord, being transformed into His image and being led by His Spirit to do acts of righteousness. Jesus promised His disciples that the Holy Spirit would "lead them into all truth and show them things to come." God will reveal His counsel in our midst, and we will know and understand what He is doing in the earth and the times in which we live.

Jesus' Prophecies About Jerusalem and Temple Worship

Out of His great love, Jesus warned the Jewish people about the future of their temple worship and the judgment that was coming.

4. What did Jesus prophesy about the Jewish temple? (Matthew 24:1)

_____

5. What did Jesus prophesy would happen to the Jewish nation because they rejected His redemptive work? (Luke 13: 37; 19:41-44)

a._____

b._____

_____

_____

_____

Jesus' prophecies were fulfilled in 70 AD when Roman legions under the direction of Titus laid siege to Jerusalem, built a wall around it and dug a trench around it so none could escape. Because the Jews refused to surrender and end their rebellion against Rome, the Roman army relentlessly attacked the city until they tore down its walls, brutally slaughtered the Jewish people who remained in Jerusalem, and destroyed the temple leaving no stone on top of another.

6. Jesus foretold this event. Extending His mercy to all who would believe in Him, what did Jesus tell the believing Jews in Jerusalem to do when they saw things lining up for this event to take place? (Matthew 24:16-20)

_____

_____

_____

Eusebius, Early Church Father of the fourth century, in his *Ecclesiastical History*, described the events which preceded the destruction of Jerusalem by the Roman army. Copies of his history still exist today in Greek, Latin, Syraic, and Armenian. At first, the Roman army surrounded the city of Jerusalem and then left. When the Christians in Jerusalem saw this sign that Jesus had predicted they fled Jerusalem, just as Jesus had instructed them to do. Esubius records:

> The whole body of the church of Jerusalem, having been commanded by a divine revelation, given to men of approved piety there before the war, removed from the city, and dwelt at a certain town beyond the Jordan, called Pella. Here those that believed in Jesus dwelt, having removed from Jerusalem, as if holy men had entirely abandoned the royal city itself, and the whole land of Judea. (3:5:3)

The *Zondervan Pictorial Encyclopedia of the Bible* also mentions Pella: "In 66 AD, the city of Pella became a refuge for *followers of Jesus* who were fleeing Jerusalem because the Roman army was coming to quiet a Jewish revolt. Pella continued as a strong Christian city throughout the prosperous Byzantine period." (Vol. 4, p. 672)

7. The book of James, believed to be written by James, Jesus' own flesh and blood brother and head of the church in Jerusalem, warned the Jews of this impending judgment. What did James tell them? (James 5:1-9) Summarize.

The prophet Daniel, also spoke of the coming of Messiah the Prince. Daniel foretold that Messiah would "finish transgression, make an end of sin, make atonement for iniquity, and bring in everlasting righteousness." Messiah would establish a firm covenant (the New Covenant) with many. This would be followed by the destruction of the city of Jerusalem and the sanctuary and the end of sacrifices. (Daniel 9:24-27) The destruction of the temple and of Jerusalem marked the end of the Old Mosaic order of ritual, animal sacrifice, and temple worship, and the establishment of the Messianic Era of the New Covenant. This marked was the end of the "last days" that Peter spoke of on the Day of Pentecost.

8. As long as the temple was still standing and the Aaronic priesthood continued, what did it signify? (Hebrews 9:7-8)_____

_____

9. Why was the temple, animal sacrifices, and the Levitical priesthood after the order of Aaron no longer needed? (Hebrews 9: 11-12; 7:11-12, 23-28)_____

_____

Trhough the redemptive work of Jesus, the human race had been launched into the Messianic age. Western civilization, most affected in the early centuries by the message of Jesus, acknowledged this fact and dated their calendar accordingly from the Advent of Messiah. BC marks the years Before Christ and AD - *Anno Domini* - Latin for *The Year of Our Lord* - marks the advent of Messiah and the years that have followed.

Jesus' prophecies about the end of the temple and destruction of Jerusalem were exact and found their fulfillment in history. It is important to remember that many Biblical prophecies have both immediate and future meaning. While we should not look for those Scriptures to be fulfilled at some future date that have already occurred, yet part of Jesus' prophecy appears to point to future fulfillment of His Second Coming at the end of time.

Since that day, with judgment against sin and the outpouring of His Holy Spirit, God continues to move history along as He judges sin and establishes righteousness among the nations. Jesus warned His disciples to be on guard against certain attitudes that could cause judgment to catch them by surprise. God does not want us to be caught up in His judgment against sin but wants us to be a part of what He is doing in the earth. Since judgment and blessing are present in varying degrees in every epoch of history, sincere followers of Jesus should stand on guard against these attitudes.

10. In what were the worldly people busily involved? (Matthew 24:38)

a._____

b._____

11. Who was taken away in judgment by the flood in Noah's day? (Matthew 24:39)

_____

12. In like manner, who will be taken away in judgment at the coming of the Lord? (Matthew 24:40-42)_____

13. Who will be left? (Matthew 24:40-42) _____

The Unshakeable Kingdom

14. According to Proverbs, who will remain in the land; and who will be cut off from the earth? (Proverbs 2:21-22)

a._____

b._____

15. Who will be removed from the earth? (Isaiah 13:9) _____

16. Who will inherit the earth? (Matthew 5:5) _____

17. In Hebrews, we read that God will shake the heavens and the earth. What will remain? (Hebrews 12:25-27) _____

18. Of what kingdom are we a part? (Hebrews 12:28-29) _____

19. Hebrews also tells us that our God is a consuming fire. When He appears, who will be fearful, and who will be able to stand? (Isaiah 33:14-15)
a._____
b. _____

20. On whom will the day of the Lord come like a trap? (Luke 21:34-35)
a._____
b._____
c._____

21. What are we exhorted to do? (Luke 21:36)_____

22. What did Jesus pray for those who put their trust in Him? (Yochanan 17:15) _____

23. Whose example does Jesus exhort us to remember? (Luke 17:28-32) _____

Lot's wife was turned into a pillar of salt because she looked back when she was fleeing from the destruction of Sodom. Her heart was still yearning after worldly ways.

Signs of His Coming

24. What signs did Jesus say would occur before His coming? (Matthew 24:3-14)
a. (5,11) _____
b. (6) _____
c. (7) _____
d. (9) _____
e. (10) _____
f. (12) _____
g. (12)_____
h.(14)_____

Historically these signs preceded the destruction of Jerusalem and marked the end of the Mosaic age. Yet, some, if not all of them have been present in every generation. We can see these things happening in the world today. Jesus calls these signs *birth pains.* Birth pains mark the fact that a birth is about to take place. What is being born? Christ's great kingdom in the hearts and minds of people everywhere as people hear the Good News of Jesus' Redemption and the kingdom of God and come to the knowledge of the Truth.

25. Paul spoke about these *birth pains* to the church at Rome. What did he say? (Romans 8:19-21) _____

_____

_____

26. Under the anointing of the Holy Spirit, how long did Peter say that Jesus would remain in heaven before His return? (Acts 3:21)_____

_____

As we read the prophets, we find that they speak of a two-fold restoration: the restoration of the body of Christ and the restoration of the nation of Israel. According to these prophets, this restoration takes place simultaneously.

27. What two-fold picture do you see in Isaiah? (Isaiah 11:10-12)

a. _____

b._____

28. What will the Jewish people say of the Lord in those days? (Jeremiah 23: 7-8)

_____

_____

29. Of what covenant will the Jewish people become partakers? (Jeremiah 31:31-34)

_____

30. What will happen when Israel returns to her Lord? Will she ever be cast out again? (Jeremiah 31:38-40)

a. _____

b. _____

31. Jesus is the Righteous Branch of David. During the days of the Righteous Branch what will happen to Judah? (Jeremiah 33:14-16) _____

_____

32. What prophet does Paul tell the Romans predicted the salvation of the gentiles and what was the prophet's prediction? (Romans 9:25-26)

a. _____

b. _____

_____

_____

Paul equates Hosea's reference to "those who are not My people" to the salvation of the gentiles - those outside the covenant of Israel.

33. At His birth what throne did the angels announce that Jesus has been given? (Luke 1:32)

_____

34. What did Hosea predict about the salvation of Israel? (Hosea 3:4-5)

_____

_____

_____

Since David had been dead for a long time, to say that the Jewish people will seek David their King is a clear reference to the Jewish Messiah Jesus. The New Living Translation says it this way: "The people will return to the Lord and to David's descendant their king."

The Salvation of Israel

35. Paul speaks of this restoration. What does he say? (Romans 11: 12-27)

_____

_____

The Lord will have one new man. The believing Gentiles joined together with the believing Jewish people will together make up the glorious body of Jesus the Messiah.

36. As the glory of God comes upon believers and His kingdom is established all over the earth through the preaching of the Gospel, and outpouring of the Holy Spirit, what will happen in the world? (Isaiah 60:1-7) _____

_____

37. When the Lord pours out His Spirit upon the Jewish people, what did Zechariah say they would recognize and what will they do? (Zechariah 12:10; 13:6)

_____

_____

This Scripture was fulfilled on Passover when Peter told the Jews that they had crucified the Lord of Glory.

38. When the Lord poured His Spirit upon the Jewish people at Passover, what did they recognize? What happened? (Acts 2:36-41) _____

_____

39. What was opened on that day? Compare these passages from Zechariah and John. (Zechariah 13:1; 1 John 1:7)

a. _____

b. _____

_____

40. When did Jesus say that the Jewish people as a nation would see Him again? (Matthew 23:37-39) _____

41. Who will rule and reign with Christ? (Revelation 2:26-27; Revelation 3:21; Matthew 19: 27-28)_____

From the prophets, we have established that before the glorious return of the Lord, both Israel and the followers of Jesus will be restored in power and glory. When the church - baptized believers - becomes glorious, multitudes of nations and kings will come into the Kingdom of God; through supernatural acts of God, all of Israel will come to repentance and the knowledge of the truth to worship Jesus as their Messiah.

42. How long did Jesus foretell the Gentiles would possess the city of Jerusalem? (Luke 21:24) _____

In recent history, we have seen a remarkable fulfillment of Bible prophecy. Israel became an independent nation in 1948 AD for the first time since 606 BC, which was 2500 years since the Jews were carried away into Babylonian captivity. In a dramatic fulfillment of Bible prophecy in 1967 AD, for the first time since Titus destroyed the city in 70 AD, Jerusalem became the possession of the Jewish people and their capital city. Other events await their fulfillment. As we see the hand of God moving to restore His body of true believers and bring salvation to the gentile world that has never believed in Him, along with the restoration of the nation of Israel, we can rejoice at the truth and accuracy of God's Word. Is there any reason to doubt that every word that God has spoken will be fulfilled in time and in history?

43. What does God say about His Word from the prophet Jeremiah? (Jeremiah 1:12)

_____

Memory Verse: Acts 3:21

_____

_____

_____

Worship our Covenant Keeping God with *Yeshua (Jesus) Kadosh (Holy)* written by Elisheva Shomron *(Holy)* <https://goo.gl/wz3Mnz>

Worship with the Gaithers, *Our God is an Awesome God* <https://youtu.be/cXx30llZ-rU>

Study 22: The Advancing Kingdom
Christ's Victory in the Nations

Charles Spurgeon, great revivalist and one of the last of the Puritans in England, wrote this prophetic admonition at the end of the 19th century:

> I believe myself that King Jesus will reign, and the idols will be utterly abolished: but I expect the same power which once turned the world upside down will still continue to do it. The Holy Ghost would never suffer the imputation to rest upon His holy name that He was not able to convert the world. Why should it not be that in this era when the population of the world has reached its height, that God will show on a yet greater scale that truth is more powerful than error, grace is more powerful than sin, and that those given to Christ are indeed "as the sand which is upon the sea-shore for multitude." (Iain H. Murray, *Puritan Hope*, Banner of Truth, P.O. Box 652, Carlisle, PA, xx)

1. When God created Adam and Eve in His image, what did He give them and tell them to do? (Genesis 1:26-28)

a._____

b._____

2. When Adam and Eve fell, they lost the dominion that God had given them to Satan. After Jesus entered Jerusalem for the last time, because the hour of His crucifixion was near, what did He call satan and what did He say was going to happen? (John 12:25-31)

_____

_____

Satan's Judgment

3. When Jesus pronounced Satan's judgment, what promise did He give? (John 12:31- 32)

_____

4. What did Paul call Jesus? (1 Corinthians 15: 45-47) _____

5. What did Jesus do and why? (Hebrews 2:14-15)

_____

_____

The Transfer of Power and Authority

6. After Jesus rose from the dead, what three things did He commission His disciples to do? What did He say had been given to Him? (Matthew 28:18-20)

a._____

b _____

c._____

d._____

7. When Jesus sent His disciples to preach what did He say that He saw? What power did He give them? (Luke 10:17-20)

a. _____

b. _____

8. John saw the resurrected Christ in all His glory on the Isle of Patmos. What did Jesus say that He possessed? (Revelation 1:18) _____

9. To Whom does the earth and all who live on it belong? (Psalm 24:1)

_____

10. Who has been made the heir of the world? (Romans 4:13; Galatians 3:29)

_____

Unfulfilled Prophecy

11. How long will Jesus remain in heaven before He returns? (Acts 3:19-21)

_____

12. What are some of the prophecies that must be fulfilled before Jesus returns?

a. Psalm 22:27_____

b. Psalm 46:8-10_____

_____

c. Isaiah 2:1-4 (Note: *mountain* in Scripture allegorically represents *kingdom)*

_____

d. Isaiah 9:6-7 _____

e. Psalm 2:7-9_____

The Kingdom of the God of Heaven

Read King Nebuchadnezzar's dream and Daniel's interpretation. (Daniel 2:27-45) Note the following:

According to biblical scholars, the statue represents different world empires that would successively rule nations and have influence on the affairs of the Jews. *Matthew Henry's Bible Commentary* explains the historical interpretation of the statue:

• *Head of Gold* - Chaldean Monarchy then in power at the time of the dream

• *Breast and Arms of Silver* - Medes and Persians

• *Belly and Thighs of Brass* - Grecian Monarchy founded by Alexander the Great

• *Legs and Feet of Iron and Clay* - Roman Empire during the time of Jesus Christ

13. What interpretation did Daniel give of the dream? (Daniel 2:44)

_____

_____

_____

14. What three things did Jesus say when He began His ministry? (Mark 1:14-15)

a. _____

b. _____

c. _____

Read Daniel 9:24 - 25. Consider the following:

Daniel specifically prophesied, "From the going forth of the command to restore and rebuild Jerusalem" until the coming of "Messiah the Prince," would be 69 weeks (Dan. 9:24-25). According to biblical measurement of time, a prophetic day equals one year, each prophetic week equals 7 years. The biblical period of 69 weeks is 69 x 7 which equals 483 years. Beginning with the exact day on which Persian King Artaxerxes gave the decree to rebuild the walls of Jerusalem - March 14, 445 BC - to the day Jesus rode into Jerusalem on a donkey hailed as the Son of David was 483 biblical years. This was the first time Jesus allowed Himself to be publicly proclaimed as the Messiah and King. As you will recall, prior to this Jesus was always telling people to go and say nothing about His miracles. A week later Jesus was "cut off" or crucified. (Sir Robert Anderson, *The Coming of Messiah the Prince*, 1841-1918. For more on this see *Matthew Henry's Commentary* on Daniel 9.)

In Babylon, Daniel was looked up to as the Chief Magi and revealer of God's secrets. Not only did he pass down this prophecy to the Jewish scribes and the Jewish people, it stands to reason that he openly proclaimed this in the King's court and gave the prophecy to the Magi who were the priestly tribe in Babylon and worshipers of the One God, Creator of Heaven and Earth. According to tradition, the Magi kept this prophecy alive and passed it down for almost five hundred years. According to tradition, Daniel told them of a new star that would appear in the heavens to mark the birth of the Messiah. They knew when to look for the star of the One who was to be the *King of the Jews,* the *Desire of all Nations,* the *Redeemer.* Because this specific timetable had been given by Daniel, many people in Judea were looking for the advent of the Messiah at the time that Jesus was alive on the earth.

d. The Scripture shows that the Jewish people believed that the time for the coming of Messiah the Prince had arrived. Who did the people think that John the Baptist might be? (Luke 3:15)_____

e. What did the priests and Levites ask John? (John 1:19-21,25)_____

_____

f. What did John say? (v19, 21)_____

_____

g. What did the Pharisees say to Jesus? (John 10: 24; Luke 22:66-70) _____

_____

The religious leaders had a hard time accepting Jesus as their Messiah because He came in a way that they did not expect - lowly and humble. Jesus' open declaration of the "fulfillment of time," and His proclamation, "the kingdom of God is at hand," was a direct reference to Daniel's prophecy. This is one reason why the Jews discount this interpretation of this very important prophetic book. The reference to Jesus being the Messiah is all too clear. Jesus was the God of Heaven who had come to establish a kingdom that could not be destroyed.

15. What did Jesus tell the Pharisees? (Luke 20:17-19)

a._____

_____

Jesus makes a direct reference to Daniel's interpretation of the stone cut out of the mountain.

According to Daniel's interpretation, what did the "stone" represent? (Dan. 2:34-35, 44-45)

b. _____

The statue set up to idolize the kingdoms of men was broken into pieces by the *stone* and ground to powder. This *stone* became a great kingdom and filled the whole earth. *Matthew Henry* (1662-1714) and *Thomas Scott's Commentary on the Bible* explains:

> The stone cut out without hands represents the Kingdom of our Lord Jesus Christ, which should be set up in the world upon the ruins of Satan's kingdom. Because the Stone is cut out without hands, it is neither to be raised nor supported by human power, but by the Spirit of the Lord of Hosts.

The Church is a kingdom of which Christ is the only Sovereign Monarch in which He rules by His Word and Spirit. It is a kingdom not of this world, yet set up in it, it is the kingdom of God among men. It was to be set up by the God of Heaven in the days of the kings of the fourth monarchy (Rome - the world empire when Jesus came to earth and ruling Palestine). His kingdom shall be victorious over all opposition. All the kingdoms that appear against the Kingdom of Christ, no matter how strong and fierce they appear to be, shall be broken before it with a rod of iron.

16. When Peter preached on the day of Pentecost, we learned that he foretold that Jesus will remain in heaven until every prophecy spoken by God's holy prophets since time began is fulfilled. What prophecy did Daniel give that must be fulfilled before Jesus returns? (Daniel 2:35, 7:27)_____

_____

_____

17. What did Jesus tell Peter about His ability to make the church successful in the world? (Matthew 16:13-20 answer from v18) _____

_____

The setting for this dramatic declaration was Caesarea Philippi, a city in the north of Israel that was a place of ancient idol worship. At this place, there was a great rocky cliff with a large cave at its foot. Within the cave was a spring that was, in those days, the beginning of the Jordan River. The Canaanites of old, who dwelt in the land before it was given to Israel, set up their pagan worship to their gods and goddesses at this spot. Here the Baals were worshipped and successive generations of Greeks and Romans had also constructed temples to their gods.

The ancients referred to this cliff as *The Rock,* and the cave at its base was known as *The Gates of Hell.* The ancients believed this was the doorway to the underworld where the gods and goddesses retreated to spend the winter. In order to gain the approval and the blessing of these gods, unspeakable practices of child sacrifice, temple prostitution, and other lewd and immoral acts were practiced.

It was at this very spot that Simon received the revelation that Jesus was "the Christ, the Son of the Living God." Jesus then changed Simon's name to Peter, which in the original Greek means *little rock.* After this, Jesus said, "Upon this rock (the original Greek meaning *a large or great rock*) I will build my church, and the Gates of Hell shall not prevail against it." Usually this idea of the great rock is taken to mean the revelation of who Jesus is. The church is built on this revelation. Yet in this geographical setting, Jesus' statement had a double meaning, something that is often the case in Scripture.

The religious leaders of Israel and Jerusalem had rejected His kingdom. Standing at the place of human debauchery and the vilest demon worship and pagan idolatry that was called *The Rock*, Jesus proclaimed that He would build His church on its ruins. In a sense, Jesus was indicating that His kingdom, which the Jews had rejected, was going to the Gentiles. He foretold that there was nothing that man or devil could do to prevail, overpower, or hold out against the success of His kingdom. Since that time, the history of the world has been a testament to the fulfillment of Jesus' prophecy.

Jesus Ascends into Heaven

18. After Jesus gave His parting words to His disciples, what happened? (Acts 1:9)

_____

19. After His resurrection, where did Jesus tell His disciples that He would go? (John 20:17)

_____

As Jesus ascended into heaven in a cloud, we pick up the scene in the book of Daniel. Daniel had seen these future events in a vision. The scene we see taking place in Daniel is after the resurrection of Jesus.

20. What did Daniel see in His vision? (Daniel 7:13)_____

_____

21. In this vision, with what did Jesus, the Son of Man, come before the throne of God in heaven? (Daniel 7:13)

_____

Jesus Receives the Kingdom

22. Answer the following questions from Daniel 7:14:

a. What was given to Jesus as He stood before the Father's throne?_____

_____

b. Why was the kingdom given to Jesus? _____

c. What type of kingdom was Jesus given?_____

_____

23. David had prophesied this. What decree did David hear God make? (Read Psalm 2; answer from vs 7-9)

a._____

b _____

c._____

24. In light of this, what does David recommend that the kings of the earth do?

a. (Psalm 2:12)_____

b. What will happen to all those who refuse and fight against Christ and His kingdom? (Psalm 2:12)_____

c. What will happen to those who trust Him?_____

Joint Heirs of the Kingdom

25. As believers, what has God made us to be? (Romans 8:16-17) _____
_____

26. If we suffer with Christ what will be revealed in us? (Romans 8:18)_____

27. What does it give the Father great pleasure to do? (Luke 12:32) _____
_____

28. What type of kingdom have we received from the Father? (Hebrews 12:28)_____
_____

The Victory of the Early Church and Christ's Unshakeable Kingdom

After His resurrection and the outpouring of the Holy Spirit, in the midst of universal idolatry, Jesus sent His disciples out to preach the Gospel. Daily, the early church broke bread from house to house, proclaiming the Lord's death, the redemption of the earth, and salvation and forgiveness of sin in His name. As they took the Lord's Supper, by His blood of the New Covenant, they claimed every nation for Christ.

As the early followers of Jesus went forth in the power of the Holy Spirit preaching the Gospel and teaching the Word of God, thrones shook and idols toppled. Early Christians were persecuted, thrown to the lions, burnt at the stake, and crucified. Both Peter and Paul were executed in Rome. Yet, every day the members of the early church shared Jesus' Holy Covenant Supper, knowing that the blood of the New Covenant redemption would eventually win the day. Every day they prayed the prayer that Jesus taught them to pray: "Thy kingdom come, Thy will be done on earth as it is in heaven." They were not believers in the ideology that things were destined to get worse and worse. The more they preached, and the more they laid down their lives for the Gospel, the more the Good News spread, until during the lifetime of the Apostles, the followers of Christ had literally taken the Gospel to every nation in the known world.

Through the preaching of the Gospel, European idolatry supported by ancient blood covenants with spiritual principalities came crashing down to the ground and was swept into the ash bin of history. Eventually, the pagan Roman Empire with its cult worship of Caesar as god came toppling down as well. The Gospel and the church of Jesus Christ, just as Jesus predicted, arose on its ruins. Christianity became the central religion of the Roman Empire. Saint Athanasius, the great church father of the fourth century, recorded the progress of

Christianity: "Since the Savior came to dwell in our midst, not only does idolatry no longer increase, but it is getting less and gradually ceasing to be."

When Christianity started 2,000 years ago, the small band of Jesus' followers were opposed by the most powerful military force in the world. They were opposed by the religious leaders of their own country. Most people would have given them no chance of surviving, but the church came out of the struggle the clear winner.

The Middle or Dark Ages of Europe 6th to 16th Century

The church was alive and well for many centuries. When the old Roman Empire was overrun with barbarian hordes, Christian monks faithfully copied the Bible, guarded literature, and kept civilization and learning alive in the monasteries. However as the years went by, the clear teaching of the early church was virtually forgotten. Most people could not read, books were rare, and the Bible was not preached. Although it had been copied for centuries as a "witness clothed in sackcloth," it was left in the monasteries. If a copy of the Bible was to be found in a cathedral, it was chained to the pulpit and the common person could kiss it, but was not allowed to read it. It was thought that the Bible was "too holy" for the common person to read. It was written in Latin and most people could not understand Latin, including many of the priests.

Consequently, the truth of the Word of God was replaced by the doctrines of men. The church backslid into darkness and idolatry. The knowledge of the Word of God and true salvation through faith in the blood of Jesus was replaced by the worship of images and holy relics. This period of history plunged Europe into spiritual darkness and became known as the Dark Ages - later called the Middle Ages. People were taught they had to earn their salvation by making pilgrimages to pray before relics and the bones of the saints, and by doing other things that were foreign to the clear teaching of the Bible. They were taught that pardons and forgiveness for sin could be bought for money. In the fourteenth and fifteenth century, a few priests discovered the Bible in the monastery libraries and tried to preach its truth. They were persecuted and killed for teaching ideas that were different from the doctrines of men, which were taught by the Roman Church. The seed of God's truth was being planted for the harvest that would inevitably follow. John Huss and other martyrs watered that seed with their blood.

The Protestant Reformation of the 16th and 17th Centuries

Finally, in the sixteenth century, one hundred years after John Huss, a priest named Martin Luther found a copy of the Bible in the monastery library and began to study and relish its words and share its truth with his students at the university. Luther was sent to Rome on a pilgrimage. When he got there, he expected to see the center of the Church as a great mecca of spirituality. Instead, he was greatly disturbed by the immoral conditions of the clergy and the great contradictions to what he had been reading about Christ's teaching from the Bible. He saw the Pope ride into Rome in a suit of armor, just coming back from a military battle. At one holy site, he bought a pardon for the forgiveness of his parents' sins. One of the conditions for this pardon to be effective was that the purchaser must climb a set of stairs on his knees.

According to a myth which shows the superstition of the day, these steps were said to be Pilate's judgment stairs, the very same stairs that Jesus walked up before He was crucified, which were miraculously transported from Jerusalem to Rome by an angel. As Luther climbed halfway up the stairs on his knees, he heard what he thought was an audible Voice thundering in his ears saying, "The just shall live by faith!" The truth of this statement took Luther by storm. He stood up and went back to preach this message in Germany. Luther composed *97 Thesis* as a list of things he believed contradicted the Bible and the Roman Church needed to change. He nailed them on the door of Wittenberg Chapel for debate.

Luther meant only to reform the Church's teaching, but his revelation was not received. Those who did embrace his teaching were thrown out of the Church of Rome. Others left on their own free will. As a result, people met in homes and fellowship groups began to spring up all over Europe. At the same time, efforts were made to translate the Bible out of the Latin into the various common languages of the people. These efforts were met with opposition, as those who sought to translate the Bible and preach its truth were persecuted, imprisoned, and burned at the stake by civil and religious authorities who were bound in darkness. But God's Truth could not be extinguished by martyrs' fires. The printing press was invented around this time. The first large book printed on it was the Bible.

The Truth continued to spread and grow and finally the Bible was available to the masses. People began to learn to read and write so they could study God's Word for themselves. They read the Bible and heard it preached. As a result, a spiritual awakening swept England and the European continent that became known as the Protestant Reformation. Europe received the message of true salvation with great joy. Men and women embraced the simple truths of the Gospel, as taught in the Bible, and came to a saving knowledge of Jesus Christ through faith in His shed blood alone for the forgiveness of sin. A heavy yoke was lifted from the population of Europe and England as the spiritual prison doors were opened and the captives were set free to experience true liberty in Christ. This was not without cost. England and the Netherlands broke away from the Pope and started their own churches independent of Rome. Other Great wars broke out as the Catholic nations tried to force nations who were embracing the Protestant faith back into the Catholic Church.

The 17th Century - The New World - A New Home for the Gospel of Liberty

About fifty years before Martin Luther dusted off a copy of the Bible from the monastery shelves, Columbus had discovered America in 1492. The curtain was rising on a New World in the West that was destined to be the new home of Christian Liberty. Among the future citizens of the New World were a group who became known as the Pilgrims. By this time, England had broken free from the Roman Church and had established a state church known as the Church of England, with the King of England as its head. However, the Pilgrims did not want to practice their Christianity the way the King of England demanded. They wanted to return to the practices of the early church, where following Jesus, and not religious rituals and doctrines, was the center of true Christianity. At first, they fled to Holland in exile to escape persecution in England.

It was their belief that the reign of Antichrist, the false substitutes for salvation, and the great Apostasy of the church foretold in Scripture (which had lasted for 1,200 years) involving the unholy alliance between the popes, cardinals and the Romand Catholic hierarchy and the kings and queens of Europe and the reign of the Man of Sin (embodied in the papal office) were coming to a close. They looked forward to the day foretold in Scripture when all the nations of the world would become followers of the Lord Jesus Christ and receive salvation. This hope gave the Pilgrims, Puritans, and those persecuted during the Protestant Reformation the faith and courage they needed to leave civilized Europe. With faith and hope in their heart, they crossed treacherous waters to seek religious freedom in the New World. In the wilderness of North America, they started the world over again. Here they were destined to found a nation where freedom to worship God would be the heritage of all. It was the Pilgrims' vision that through their new nation of liberty, all the nations of the earth would be blessed.

In the New World, the Pilgrims, and later the Puritans who followed them, looked for a greater reformation and transformation of Christianity. John Winthrop, a Puritan Governor and one of the Founders of the Massachusetts Bay Colony, summarized the Puritans' view. He wrote that they purposed to establish a nation where God was to be recognized as Sovereign, and the Bible was to be the rule of man's conduct. Their new nation was to be one in which human rights would be respected, and everyone would do what was right and just to their fellowman. Winthrop writes that their new nation was to be "a city set upon a hill" to give light to the nations. By 1674, it is estimated that 80,000 Puritans came to Massachusetts seeking freedom of worship. By the early 1700s, their number increased to over 106,000. This was the spiritual seed needed to lay the foundation of our nation in truth and righteousness. Soon persecuted Protestants from all over Europe fled to North America.

The Pilgrims and Puritans entered into a covenant with God for this new nation that would become the model of spiritual liberty for all nations to follow. Liberty would become its greatest export. From this new beachhead for Christianity, which later became the United States of America, individual believers would take the blessings of the Gospel and Christian Liberty to the world. Winthrop envisioned that everyone would respect Sunday as the Christian Sabbath, and the time set aside to adore and worship God and listen to the teaching of the Bible. The Founders' vision for the Sabbath was reflected in the practices of our nation for three hundred years after the Pilgrims came here. Until the later years of the twentieth century, businesses were closed on Sunday as the American people observed the Christian Sabbath rest according to God's command - "six days you are to labor and do all your work. The seventh day you are to rest for it is the Lord's Sabbath."

Mistreatment of the Indians and slavery later became blights on this vision. It took two hundred years to overthrow slavery - an institution as old as the human race - and to rectify national intentions, but ultimately the Puritan vision born of the Spirit of God won the day. The United States has realized this founding vision and has stood for the recognition of human rights around the world. This is a Christian idea! This is a victory for the teaching of Christ in time and in history. This is a fulfillment of Jesus' commission: "Go and teach all nations to observe everything I have taught you." (Matt. 28:20) His Truth is marching on!

Victory for Christ in the 18th Century - First Great Awakening

In the mid 1700s, the First Great Awakening, which followed on the heels of the Protestant Reformation, was sweeping England and the American Colonies and fueling the flames of liberty. This new-found liberty and understanding of biblical truth eventually led to the American Revolution as the colonists dissolved their relationship with the oppressive rule of the British King and the British Parliament. Rejecting the age-old idea that God had ordained certain people to be Kings to rule over others, the colonists declared they would return to Moses' government in the wilderness - they would have no king but Jesus! The colonists would live under the rule of law, not under the rule of men. They declared that their government would be "of the people."

Of the fifty-five delegates who framed the United States Constitution, many of the delegates were ministers, and all but three were Christians. Of those three, two believed the Bible should be the foundation of our national life. The Founders of the United States acknowledged that it was true faith in Christ, enshrined in the hearts of men and women through the ages, that gave birth to their civil freedoms, prosperity, and their free form of self-government. Noah Webster, one of the leading thinkers and framers of the U.S. Constitution, wrote in 1823, in his book *History of the United States*, "The religion which has introduced civil liberty, is the religion of Christ and His apostles, which enjoins humility, piety and benevolence; which acknowledges in every person a brother, or a sister, and a citizen with equal rights. This is genuine Christianity, and to this we owe our free constitutions of government."

In the Bill of Rights to the U.S. Constitution, the Founders made sure that they enshrined religious liberty into civil law. The First Amendment to the U.S. Constitution clearly states: *Congress shall make no law respecting an establishment of religion, or prohibiting the free exercise thereof; or abridging the freedom of speech, or of the press; or the right of the people peaceably to assemble, and to petition the Government for a redress of grievances.* The Founders believed that this form of Christian self-government would eventually spread throughout the world.

First in North America, and later in England and Europe, the Divine Right of Kings was overthrown. Since Israel had rejected God as their King thousands of years before, almost every nation had lived under the oppression of Ruler's Law. Ruler's Law has been a trail of bloodshed and tears for the human race. The United States rejected Ruler's Law, and established a nation ruled by laws and not by men. Those laws, at their inception, were based on the Ten Commandments and the Law of God as recorded in the Scriptures. The Founding Fathers believed that God had given every person the degree of reason necessary to govern themselves according to His Commandments.

This free form of self-government that had its birth from the teachings of Jesus Christ, gave "eagle wings to the human spirit." The Liberty of Christ enshrined in civil government broke the class system that was prevalent in Europe. This system kept people confined to their social status, unable to break free to change their economic situation, their occupation, and their lot in life. Christian Liberty in North America began putting people in charge of their own destiny. It has allowed individuals, no matter what their social status of their parents, to prosper, keep the fruits of their labor, and try to accomplish anything they have wanted to try.

Victory for Christ in the 19th Century - Second Great Awakening

During the 1800s, the idea of Christian Liberty under God was spurred on by the Second Great Awakening that was taking place in the United States and England. As the light of God's Word shone brightly on the affairs of state, both nations rose up in that century and overthrew slavery as a legal institution - an institution that was over 5,000 years old. Today institutional slavery sanctioned by law is illegal in every nation on earth. Christians believed that this was the will of God, played out in civil government, and was the fulfillment of Jesus' promise "to open the prison doors and let the captives go free."

After the Civil War, nineteenth century historian Charles Coffin echoed the Christian idea of history. In 1881, he pondered what would happen to the newly freed African race as they grew up as free men and women in North America. Coffin asked, "What part are the four millions of the African race to take in the future of our country? What will they yet do for Africa? Who knows but they will be the means of carrying a Christian civilization and Republican institutions to the country of their origin?" (Coffin, *Sweet Land of Liberty,* Maranatha Publications)

During the nineteenth century, great mission movements were formed on both sides of the Atlantic, as missionaries were sent out to preach the Gospel around the world. Christians formed foundations and philanthropic missions to help the poor. Philanthropy and charitable works was a Christian idea! Not only were the lights turning on spiritually to enlighten the dark hearts of men, the "lights" were going on physically too. After ten thousand experiments, Thomas Edison discovered the electric light bulb. As a result, people advanced from what was a 6,000 year-old practice of lighting their homes and caves by fire, torch, and lamp to electric lights at the flip of a switch.

Victory for Christ in the 20ᵗʰ Century - The Outpouring of the Holy Spirit

In the twentieth century, miracles were taking place on every level of human endeavor. The Baptism of the Holy Spirit was poured out all over the world as God's power began to be restored to the church. The United States' experiment in liberty and free enterprise, which allowed the individual to work in an atmosphere of freedom and keep the profits from his labor, unleashed a stream of inventions and creativity.

Men went from traveling by horse and buggy to walking on the moon in one generation. A deluge of creativity pouring forth from the ideas of self-governed individuals produced modern conveniences to bless the world. Among these advances were hot and cold running water, the indoor toilet, the automobile, the vacuum cleaner, the dishwasher, the electric stove, the microwave, the plow and the tractor, the combine, the airplane, the jet engine, the satellite, the telephone, the ability to record the human voice, moving pictures, electric heating and air conditioning, television, film, the computer, the DVD, the cell phone, the internet, miracle drugs that cured plagues that had afflicted the human race since the beginning of history, and advances in science and medicine.

Victory for Human Rights

Elevation of Women

In the twentieth century, movements to protect and lift up women and children were led by dedicated Christians. In the early part of the twentieth century, God began to roll back the oppression of women in civil society. Throughout world history, women were viewed as less than men and did not have equal rights. Although there is an obvious difference between men and women and their basic functions in the family, Paul taught that there is no such thing as male and female in Christ. As God shed more light on His Word, Christians discovered that Jesus elevated the status of women by allowing them to fully participate in the spiritual life of the church and follow Him wherever He went - a position in Jewish society reserved only for the men. In the United States and many other nations, Christians began to insist that women's rights be legally established; women gained the right to vote, work, study, and learn.

Protection of Children

Child labor laws were enacted in both the United States and England to protect small children from being coerced to work at hard labor. Many children had been forced to spend their childhood as early as the age of four, slaving away in dark factories. Catherine Booth and the Salvation Army led the fight to get legislators to pass laws to protect children, and worked tirelessly until measures were signed into law on both sides of the Atlantic. The fact that childhood should be a joyful time of learning and discovery was a new idea for the human race. People began to realize that childhood was a sacred time to be cherished and studied.

Jesus' central teaching about children was enshrined in civil life: "Allow the little children to come to Me and forbid them not, for of such is the kingdom of heaven"... "And He took a small child and set him in the midst of His disciples, and He said, 'Unless you become like this little child, you will not ever be able to enter the kingdom of God. Whoever receives one little child like this in My name receives Me. If anyone causes one of these little ones to sin it would be better for him if he had a millstone tied around his neck and he was drowned in the depths of the sea.' " (Matt.18:2-6; 19:14). God's Truth was marching on!

Overturning the Evil of Nazism and Japanese Imperialism

In the twentieth century, Nazism and Japanese Imperialism attempted World dominance as declared enemies of Christ, but were defeated. Christ's love and His kingdom in the hearts of men continued to spread around the world and bring God's blessings. After World War II, the United States reached out to both Japan and Germany. Instead of treating conquered enemies as slaves and excising taxes and servitude as was customary, the United States helped to rebuild these nations, encouraging them in principles of self-government and free enterprise, and welcomed them into the family of those nations who love peace. Jesus' teaching to "love your enemies and do good to those who hate you" was actually put into practice among nations. Nothing like this had ever been done in world history.

Civil Rights Movement and the Overturning of Communism

Through nonviolent protests under the leadership of Baptist minister Dr. Martin Luther King, the United States was brought face to face with racial inequality. The oppression of segregation was overturned, and the Black race in America received the opportunity to participate in full citizenship rights that had been won for them in the struggle of the Civil War a hundred years earlier. At the end of the twentieth century, in South Africa, Nelson Mandela, a Christian antiapartheid leader, reconciled the black and white communities, and the oppressive practices of segregation in South Africa were eliminated.

In the last decade of the twentieth century, the Soviet Union - which opposed Christianity, banned the Bible, and proclaimed that the state was god - rejected atheism and Marxism and opened their doors to freedom of religion. Nations that had been forced into the Soviet Block were set free and established their independence. The nation of Russia and the former Soviet countries began experiencing revivals of Christianity. They rejected the idea of Marxism and centralized state planning and embraced the concepts of freedom of speech, personal responsibility, and free enterprise economics - all biblical ideas!

Victory for Christ in the 21st Century

Jesus commissioned His disciples 2,000 years ago to "go and teach the nations" to "observe everything" that He had taught them. The importance of human rights and love and caring for one's fellowman, truths that Jesus taught, are gaining dominance on the world scene. Throughout history it has been common practice to rejoice at the destruction of other nations and to try to loot and pillage as many people as possible. We have seen what man's inhumanity to man can do through terrorism in nations that do not know about the love of God as Jesus taught it. Yet, in the face of that darkness, in the early years of the twenty-first century, we have seen what the love of God can do. In the face of earthquakes, tsunamis, and untold devastation that opened the twenty-first century, nations around the world sent their military and their money to help care for these devastated people and helped rebuild their nations. Individuals of different nations gave both their money and service to help others in these devastated areas. Jesus' teaching on love has taken root on a world-wide scale. Among the nations influenced by Christianity, Jesus' teaching is the foundation for their standard for human rights - "love your neighbor as yourself."

Fruit is now being reaped from over 150 years of mission work as spiritual revivals break out in South America, Africa, and Asia. Africa and the Philippines are sending out their own missionaries. The small nation of South Korea is among one of the largest missionary-sending nations in the world. In China, the work of missionaries that began in the 1850s has gone viral underground as millions are giving their lives to Christ to fill the spiritual vacuum that has been left in the hearts of the Chinese by the years of atheistic communism and the more recent emptiness of materialism. There is still persecution against Christians in China, yet it is diminishing, and we know that one day in the near future China will most certainly have religious freedom. Australia continues to be a beachhead for the Gospel.. Singapore is considered an Antioch country and is raising up people to go into Asia and the world for Christian missions. The spiritual awakening taking place in Russia has now caused Russia, a nation who declared themselves atheists in the 20th century to proclaim that they are a Christian nation. The Bible once a banned book is nor required to be taught in their schools.

Although there is still tension in the Moslem world, and many Christians are being persecuted and killed, Moslems around the world are receiving a personal revelation of Jesus Christ as a loving Savior. Indonesia, the largest Moslem nation in the world, is experiencing spiritual awakening. So many are coming to the Lord it will soon be a Christian nation. Regardless of nation, race, or religious background, the world mission is being fulfilled that Jesus proclaimed over two thousand years ago: "For God so loved the world that He gave his only begotten Son that whoever will believe in Him will not perish, but will have eternal life. God sent His son into the world not to condemn the world, but to save it" (John 3:16-17).

Although only 2.3% of India's population are Christians today, India, with its multitude of people, joined the UK and the United States as being one of the largest missionary-sending nations of the world. India one day will also be swept into the kingdom of God. Every false religion will be eclipsed by the love Jesus shed abroad in the world and every idol will definitely fall. E. Stanley Jones, missionary to India in the last half of the twentieth century made this prediction in *Christ of the India Road*:

> It is a most significant thing for India and the world that a great people of amazing spiritual capacities is seeing with remarkable insight that Christ is the center of Christianity. That total commitment to Him and catching His mind and Spirit, and living His life, constitute a real Christian. I cannot help wondering if there is not a Providence in the fact that India has not accepted Christianity without this clarification. It may mean that the most potentially spiritual race of the world may accept Christ as Christianity, may put emphasis upon Him, may restore the lost radiance of the early days when Jesus was the center and may give the church a new burst of spiritual power. For in all the history of Christianity, whenever there has been a new emphasis upon Jesus, there has been a fresh outburst of spiritual vitality. Whenever Christianity has struck out a new path in her journey, it has been because the personality of Jesus has again become living and a ray from His being has once more illuminated the world. Some of us feel that the next great spiritual impact upon the soul of the human race is due to come by the way of India.

Is there still work to be done for Christ's kingdom? Yes, there is. Is there still darkness in the nations? Yes, there is. But the world has come a long way in its march from slavery to freedom, as the earth's people learn to turn from the power of self and Satan to the power of God and to Jesus, the Author of love, life, and liberty. In *The Story of Liberty*, nineteenth century historian Charles Coffin sums up the Christian idea of history:

Men act freely in laying their plans, but behind the turmoil of human events a Divine hand can be seen directing the counter plan...whoever fails to recognize this feature fails to comprehend the meaning of history...Nations rise and fall, generations come and go yet through the ages there has been an advancement of Justice, Truth, Right, and Liberty.

One thing is certain, "All the earth will worship Him and sing unto His name," as God has proclaimed it. He will bring it to pass through spiritual awakenings and revivals of Christianity, as His people all over the globe are faithful to take the Good News of the Gospel into all the earth. His kingdom is not a worldly kingdom, one of top down dominance. It is not a political kingdom. It is a kingdom of love that rules in the hearts of people. As David surmised, "The heathen rage and imagine a vain thing against the Lord and His anointed," but God proclaimed the victory of Christ thousands of years before His birth through the psalmist David - "I have installed my King on Mt. Zion" (Psalm 2:6). The reign of the love of Jesus in the hearts of men and women and boys and girls will continue to usher in new eras of brotherhood, peace, and abundance. The love of God in the hearts of people will continue to establish governments that protect the liberty of its people and bring God's blessing.

The "pinnacle" toward which all the world is moving is not communism, as Karl Marx once proclaimed, or any other false religion, but the *pinnacle* toward which all the world is moving is the day when "the kingdoms of this world will become the kingdoms of our God and of His Christ and He shall reign forever." This Truth was proclaimed by God David, Isaiah, Daniel, Malachi, Jesus, Paul, Peter, and John. Is there any reason to doubt its fulfillment? (Psalms 22:27; 65:5; 67:3-4,7; 86:9;117:1; Isaiah 2: 2-4; 11:9; 42:10-12; 49:22-23; 29. Daniel 7:14; Malachi 1:11; John 3:16; Matthew 28:18-20; Revelation 15:4).

29. Will the Jews be able to withstand Christ? What did Paul say will happen? (Romans 11:25-26)_____

30. How long will Jesus reign in heaven? What is the last enemy to be destroyed before Christ's return? (1 Corinthians 15:24-26)

a. _____

b. _____

31. When death is destroyed, the dead are raised and those who are alive will be changed and receive an immortal body. When did the Apostle Paul say this would take place? (1 Corinthians 15: 50-54) _____

32. John refers to the *last trumpet* in the book of Revelation. There are seven angels that blow seven trumpets. When the seventh angel begins to sound and blow his trumpet, what has actually happened on earth? (Revelation 11:15-18) _____

Consider this passage from the *Amplified* and *New King James* versions:

> The seventh angel then blew his trumpet, and there were mighty voices in heaven, shouting: 'The dominion, kingdom, sovereignty, rule of the world has now come into the possession and become the kingdom of our Lord and of His Christ, the Messiah, and He shall reign forever and ever, for the eternities of the eternities!" And the twenty-four elders who sat before God on their thrones fell on their faces and worshiped God, saying: "We give You thanks, O Lord God Almighty, The One who is and who was and who is to come, because You have taken Your great power and have reigned." (Revelation 11:15-18)

The Sons of God

Finally, we will consider how God's kingdom blessing will fill the earth.

33. What is the world waiting for? (Romans 8:19-21) _____

_____

34. Who are the sons of God? (Romans 8:14) _____

35. When Jesus began His ministry He announced His program for the human race. What was this program? (Luke 4:17-19)

a. _____

b. _____

c. _____

d. _____

e. _____

f. _____

The Outpouring of the Holy Spirit

36. How did Jesus say He was going to accomplish this mission? (Luke 4:18)

_____

37. What promise did Jesus give to all those who are thirsty and come to Him? (John 7:37-39) _____

John tells us that this "living water" that Jesus spoke of represents "the Holy Spirit who those who were to believe in Him would receive." We see this picture again in Revelation as the water flows from the Throne of the Lamb. Although this scene may be seen literally in heaven, it can also be taken as an allegory of the life of the believer. The heart of every believer is to enthrone Jesus Christ as King.

38. What happens as the rivers of Living Water are flowing out to the nations from the life of the believer where Jesus Christ is the undisputed Lord and Ruler? (Revelation 22:1-3)

a. _____

b. _____

c. _____

39. What did Jesus say the Holy Spirit will give us power to do? (Acts 1: 4-8)

_____

For the Early Christians, the Protestant Reformers, the Pilgrims and Puritans, and the Christians of America's first two centuries, the goal was clear. Christianity meant the victory of Jesus and His teaching of love, forgiveness, and the deliverance from sin that actually transforms the behavior of people. It was not a victory that somehow would suddenly take place in "the last chapter" of the Bible where all we have to do is "peek" at it and learn that the Jesus won. It was not an optimistic "everything will work out somehow" idea. The saints of old saw history as His Story, as a spiritual struggle between Light and darkness, Truth and error, Good and evil, and at the end of the conflict, they believed that Truth, no matter how persecuted, would come out victorious.

Christ's Ultimate Triumph

The conquering power of Truth is confirmed throughout the pages of the Bible and is figuratively pictured in the book of Revelation.

40. As the book opens describe the Rider on the white horse and tell what is He doing? (Revelation 6:2)_____

_____

Who is this mysterious Rider on the white horse? The Bible doesn't ask us to guess. The Bible tells us the meaning of its own symbols. The white horse appears again.

41. Describe and identify the Rider on the white horse. (Revelation 19:11-16)

_____

_____

_____

This time the Warrior who sits upon the white horse is crowned not with one crown, but with many diadems, signifying that He has conquered many nations. The Mighty Warrior is identified as the Word of God, Jesus Christ, and all the armies that are in heaven are following Him. From His mouth comes a sharp sword and with it He smites the nations. He is also given the name, "The King of Kings and the Lord of Lords." Thus the message seems to be clear. The all powerful Word of God will inevitably, as history progresses, conquer every nation, and Jesus will be Lord of all.

It is the empowering, anointing, and filling of the Holy Spirit that will give us the ability to be witnesses for Him. And not only that, through the power of His Holy Spirit, Jesus will work with us, sending great outpourings of the Holy Spirit and Spiritual Awakenings as the

Word of God is faithfully preached, until "the earth is full of the knowledge of the Lord as waters that cover the sea." Wrongs will be righted and good will conquer evil. So it has been in the history of the church and the nations of the world, and so it will continue to be until the end of time. As a result, the saving knowledge of Jesus Christ will fill the earth, and the kingdom of God will be established on earth in the hearts of people just as it is in heaven. This will be the fulfillment of the Lord's prayer that Jesus taught His disciples to pray, "Our Father who art in heaven, Hallowed be Your name. Your kingdom come. Your will be done on earth as *it is* in heaven."

Memory Verses: Matthew 6:9-13

When He first the work begun
Small and feeble was His day:
Now the Word doth swiftly run,
Now it wins its widening way:
More and more it spreads and grows,
Ever mighty to prevail,
Sin's strongholds it overthrows,
Shakes the trembling gates of hell.

- Charles Wesley
1707-1788

Worship with the Gaithers, *Let Freedom Ring*, <https://youtu.be/FRpUgRkSI1M>

History of *Battle Hymn of the Republic* (history Orson Wells)<http://goo.gl/TTVybw>

Battle Hymn of the Republic - <https://youtu.be/-7GzUvGiF48>

Worship, *I Pledge Allegiance to the Lamb*, <http://goo.gl/na0lII>

Worship with Rob Sterns, *March On!* <http://goo.gl/nSYtda>

For more on the Progress of the Gospel as the foundation of our national freedom go to <www.weinermedia.com>The Story of Liberty, Sweet Land of Liberty, with study guides and Boy's of '76.

Study 23: How to Have Great Faith in God

1. Before we can leave the foundational teaching about Christ and press on to maturity, what foundation must we have? (Hebrews 6:1-3)

a. _____

b. _____

c. _____

d. _____

e. _____

f. _____

Faith in God is a necessary ingredient for a strong foundation. Without a true understanding of biblical faith, we will find it impossible to grow into that spiritual maturity that God desires to see in each one of His children. Faith makes the difference between defeat and victory in our Christian life.

"Without faith, it is impossible to please God." By faith, the men of old gained approval from God. By faith, they "conquered kingdoms, performed acts of righteousness, obtained promises, shut the mouths of lions, quenched the power of fire, escaped the edge of the sword, from weakness were made strong, became mighty in war and put foreign armies to flight. They were stoned, sawn in two, put to death with the sword; they were destitute, afflicted and ill-treated. All these gained approval through their faith." These men and women believed God, and it was accounted to them as righteousness.

If we build a strong foundation of faith, each believer may show the same diligence as those great men of faith who went before us so that we "will not become sluggish but will be an imitator of those who, through faith and patience, inherit the promises and press on to maturity in God." (Portions of Hebrews 11)

2. What do we need in order to please God? (Hebrews 11:6)_____

3. What has God given to every person? (Romans 12:3) _____

Every person has been given the measure of faith. The question is, what are you doing with the measure of faith that God has given you? Faith is not a mysterious thing; you use faith all the time. You use faith every night when you go to bed. You have faith that you will wake up in the morning. You use faith to drive your car, ride a plane, and walk across the street. You believe you will arrive at your destination in safety. You can use your faith to believe what God says is true, or you can use your faith to believe that what the Word of God says is false.

What is the source of your thoughts? *Who* are you believing? Are you believing the lies of the devil, the philosophy of this world, or are you believing and putting your trust in what God has promised? The choice is yours.

4. In order to please God, what must we use our faith to believe? (Hebrews 11:6)

a. _____

b. _____

God has told us that without faith - faith in what He has said and promised - it is impossible to please Him. Not only that, God has told us in His Word that we can have faith in Him and what He says. If we do not have faith and do not put our trust in Him, it is not God's fault. To blame God for our lack of faith is ignorance, because God has provided the way that everyone can have faith in Him. Let's examine a few Scriptures to discover the provision for faith that God has made.

5. Through what are we saved? (Ephesians 2:8)

_____

6. How do we get the faith to be saved? (Romans 10:17)

_____

So then, we see that faith comes through "hearing the Word of God."

Faith that Comes by Hearing

7. What three steps does a person take to receive salvation? (Romans 10:8-10)

a. _____

b. _____

c. _____

8. As Cornelius was praying, God sent an angel to his house. The angel told him to send for Simon Peter. What was Peter supposed to tell Cornelius? (Acts 11:13-14)

_____

Cornelius had not yet heard the Gospel; he was not saved. The expression "who shall tell you words by which you will be saved" shows that people are saved by hearing the Words of God. "Faith comes by hearing, and hearing the Word of God." In order to be saved, we must first know what Jesus has done for us, and then we must believe it and then receive it.

9. In the following passage, what three things did Paul do, and what three things did the lame man do? (Acts 14:7-10)

Paul: 1. (7) _____

     2. (9) _____

     3. (10) _____

Man: 1. (9) _____

     2. (9) _____

     3. (10) _____

10. Where did the lame man get the faith to be healed? (Acts 14:9)

_____

11. What is faith? (Hebrews 11:1)

_____

Moffatt's Translation of this verse reads: "Now faith means that we are confident of what we hope for, convinced of what we do not see." Many people want to receive something from God, and then believe. However, biblical faith is believing first, then receiving the visible manifestation of it. This is the kind of faith that God has.

12. How did God form the world? (Hebrews 11:3)_____

_____

Jesus' Instructions on Faith

13. We see this faith of God outlined by Jesus. What principles of faith are found in the following passage? (Mark 11:22-23)

a. _____

b. _____

c. _____

d. _____

14. We see this kind of faith operating in the heart of God when He created the world. What did He do? (Genesis 1:1-3)

a. _____

b. _____

c. _____

God was brooding over the waters. He was thinking of something. He had the creative idea, the design, that He wanted to create in His mind. He spoke these things into existence, commanding them to come forth. Then they appeared just as He had thought and declared.

15. When we pray for something, what are the conditions for receiving an answer to our prayer? (Mark 11:23-25)

a. _____

b. _____

c. _____

Jesus tells us that we have to believe it before we can receive it. Faith says, "I have it, even though I can't see it." We must believe it because God's Word says it, then that which is in the invisible realm of the spirit becomes visible. Stand firm on God's Word, and results will be forthcoming. However, if we sit around and groan, sigh, gripe and complain - waiting until we see the manifestation of the promise before we believe - we will never get very far. "For faith is . . . the evidence of things not seen."

16. What other promises did Jesus give us on which to base our faith? (John 14:13-14, 15:5-7: 16:24)

a. _____

b. _____

c. _____

d. _____

Let's examine two types of faith:

1. Head knowledge faith - seeing is believing.

2. Heart knowledge faith - I believe it because God says it is true.

17. Why did Thomas find it hard to believe that Jesus was alive? (John 20:24-25)

_____

_____

18. At what point did Thomas believe? (John 20:26-29) _____

19. What exhortation did Jesus give him? (John 20:29) _____

The Faith of Abraham

Abraham is an example of a man who did not see and yet believed. He had that "heart" kind of faith. Abraham was a hundred years old when God told him that he would have a son before the year was up. His wife was ninety - well past the years of childbearing. Regardless of the circumstances, Abraham believed the promise because *God said it was true.*

20. Describe Abraham's *heart* faith. (Romans 4:17-21)

a. (17) _____

b. (18) _____

c. (19) _____

d. (20) _____

e. (21) _____

Notice that Abraham did *not consider his body.* Many people who want to be healed look at their body for symptoms of sickness or healing.

21. According to the above passage, if Abraham did not consider his physical body or feelings, what did he consider? (Romans 4:17-21) _____

Abraham did not consider his body; he looked *only* to the promise of God.

22. How do we put our faith in God's Word? (1 John 5:9) _____

John tells us that if we receive the words of our friends as true, how much more should we receive the words of God as true. Faith is a matter of simply receiving God's Word as true. This is the most crucial and important principle of faith. "If we receive the word of men, the words of God are greater."

An Example of Faith

Kenneth Hagin gives the following example of the truth of this Scripture:

Mary went shopping on Monday morning. In one of the shops, she met a school friend whom she had not seen in three years. Mary asked the girl to come to her home for dinner that evening. The friend accepted. Mary did some last minute grocery shopping and spent the rest of the afternoon preparing for the visit.

She did *not* worry and fret all afternoon wondering if her friend would arrive; she did not worry whether her friend would keep her word. Instead, she looked forward with great anticipation to the meeting that they were going to have together. At 7 o'clock everything was ready, and she was expectantly awaiting her guest with joy in her heart. Mary *received* the witness of a friend. Her actions for the rest of the day were based upon that word.

Mary is also a Christian. She read in Matthew 6 that she should not be anxious for what she will eat or drink or for her clothing, for God knows that she needs all these things. She read in the Bible that if she would "seek the kingdom of God first and His righteousness," all these needs would be taken care of by God. This promise seemed too good to be true.

The mail carrier came and Mary went to the door to get her mail. She received three bills in the mail which totaled $300 more than she had to pay. Mary spent the rest of the day worrying and fretting about whether God would really meet her need. She wondered if God's Word to her was really true? She thought, "If only I could have enough faith, I could *make* the word happen." She became so worried that she found her thoughts filled with the cares of this life and found it hard to think on the things of the Lord. Mary spent the rest of the day worrying about whether God would keep His promise to her.

Her thoughts and actions were opposite from the Word of God. "If we receive the word of man, the Word of God is greater." Mary found it easy to believe the word of her friend. She never gave the truth of it a second thought. But to believe that God's Word was true was very difficult.

23. In light of God's Word, what should Mary have done? _____

_____

Mary naturally acted in faith toward her friend's word, yet failed to act in the same kind of faith toward God's Word. Faith is *not* something that we try to *get* to make the Word of God true and work for us. Faith is accepting the Word of God at face value, receiving it as we would the word of a trusted friend. Let the Word of God dwell in your heart, cast away every thought that causes you to doubt the promises of God.

24. What promise do we have regarding the validity of God's Word? (Numbers 23:19)

_____

Memory Verse: 1 John 5:9a

_____

_____

_____

Watch Jesus show Peter where to fish from *The Bible Mini Series*
<https://youtu.be/33O4s_DT8bA>

Worship with Wintley Phipps, *You'll Never Walk Alone* <http://goo.gl/NptmUE>

Worship with the Gaithers, *It is Well with My Soul* <https://youtu.be/0nJ6wQpLmuo>

Worship with Don Moen, *Great is Thy Faithfulness* <https://youtu.be/2iZzsrwf_aE>

Worship with Casting Crowns, *Tis' So Sweet to Trust in Jesus*
<https://youtu.be/-DdgkvnsHjM>

Worship with Daniel Ortega, *I Need Thee Every Hour* <https://goo.gl/KxwcBJ>

Study 24: How to Grow in Faith
How to Be a Doer of the Word

How are you using your faith? We have seen that faith is not hoping that we will see the answer in the future; faith is believing that we have the answer now. Faith sees the answer by continually looking into the Word and acts according to what it sees.

1. How does the kind of faith that contradicts circumstances and sees the answers grow strong in your life? (Proverbs 4:20-22) _____

_____

To "give attention" to God's Word means to study and obey God's Word. Many Christians have failed, been defeated, and are weak and sickly because they have disobeyed this basic command of God. They do not study and meditate on the Word of God. However, if you will obey God's command to keep the Word of God ever before you, you will see yourself as more than a conqueror because of Christ; you will walk in health and in God's blessings.

Many people pray, and instead of seeing themselves with the answer, they imagine things getting worse. Forgetting to look continually at the Word of God, they look at the wrong thing - at the symptoms, at conditions, at themselves, at their lack - and so they walk in unbelief and destroy the effects of their prayer.

2. Abraham had a faith that contradicted circumstances. What did Abraham look at, and what did he refuse to consider? (Romans 4:19-21) _____

_____

As children of God and sons of Abraham through faith in Jesus Christ, we must constantly stand firm upon God's Word even in the face of adverse circumstances and contradictory evidence.

3. What assurance do we have from the Lord concerning the truth and steadfastness of His Word? (Isaiah 55:11) _____

_____

Faith contradicts circumstances. Faith agrees with God's Word. Faith acts on God's Word.

The Importance of What We Say

4. What is the evidence of what a person really believes in his heart? (Romans 10:10)_____

Our faith in God becomes stronger as we vocalize what is in our heart.

5. We find this principle given in the teachings of Jesus. What did He say about our confession? (Mark 11:23) _____

_____

6. To see our prayers answered, what did Jesus teach we must add to the belief we hold in our heart? (Mark 11:23) _____

Jesus reminds us, "Out of the abundance of the heart, the mouth speaks." What you say reveals what you believe in your heart to be true. God and His Word are inseparable. God's Word is an expression of Himself. As we grow in love and trust toward God, we must begin to say about ourselves what the Word of God says. We *have* what God says we have. We *are* what God says we are. If God says we are strong, then we are. If He says He cares for us, then He does. If He says we are healed, then we are.

7. How do we overcome the enemy? (Revelation 12:11)

a. _____

b. _____

c. _____

Joshua's Acts of Faith

In both the Old and New Testaments we see examples of people who put their faith into action. God's people were able to accomplish mighty deeds, and mighty miracles were wrought by humble men, who in childlike faith, acted upon God's Word.

Look at the example of Joshua's faith at the Battle of Jericho.

8. What did God tell Joshua? (Joshua 6:2) _____

9. Did this mean that Joshua and the children of Israel could sit back and relax while the city automatically became theirs? (Joshua 6:3-5)_____

10. What explicit instructions did God give Joshua about possessing the land that He had already given them by promise? (Joshua 6:3-5)_____

_____

_____

_____

God told the Israelites exactly what to do. They had to believe God's word and *act* on it. Acting on God's Word was their faith in action. Notice that they were to shout while the walls were still up. Anyone can shout when the walls are down; it does not take any faith to do that. The Israelites were required to act out their faith. They "shouted" first; then they saw the results. We must be careful not to sit and wait for something to come to us. We must have an active faith and go up and possess the land that God has given us for an inheritance. We see this same faith in action in the New Testament.

A Faith that Can be Seen

11. While Jesus was teaching in a house, some men brought their friend to Him to be healed. Because they had difficulty in reaching Jesus, did they give up? (Luke 5:18-19)

12. What did they do? (Luke 5:18-19)

Notice that they did not shrug their shoulders and go back home. They did not say, "Well, at least we tried. We did the best we could." They did not give up that easily.

13. What did Jesus "see"? (Luke 5:20)

Jesus saw their *action* as a demonstration of the faith that was in their hearts.

14. How did the invalid demonstrate his faith? (Luke 5:24-25)

As we act out our faith in God's Word to us, we will reap the results. One of the best definitions of faith is this - *believing God's Word means acting as though it is true.*

The following is the biblical formula for faith:
   1) Find a promise in God's Word for whatever you are seeking.
   2) Believe God's Word as you would the word from a friend.
   3) Do not consider the contradictory circumstances.
   4) Thank God for the answer that is on its way and praise God.
   5) Act on the Word of God.

15. What are we exhorted to do? (James 1:22)

16. How is faith demonstrated outwardly? (James 2:17-18)

17. How did Abraham demonstrate his faith by works? (James 2:21)

18. When Abraham acted on God's Word by offering up his only son, what was he demonstrating? (Hebrews 11: 17-19)

19. How did Noah demonstrate his faith by works? (Hebrews 11:7) _____

_____

20. How is faith perfected or made more perfect? (James 2:22) _____

It is in the "doing" of God's directive Word that our faith is made stronger day by day. If we have seen that God has been faithful to His Word in small things, we will not doubt when the big things come along.

21. David's faith in God was developed in this way. Why did he believe he could defeat Goliath, the Philistine giant? (1 Samuel 17:33-37)_____

_____

_____

22. What is a hearer of the Word but not a doer like? (James 1:23-24) _____

_____

As the New Creation of God, we can discover what our lives in Him are to be and what we are like as a new creation by looking into the Word as we would look into a mirror. We must be careful that we do not walk away and act like the old earthly creatures we used to be. We must be careful that we do not forget what God says we are, what He says we can have, and what He says we can do.

23. How can we avoid this? (James 1:25)

a. _____

b. _____

c. _____

24. What kind of life will we have? (James 1:25) _____

_____

Memory Verse: James 1:25

_____

_____

_____

Watch Joshua March Around Jericho by Faith <https://youtu.be/APWvdaXTtak>

Watch David Defeat Goliath by Faith <https://youtu.be/PlTpu5yHXz8>

Watch God's Provisions by Faith <https://youtu.be/pMs8N6Wzwg4>

Study 25: The Power of Confessing God's Word

Confession is faith's way of expressing itself. Meditating continually on God's promises and faith's confession creates reality. It is always possible to discover a person's belief by what he says. Jesus reminds us, "Out of the abundance of the heart, the mouth speaks" (Matthew 12:34). If a person's confession is wrong, his believing is wrong. If his believing is wrong, his thinking is wrong. If his thinking is wrong, it is because his mind has not been renewed by the Word of God. All three - believing, thinking. and saying - go together. God has given us His Word to get our thinking straightened out. Confession, then, is affirming something we believe. It is testifying to something we know. It is witnessing for a truth we have embraced.

1. How is God's Word to be given to the lost? (Mark 16:15)

_____

It is through our confession or preaching of the Word that the world hears the Gospel. If we do not carry the Word to the world, then we waste our time praying for God to do something. If we could just pray and get people saved, we would not need to send missionaries all over the world. In obedience to Jesus' command, the disciples went out preaching the Word everywhere.

2. As the disciples went forth and preached the Word, what did the Lord do for them? (Mark 16:20) _____

_____

God did not do anything until the disciples preached the Word; then the signs followed. Notice also that the signs did not follow an individual but followed the preaching of the Word. There is no faith without confession. Paul wrote, "And how shall they believe in Him Whom they have not heard. And how shall they hear without a preacher—a confessor?" (Romans 10:14)

Likewise, in our daily lives and conversation, confession is faith's way of expressing itself. Faith, like love, is of the heart and of the spirit. We know that there is no love without word or action. We cannot reason love into people, nor can we reason love out of them. It is of the heart. In the same way, there is no faith without confession. Without confession of your faith, there is no outward sign of your belief. Your confession can determine your future.

The Power of What You Believe

3. What did Jesus say about our confession? (Mark 11:23)

_____

According to the words of Jesus, if we believe what we say will come to pass, it will - whether it be failure or success, sickness or health, weakness or strength. The reason the majority of Christians are weak is that they never have dared to make a confession of who they are in Christ. Your confession can affect your future and establish the events and circumstances of your life.

According to Jesus, the law of faith prescribes that you get what you believe. If you hold competing thoughts, beliefs, or images in your mind (believing God's Word, and then doubting God's Word), you become double-minded, you break the law of faith, and you are not able to receive anything from God.

4. We see an example of this when Peter was walking on the water. What did he do that caused him to start sinking? (Matthew 14:29-31)_____

_____

Peter took his eyes off Jesus and His Word and looked instead at the circumstances around him and the natural impossibility of doing what he was attempting to do.

5. What did Jesus say to Peter? (Matthew 14:31)_____

_____

Notice that Jesus did not congratulate Peter for trying to walk on water when none of the other disciples had the courage to do so. Jesus asked, "Why did you doubt Me? You have such little faith." Jesus corrected Peter for not having absolute and total faith in His words. Peter used his faith to believe in Jesus' words to come out and walk on the water. He simply accepted that Jesus' words were true. But Peter also used his faith to believe that the stormy waves were more powerful than Jesus' command. Peter let fearful images crowd out Jesus' word and was not able to receive Jesus' promise to walk on water. Because Peter believed the power of the waves were stronger than Jesus' words, Peter got what he believed for - he sank.

6. What happened when Jesus went to Nazareth and why? (Mark 6:1-6)_____

Although Jesus was God incarnate in human flesh, He was not able to do mighty works in Nazareth because of their unbelief. The people in Nazareth used their faith to believe that Jesus was not anyone special. They used their faith to believe that He was not the Son of God. They used their faith to believe that Jesus had no mighty power. As a result they received what they believed for - no miracles.

The Twelve Spies and the Result of Their Confession

In the Old Testament, we find this truth illustrated in the lives of the twelve Israelites who were sent to spy out the land.

7. What confession of faith did ten of the spies make? (Numbers 13:25-33)

8. What confession of faith did Caleb and Joshua make? (Numbers 13:30; 14:6-10)

9. What limitations did the ten spies set up in their lives because of their negative confession? (Numbers 14:36-37)

The ten spies used their faith to believe that they were going to die in the wilderness and they got what they believed for - exactly what they said - death in the wilderness!

10. What consequence did the congregation of Israel reap as a result of all their grumbling and complaining? (Numbers 14:27-29)

11. What events did the fathers set in motion in the lives of their children? (Numbers 14:31-33)

12. What events did Joshua set in motion in his life through his confession? (Numbers 14:38; Joshua 1:1-8)

13. What events did Caleb set in motion in his life through his confession? (Numbers 14:24; Joshua 14:6-14)

Caleb and Joshua used their faith to believe that God was going to keep His promise and give them the land, and they got what they said and what they believed for.

14. What is in the power of the tongue and with what will a man be filled? (Proverbs 18:20-21) _____

15. What are we exhorted to do as believers in light of Israel's failure? (Hebrews 3:16-19; Hebrews 4:1-2)_____

_____

16. Why did the Word of God not profit them? (Hebrews 4:2) _____

_____

The Amplified Version of this verse reads: "But the message they heard did not benefit them, because it was not mixed with faith (that is, with the leaning of the entire personality on God in absolute trust and confidence in His power, wisdom and goodness) by those who heard it."

If you find yourself at the bottom of life, it is because that is all that you have believed you would receive. There is a God-ward side and a man-ward side to every battle. Every victory, and everything that we have, we receive from God. Yet, we have our part to play. If there is any failure, it has to be on our part. God is not going to fail. If we see to it that we do our part, then we can be sure that there will be an answer and a victory from our Heavenly Father - He will always do His part.

Whether you believe that God's Word is true, and you confidently trust in it, is really based on one thing - the opinion you hold of the One who promised it.

17. Where did the spies' doubt and unbelief in God's promise begin? What picture were they holding in their imaginations and thoughts? (Numbers 13:31-33)

_____

_____

The Power of David's Thoughts

18. When Goliath, the Philistine giant, challenged the armies of Israel, what was their response? (1 Samuel 17: 1-11)_____

19. All the armies of Israel could see what Goliath looked like. Describe Goliath. (1 Samuel 17:4-7)_____

_____

_____

20. When David went out to fight Goliath, what thoughts did David hold in his imagination? (1 Samuel 17:1-12-37, answer from v. 34-37) _____

David *acted* upon his faith in the power of God. If David had been led by his natural senses, if he had listened to human reasoning, he would have known that it would be impossible to kill a giant with a shepherd's sling. He was focused on faith in God's promises and in God's ability. He was not listening to the voice of human reasoning.

21. Images of God helping him kill the lion and the bear filled the thoughts and imaginations of David's heart. As a result, when David went out to face Goliath what did he say and what were the results? (1 Samuel 17:40-53) _____

_____

_____

_____

_____

_____

David had faith, not in his own strength, but in God's power and might. He was not trusting in himself. He was trusting in the Lord. He *confessed* what he believed in his heart. First, David thought, second, David said, and third, David acted. David believed that what he thought and said would come to pass. As a result, his faith moved God, and Goliath came tumbling down. David got the result that he had pictured and believed that he would get.

22. What is the fourth thing that David did? (1 Samuel 17:54)

_____

David *published* the news of his victory throughout the land. We must first, *say* what we believe to be true; second, *act* on what we believe to be true; third, *receive* what we believe to be true; fourth, *tell* others about what we have received from God so that they too might believe.

In doing this, we can fix the landmarks of our lives for good and win victories for the kingdom of God, ourselves, and our brothers and sisters in the Lord. Out of weakness, we will be made strong and will be able to put to flight the armies of the evil one.

The Faith Formula in Action

23. A certain woman who had been sick for twelve years came to Jesus for healing. What did she do as the result of hearing the Word of God? What did the woman think and say? (Mark 5:25-34)

a. _____

b. _____

Hearing the Word of God activated this woman's faith in God. As a result she acted upon what she believed. She was a doer of the Word and not a hearer only. Our actions either defeat us, or they cause us to overcome. According to our actions, we either receive or are kept from receiving. The woman acted out her faith. The woman thought and said what she believed. She could have made a negative confession instead of a positive one. She could have thought that it was no use and that it was best for her to die. But she spoke positively. If we are defeated, we are defeated by our own thoughts and with our own words.

24. What was the result? (Mark 5:29) _____

_____

The woman got what she believed. Notice that the feeling and the healing followed the saying and the acting. Many people fail to receive because they want the feeling and the healing before they are willing to say it and do it.

25. What is the fourth thing the woman did? (Mark 5:33)

_____

If we are entertaining vain imaginations that are contrary to the Word of God, it is important to realize that these imaginations have the power to keep us from receiving God's promises.

26. What does Paul exhort us to do? (2 Corinthians 10:4-5) _____

_____

Memory Verses: Mark 11: 22-23

_____

_____

_____

_____

Watch this video clip of Jesus and Peter Walking on Water <http://goo.gl/1mjTzV>

Worship with Michael W. Smith, *Ancient Words,* <http://goo.gl/3qDLVA>

Worship with Robin Mark, *All I Once Held Dear* <http://goo.gl/MB7zGr>

Study 26: How to Become a Bold Confessor

Very few Christians realize the place that confession holds in God's scheme of things. Whenever the word "confession" is used, many invariably think of confessing sins, weaknesses, and failures. That is one side of confession. Confession of sins to God is a very positive thing. We are forgiven and cleansed from all unrighteousness. "If we confess our sins, He is faithful and just to forgive us of all our sins and cleanse us from all unrighteousness."

But, here we are speaking of a different type of *confession*, about which the Bible has a lot to say. *Webster's Dictionary* defines *confession* not only as "a confession of sins," but also as a "statement of one's beliefs; especially those of the Christian faith." That is why true Christianity throughout the centuries has been known as "The Great Confession." *Webster's Dictionary* also defines a *confessor* as "a Christian who has suffered for his faith. "

The apostles and early church fathers of the faith, as well as many who came before them and followed in their train down through history, in both the Old and New Testaments, were "bold confessors" of the Word of God. We will look at five of these "bold confessors."

1. We find the first three bold confessors defying the king's order to bow down before the golden image. What was the "bold confession" of Shadrach, Meshach, and Abednego? (Daniel 3:16-18)_____

_____

2. As a result of the "bold confessions" of their faith, what happened? (Daniel 3:21)_____

3. Because of their faith and commitment to God, loving not their lives unto death, what did the Lord do for them? (Daniel 3:24-27)

_____

4. What four things did the King say about their "bold confession" of faith? (Daniel 3:28)

a. _____

b. _____

c. _____

d. _____

As a result of these men's "bold confessions" of faith, God was exalted and glorified; and according to the Scripture, they prospered greatly in the province of Babylon.

Daniel

5. We find our fourth confessor denying the edict of the king which said that anyone making a petition to any god or man besides the king was to be thrown to the lions. What was Daniel's "bold confession"? (Daniel 6:10) _____

_____

6. As a result of the "bold confession" of his faith, what happened? (Daniel 6:16-17)

_____

7. Because of Daniel's faith and commitment to God, loving not his life unto death, what did the Lord do for him? (Daniel 6:20-23) _____

_____

8. Because of the "bold confession" of Daniel's faith, what did the king recognize about Daniel's God? (Daniel 6:25-27)

a. _____

b. _____

c. _____

d. _____

So God was glorified and exalted through the faith of Daniel, and as it is written in verse 28: "Daniel enjoyed success in the reign of Darius and in the reign of Cyrus the Persian."

Stephen

9. We find the fifth "bold confessor" of faith boldly proclaiming and confessing the Word of God before the high priest and elders of Israel and the synagogue of the Freedmen. What was the "bold confession" of Stephen? (Acts 7:51-52, 55-56)_____

_____

_____

_____

10. As a result of the "bold confessions" of Stephen's faith, what happened? (Acts 7:57-60)

_____

11. Because of Stephen's faith and commitment to God, loving not his life unto death, what happened? (Acts 7:58, 60; Acts 9: 15) _____

_____

As a result of Stephen's "bold confession" and his forgiving spirit, a young man named

Saul, who was later to become the great Apostle Paul, heard the Gospel. Because Stephen asked Jesus to forgive the sin of his murderers, Saul was released from his sin of murder. This opened the door for the visitation that Saul had from Jesus when he was blinded by light from heaven on the Road to Damascus.

12. What blessing did Stephen's interceding for his murderers and his bold confession bring to the world? (Acts 9:11-16) _____

13. Where did the early church get their power to so boldly confess the Word of God? (Acts 4:29-31)_____

14. What great victories were won by the bold confessions of men and women of faith? (Hebrews 11:33-38)

a._____ g._____

b._____ h._____

c._____ i._____

d._____ j._____

e._____ k._____

f._____

By faith great victories were won for the kingdom of God, and by faith men were willing to give their lives for Truth. This kind of faith is the very essence and heart of the Gospel. It is the kind of faith that agrees with God's Word and stands for it; never backs down, even in the face of death. By this faith, the men and women of old gained approval from God. This is faith in its maturity. This is the faith that continues to conquer the world.

15. What does the Bible say about those who gave their life standing for Truth and righteousness? (read Hebrews 11:36-38 answer from v 38)_____

16. How will we overcome the enemy? (Revelation 12:11)

a. _____

b. _____

c. _____

Memory Verses: Revelation 12:11

_____

_____

_____

Watch Shadrach, Meshech and Abednego's bold confession <http://goo.gl/oz1CBD>

Worship with the Gaithers, *It is Finished,*<https://youtu.be/TxaAmNuL7BU>

Worship with Steve Green, *God Defeats Pharaoh at the Red Sea* <http://goo.gl/ueHDxh>

Study 27: God's Predetermined Purpose and Your Free Will

Is everything that happens God's direct will? Is God's will always done? Human beings cannot thwart God's ultimate plan for the world; but they can and do thwart His plans for their personal life, their generation, and their nation. Men and women cannot prevent God's ultimate plan from achieving its end. "He has come to make His blessing flow as far as the curse is found." (from the hymn *Joy to the World!*) The kingdom of God will come upon the earth as it is in heaven - first in the hearts of people. From there, the river of God's Spirit will flow out until the glory of the Lord fills the earth and culminates in His Second Coming. In this sense, we may well cry "Hallelujah, the Lord our God, the Almighty reigns! The kingdoms of this world will become the kingdom of our God and of HIs Christ and He shall reign forever!" (from Revelation and "The Hallelujah Chorus" Handel's *Messiah*)

However, men and women can personally drop out of God's kingdom, or from their appointed places in it, which can affect those around them. God ordains that the kingdoms of this world will become the kingdoms of our God and of His Christ. However, He does not force people to accept His plan for them in His kingdom.

1. What does Isaiah foretell about God's predetermined purpose in the earth? (Isaiah 46:10-11)_____

2. As individuals, how did the Pharisees and lawyers respond to God's purpose for them? (Luke 7:30) _____

_____

Even though God's plans for the universe will certainly succeed, an individual may still reject God's plan or his part in it. Luke clearly states: "the Pharisees rejected God's purposes for them." God does not want mule-like servants who have to be forced to obey Him all the time. He wants those who will freely love Him and accept His instruction and counsel.

God wants relationships with His children based on mutual affection and love. God will not force us to love him. God wants everyone to repent and freely enter into a love-relationship with Him. But, if He "forced" people to repent, then their allegiance would not be freely given. Therefore, God leaves a person with a free choice. He does not "force" anyone to follow Him.

Let's search the Scriptures to discover more about man's responsibility and his free will to defy the will of God or to follow that will.

God Gives Us a Choice

3. When God called Abraham to follow Him, what was His response, and what did Abraham receive from God? (Genesis 12: 1-7)_____

4. What other promises did Abraham receive? (Genesis 13:16; 17:4-6; 26:4)

a. _____

b. _____

c. _____

d. _____

e. _____

5. In the story of God choosing a wife for Isaac, what was God's plan, and what part did the woman have in that plan? (Genesis 24:7-8)

a. _____

b. _____

6. What was Rebekah's choice? (Genesis 24:57-58) _____

7. Judas was also called by God. What was Judas called to, and what was his choice? (Acts 1:24-25) a. _____

b. _____

God called Abraham, Rebekah, and Judas to fulfill certain roles in his unfolding purposes. What God did not ordain was how they would respond to the task He had given them. Rebekah, through the act of her will, chose to fulfill her calling through the power of the Spirit. Judas did not. It was his own choice. It was not that he could somehow "unchoose" or "uncall" himself - for both calling and election were Jesus' decision. What Judas could and did do was to fall away from the ministry he had been given and so forfeit the blessing he could have enjoyed. God then used Judas' betrayal to fulfill His purpose.

8. As a result of Rebekah's choice, what blessing did she receive? (Genesis 24:60)_____

9. The Lord established this principle of free will very early in Israel's history as a nation. What choice was set before Israel? (Deuteronomy 30:11-20)_____

10. What was God's desire for them? (Deuteronomy 30:19-20) _____

_____

11. Was this commandment too difficult for them or impossible for them to follow? (Deuteronomy 30:11-14) _____

Again and again throughout Israel's history, God gave Israel choices and the freedom to choose His way or not. Rabbi Ginsburgh in *Hebrew Letters*, writes, "Free choice is fundamental to Jewish faith. Only *today* do we possess the opportunity to choose between good and evil. And so in accordance with our choice do we, ourselves, define the reward and punishment of *tomorrow.*"

12. What did Israel desire for Samuel to do for them? (1 Samuel 8:4-5)

_____

13. In demanding a king, what did the Lord say they were doing? (1 Samuel 8:6-8)

_____

God's Warning of the Result of Wrong Choices

14. Was it God's will for Israel to have a king? (1 Samuel 12:12-18) _____

_____

15. Briefly summarize the warning that the Lord gave them concerning the actions of the king who would reign over them. (1 Samuel 8:9-17) _____

16. What did the Lord say that Israel would do because of their oppression, and what would be God's response? (1 Samuel 8:18) _____

17. After hearing all this, what did Israel *choose* to do? (1 Samuel 8:19-20)

_____

18. As a result of Israel's choice, what did God choose to do? (1 Samuel 8:21-22)

_____

Israel rejected God's perfect will for them. They defied God's plan and frustrated His purpose. It was *never* God's will for them to have another king besides Himself. Israel missed God's perfect will as a nation and moved into His permissive will. They could not, however, prevent God's ultimate plan from being achieved. Because of God's loving kindness and mercy, He continued to try to work with Israel to bring forth His ultimate purpose. God chose Israel to bring forth the Messiah and ultimately the salvation for the world. He now has a kingdom, a holy nation (the church), and *He is the King.* However, because of their choice, they reaped the fruit of their choice and brought upon themselves all the sorrow and misery about which God had warned them. Let's examine the life of Saul, their king, to see an example of God's purposes and the free will of the individual.

The Result of Saul's Choices

19. Who chose Saul to be King over Israel? (1 Samuel 9:15-17) _____

20. What choice was set before Saul? (1 Samuel 12:24-25)_____

21. What did Saul choose to do? (1 Samuel 13:8-13)_____

22. What was God's will for Saul? (1 Samuel 13:13)_____

23. Because Saul chose to disobey the Lord, what happened? (1 Samuel 13:14)

_____

_____

24. What did the Lord tell Saul to do in the battle with Amalek, and what did Saul choose to do? (1 Samuel 15:2-3, 8-9) _____

_____

25. What did Saul do after the battle with Amalek and what did it reveal about his heart? (1 Samuel 15:12)

a._____

b._____

Notice that Saul did not lead the people in the worship of God for giving them the victory over their enemy. He took the credit for himself and set up a monument so people could honor him.

26. Because of Saul's choice, what happened? (1 Samuel 15:22-28) _____

_____

God had called and chosen Saul. What God did not ordain was how he would respond to the task He had allotted him.

27. What was God's reaction to Saul's disobedience? (1 Samuel 15:11,35)

_____

_____

28. Why does God test man? (Deuteronomy 8:2) _____

_____

This is why there are periods of heavy testing before God gives a person responsibility. By the way we react through trials, God determines faithfulness.

29. What does God require of those to whom He has given a stewardship? (1 Corinthians 4:2)

_____

30. When Saul was disobedient to God and didn't faithfully fulfill the office that God had given him, what did God do? (1 Samuel 15:28) _____

To Obey or to Disobey

31. Before God brought the judgment of Babylonian captivity upon Judah, the Lord had Jeremiah warn Judah of the coming judgment. Why? (Jeremiah 36:2-3)

32. What was the attitude and choice of King Zedekiah and his servants? (Jeremiah 36:24-26)

33. The Chaldeans began to besiege Jerusalem. Because of His long-suffering and loving kindness, God did not want anyone to perish. God gave them an opportunity to save their lives. What did God tell them to do? (Jeremiah 38:2,17-20)

34. After the deportation to Babylon, there was still a small remnant of Judah in the land. What was the Word of the Lord to them? (Jeremiah 42:10-19)

35. What was their choice? (Jeremiah 43:4; 44:16-17)

36. If a nation hears that God will judge them for their sin, what is God's response if that nation repents and turns from evil? (Jeremiah 18:7-10)

37. What will happen if a nation that God is building up disobeys God and does evil? What will God do? (Jeremiah 18:7-10)

38. Does God want to change His mind about judging people? (Jeremiah 26:13; Ezekiel 24:13)

It is man's free choice to defy God's Word or to repent and obey it. It is God's hope that every person will be faithful to Him and enjoy the privileges of His kingdom.

39. What was God's perfect will and desire for Israel? (Isaiah 48:17-19)

Because of the free choice God gives every person, individuals as well as entire nations have missed God's perfect will for their lives. Those who openly defy His Word and rebel against His counsel, reject God's Word to them personally, miss their calling and their part in God's ultimate purposes for the world.

The Path of Faith

40. Abraham is called the Father of Faith because of the example he set for all God's children for all ages to come. What example did Abraham give us. Summarize.(Romans 4:16-25)

_____

_____

_____

_____

Abraham believed in the God who brings into existence what didn't exist before. Abraham believed God even though such a promise seemed utterly impossible! Abraham never wavered in believing God's promise. His faith grew stronger, and in this he brought glory to God. He was absolutely convinced that God was able to do anything He promised.

41. What has been given to us as children of God through faith in Jesus Christ? (2 Peter 1:4)

_____

_____

_____

42. What eight things are we exhorted to practice that will assure us of never stumbling? (2 Peter 1:5-8)

a. _____ e. _____

b. _____ f. _____

c. _____ g. _____

d. _____ h. _____

43. If we have these qualities, of what can we be sure? (2 Peter 1:8)

_____

_____

44. If we lack these qualities, what is our spiritual condition? (2 Peter 1:9)

_____

_____

45. What exhortation does Peter give, and if we do this, of what can we be assured? (2 Peter 1:10-11)

a._____

b._____

c._____

46. What does Hebrews warn us about and advise us to do? (Hebrews 12:13-29).

a. (13)_____

_____

b. (14) _____

c. (14)_____

d. (15) _____

e. (16)_____

f. (25)_____

g. (28)_____

47. In the day when God created man and woman, what did God name them? (Genesis 5:2)

_____

Both Men and women were evangelists, pastors, and teachers great pillars of the early church.

48. What did Paul teach about the body of Christ? (Galatians 3:28)

_____

Memory Verses: Deuteronomy 30: 19-20

_____

_____

_____

_____

When you listen to the worship below, think of the impact of the Living Christ in time and in history. The disciples were sent out to preach the Gospel against the universal disapproval of their own religious leaders and were opposed by the greatest Military Power in world history. Since then, Christ's kingdom has grown from a little Stone to a great mountain and is destined to fill the entire earth - "All the earth will worship Him and sing praise to His name!"

Worship with Passion Band/Chris Tomlin, *We Fall Down* <http://goo.gl/NWp6fx>

Worship, *I'd Rather Have Jesus* <https://youtu.be/ZqFsFY0M8WI>

Singapore <http://goo.gl/DJvlVs>   *Korea* <http://goo.gl/8Ix3TH>

Moscow Russia <https://goo.gl/mNVkIS>   *India* <http://goo.gl/us6EEE>

Kiev, Ukrain <http://goo.gl/7Za6sU>   *Philippines* <http://goo.gl/cDUVKD>

Brazil <http://goo.gl/p3kjpi>   *Indonesia* <http://goo.gl/JRbSt8>

Africa <http://goo.gl/V22H2e>

Study 28: Called into His Glory

1. Why did God call you through the Gospel? (2 Thessalonians 2:14)

_____

Paul wrote to the Thessalonians, "It was for this He called you through our Gospel, that you may gain the glory of our Lord Jesus Christ."

2. When we were rescued from the realm of sin and darkness by faith in the blood of Jesus, what was the purpose of Christ's rescue mission? (Hebrews 2:10)

_____

3. Who are the sons of God? (Romans 8:14) _____

From the clear teaching of Scripture, we see that it is God's desire to bring many sons into glory. We also clearly see that the sons of God are neither male nor female, but are those who have learned how to be led by His Spirit.

4. What is the world waiting for? (Romans 8: 17-19)

_____

5. What will those who are led by the Spirit be able to do for the world? (Romans 8:21)

_____

_____

Throughout the church age, those who have been led by God's Spirit have been able to bring people, and eventually nations, into true spiritual liberty.

6. Where the Spirit of the Lord is, what is always there? (2 Corinthians 3:17)

_____

The Calling of God

7. What has God called us to and how are we to live? (1 Thessalonians 2:12)

a. _____

b. _____

8. What else has God called us? (Romans 8:28)

_____

9. What has God predestinated us to become, and who is Jesus to us? (Romans 8:29)

a. _____

b._____

Called to Receive His Glory

10. What has God promised to those He has called? (Romans 8:30) Answer from *Living Translation*: "And having chosen them, He called them to come to Him. And He gave them right standing with Himself, and He promised them His glory."

_____

11. Because we have believed in Jesus as our Lord and Savior, what have we received and what do we look forward to sharing? (Romans 5:1-2)

Answer from the *Living Translation*: "Therefore, since we have been made right in God's sight by faith, we have peace with God because of what Jesus Christ our Lord has done for us. Because of our faith, Christ has brought us into this place of highest privilege where we now stand, and we confidently and joyfully look forward to sharing God's glory."

a. _____

b. _____

c. _____

d. _____

12. What are those who have received the abundance of grace and the gift of righteousness called to do? (Romans 5:17)_____

13. When God first created Adam and Eve, what were they crowned with? (Hebrews 2:6-7)

_____

14. What happened when Adam and Eve sinned? (Romans 3:23)

_____

15. In Jesus' prayer right before He was crucified, what did He give us? (John 17:22)_____

16. In this prayer, what did Jesus pray that we would be able to see? (John 17:24)

_____

17. When God gave Moses the Ten Commandments, what happened to Moses' face? (2 Corinthians 3:7) _____

18. What were two characteristics of this glory? (2 Corinthians 3:7)

a. _____

b. _____

19. What is the glory of the New Covenant like in comparison? (2 Corinthians 3:10-11)

_____

20. How do we receive this glory? (2 Corinthians 3:18)

_____

21. Why has God shown His light in our hearts? (2 Corinthians 4:6)

_____

22. What is another way that we receive this glory? (2 Corinthians 4:17-18)

_____

23. What did God promise to do in both the Old and New Covenants? (Isaiah 60:1-5, 7; Ephesians 5:27)

a. _____

b. _____

24. What is God able to do, and what does God want in the church? (Ephesians 3:20-21)

a. _____

b. _____

God is able to do abundantly above all we can think, dream, or imagine. And He wants glory in His church. He wants the glory of His Presence in our meetings, but beyond that, He wants His glory displayed through your life. He wants others to look at you and see and feel His glory and His love through your life that is well lived and full of His blessings for others. So cast out all images of doubt, fear, and unbelief and get busy dreaming the dreams of God and imagining all the good He has stored up for you in this life, not just in the world to come.

The following are three of the New Covenant's greatest prayers. If you pray these prayers everyday, your life will be transformed beyond recognition of your old, former self. Paul prayed these prayers for the early church, and he knew they would end up conquering the world.

25. The disciples came to Jesus and asked Him to teach them to pray. Read Matthew 6:9-13. When we pray, what attitude should we have? Should we scream and yell at God? (Matthew 6:9) _____

_____

The Lord's Prayer

26. What does Jesus tell us to ask for in prayer? (Matthew 6:10-13 a)

a. _____

b. _____

c. _____

d. _____

e. _____

It is important to remember that God does not lead us into temptation. "Lead us not into temptation" means "Do not let us yield to temptation."

27. What does James remind us about this? (James 1:13) _____

_____

In this prayer, Jesus told us to ask God to forgive our sins just like we forgive the sins of others. This means God will only forgive us in the measure that we forgive others. The *Amplified* gives the verse this way, "Forgive us our debts (sins) as we also have forgiven, remitted, and let go of the debts (sins), and have given up resentment against our debtors."

28. What did Jesus explain about what it takes to be forgiven of your sins? (Matthew 11:14-15) _____

29. Jesus instructed His disciples to end their prayer with a declaration of faith and a decree. What was that decree? (Matthew 6:13b)_____

_____

The power in the Lord's Prayer is undeniable. The early church took the Lord's Supper everyday, remembering His death and His covenant to save the world. They also prayed the Lord's prayer. With these two spiritual weapons, they saw Rome and the continent of Europe "cast their idols to the moles and the bats" and turn to the Living God as Isaiah prophesied. (Isaiah 2:18-20)

Paul's Prayer for Revelation for the Church

30. Here is the second prayer of utmost importance in the New Testament. What did Paul pray for the church? Answer from *The Living Translation:*
Make this scripture your own personal prayer. (Ephesians 1:15-23)

> I pray for you constantly, asking God, the glorious Father of our Lord Jesus Christ, to give you spiritual wisdom and understanding (the spirit of wisdom and revelation in the knowledge of Him), so that you might grow in your knowledge of God. I pray that your hearts will be flooded with light so that you can understand the wonderful future He has promised

to those he called. I want you to realize what a rich and glorious inheritance He has given to His people. I pray that you will begin to understand the incredible greatness of His power for us who believe Him. This is the same mighty power that raised Christ from the dead and seated Him in the place of honor at God's right hand in the heavenly realms. Now He is far above any ruler or authority or power or leader or anything else in this world or in the world to come. And God has put all things under the authority of Christ, and He gave him this authority for the benefit of the church. And the church is His body; it is filled by Christ, who fills everything everywhere with his presence.

a. _____

b. _____

c. _____

d. _____

e. _____

Paul's Prayer for Love for the Church

31. Here is the third New Covenant prayer of great power and significance. Read this prayer from the *Living Translation* (Ephesians 3:14-21), then answer below:

When I think of the wisdom and scope of God's plan, I fall to my knees and pray to the Father, the Creator of everything in heaven and on earth.(v14). I pray that from His glorious, unlimited resources He will give you mighty inner strength through His Holy Spirit. And I pray that Christ will be more and more at home in your hearts as you trust in Him. May your roots go down deep into the soil of God's marvelous love. And may you have the power to understand, as all God's people should, how wide, how long, how high, and how deep His love really is.

May you experience the love of Christ, though it is so great you will never fully understand it. Then you will be filled with the fullness of life and power that comes from God (vs.15-19). Now glory be to God! By His mighty power at work within us, He is able to accomplish infinitely more than we would ever dare to ask or hope. May He be given glory in the church and in Christ Jesus forever and ever through endless ages. Amen.

In the prayer above, what did Paul do when he prayed and why? (Ephesians 3:14)

_____

_____

32. In the prayer above, for what six things does Paul pray? (Ephesians 3:15-19)

a. _____

b. _____

c. _____

d. _____

e. _____

f. _____

33. What declaration of praise and faith does Paul make? (Ephesians 3:20-21)

a. _____

b. _____

c. _____

_____

The *Amplified Version* ends Paul's prayer this way: "Now to Him who is able to do...superabundantly, far over and above all that we dare ask or think, infinitely beyond our highest prayers, desires, thoughts, hopes, or dreams. To Him be *glory in the church* and in Christ Jesus throughout all generations forever and ever. Amen - So be it!"

Memory Verse: Hebrews 2:10

_____

_____

_____

Worship with Larnell Harris and Sandy Patti, *I've Just Seen Jesus* <https://youtu.be/_yLgtd_kkxw>

Worship with Keith Green, *The Victor* <http://goo.gl/jttnO0>

All the Ends of the Earth Shall Remember and Turn to the Lord:

England: London - *The Hallelujah Chorus, Handel's Messiah* <http://goo.gl/38ExRR>
          Oxford, King's College <http://goo.gl/Etkz86>

New York: *The Hallelujah Chorus, Handel's Messiah* <http://goo.gl/dCm0HH>

Korea: Seoul - *The Hallelujah Chorus, Handel's Messiah* <https://youtu.be/79M0P74d6ZA>

Spain: Madrid - *The Hallelujah Chorus, Handel's Messiah*<http://goo.gl/6mpu3E>

Canada: Must See! - *The Hallelujah Chorus, Handel's Messiah* <http://goo.gl/nho1zZ>

Answers

"Who is like the wise man and who knows
The interpretation of a matter? A man's wisdom
Illumines him and causes his stern face to beam."
--Ecclesiastes 8:1

Study 1: Set Free from Sin!

1. They chose to disobey God and rebel against Him.

2. They desired to exalt themselves above God and be God themselves.

3. a. The lust of the flesh (the tree was good for food). **b.** The lust of the eyes (it was a delight to the eyes).

c. The pride of life (it was desirable to make one wise).

4. He was walking in the garden, calling Adam, and desiring their fellowship.

5. a. None of them are righteous. **b.** None of them understand. **c.** None of them seek for God.

d. All of them have turned aside and become useless. **e.** None of them does good. **f.** Their mouth is full of death, deceit, poisons, cursing and bitterness. **g.** Their feet are swift to shed blood. **h.** Destruction and misery are in their path. **i.** They have no peace. **j.** They do not fear God. **k.** All of them have sinned and come short of God's glory.

6. God sent a savior and a deliverer, the Son of Man, who came to seek the lost. It is the Spirit of God that draws men unto Him.

7. God's kindness.

8. No.

9. No.

10. As to the righteousness which is in the law, he was blameless; yet he was the chief of sinners.

11. Through the law comes the knowledge of sin, that all the world may be accountable to God.

12. a. True repentance - forsaking sin and obeying God's commandments **b.** By the shedding of the blood of animals.

13. Blood is needed to make atonement, a sinless sacrifice must be offered, and without the shedding of blood there is no forgiveness.

14. Animal sacrifices sanctified for the cleansing of the flesh and the forgiveness of sins.

15. He will save His people from their sins. He appeared to take away sins.

16. Behold the Lamb of God which takes away the sin of the world.

17. The blood of Jesus will purge your conscience from dead works to serve the Living God.

18. a. Bore our sins. **b.** Bore our sickness. **c.** Redeemed us from the curse. **d.** Took upon Himself the body of sin, that we may no longer be slaves to it.

19. a. I will put My laws in their minds and write it upon their hearts. **b.** I will be their God and they shall be My people. **c.** They shall know the Lord. **d.** I will be merciful to their iniquities and forget their sins. **e.** Give you a new heart and a new spirit. **f.** He will remove the heart of stone.

20. a. Repent. **b.** Confess Jesus as Lord and believe God raised Him from the dead.

21. To save the world and give them eternal life.

22. Those who have rejected Jesus and who love darkness rather than light.

23. They will be cast into the lake of fire.

24. That none should perish, but all come to repentance and the knowledge of the truth.

Study 2: What is True Repentance?

1. That God has made Him both Lord and Christ Messiah.

2. They were pierced to the heart and asked, "What shall we do?"

3. a. Repent. **b.** Be baptized. **c.** Receive the gift of the Holy Spirit.

4. a. Repentance means to confess our sin. **b.** Turn away from it, forsake it and walk in a new direction; **c.** Ceasing to do evil and learning to do good.

5. Your sins.

6. 1) Worship God only. **2)** Do not worship idols or images or bow down to them. **3)** Don't take God's name in vain. **4)** Keep the Sabbath holy. **5)** Honor your father and mother. **6)** Do not murder. **7)** Don't commit adultery. **8)** Don't steal. **9)** Don't bear false witness against your neighbor. **10)** Don't covet your neighbor's house, wife, or anything that belongs to him.

7. If you break God's commandments or teach others to do so you, will be least in the kingdom of Heaven, but if you keep God's commandments and teach others to keep them, you will be great in the kingdom of heaven.

8. a. Anger is the same thing as murder. **b.** Lust in the heart is the same as adultery. **c.** Bless and show love to your enemies.

9. Adultery, fornication, uncleanness, lewdness, idolatry, sorcery, hatred, contentions, jealousies, outbursts of anger, selfish ambitions, dissensions, heresies, lust of the flesh, the lust of the eyes and pride of life, homosexuality, sodomy, sexual immorality.

10. To the one who knows to do right and doesn't do it, to him it is sin.

11. Disobeying God's Word.

12. They did not practice what they preached but did things to be seen and honored by men.

13. Don't be called teacher, leader, or father. Remember you are all brothers.

14. You won't be able to believe (or have faith).

15. If they persecute Me, they will persecute you. You are blessed when you are persecuted for righteousness sake. Yours is the kingdom of heaven.

16. He who loves father, mother, son or daughter more than me is not worthy of me. Your desire for your family's approval cannot be greater than your desire to do the will of God. You must take up your cross and follow after Him.

17. He who tries to save his life will lose it, but if you lose your life for Christ's sake you will find it.

18. He is faithful and just to forgive our sin and cleanse us from all unrighteousness. We shall be as white as snow and eat the good of the land.

19. Neither do I condemn you. Go and sin no more.

20. Return or pay back what you have stolen and keep God's laws.

21. He received Jesus gladly saying that he would give half his possessions to the poor and if he had defrauded anyone, he would give back four times as much.

22. a. This day salvation has come to your house. **b.** The Son of Man came to seek and save that which is lost.

23. a. Do not have fellowship with the ungodly. **b.** Come out from the world and be separate. **c.** Touch not the unclean thing.

24. He squandered his estate with loose living and wound up feeding pigs and eating swine food.

25. He decided to leave his sinful ways and worldly influences and go to his father and confess his sin and wrong doing.

26. His father saw him coming and ran to meet him, embraced him and kissed him.

27. He made him a son.

28. a. Make no covenant with them. **b.** Show them no favors. **c.** Do not allow your sons and daughters to intermarry with them.

29. a. They will turn your heart away from the Lord. **b.** You are to be a holy people set aside for the Lord alone. **c.** In order that you may live and multiply and go in and possess the land. (This obedience was conditional to receiving God's continued blessing).

30. A marriage relationship.

31. Your God delights and rejoices over you as a bridegroom does his bride.

32. A harlot or prostitute.

33. a. Adultery. **b.** Hostility toward God. **c.** Make yourself an enemy of God.

34. He jealously desires the Spirit He has put in them.

35. The love of the Father is not in Him.

36. a. The lust of the flesh **b.** The lust of the eyes. **c.** the boastful pride of life.

37. They abide forever.

38. a. Love the Lord thy god with all your heart, soul, mind and strength and love your neighbor as yourself. **b.** Seek the kingdom of God first and His righteousness.

39. You must give up everything.

40. Sit down and count the cost.

41. Eternal life.

42. I have kept all God's commandments since I was a child, what more do I lack?

43. Sell everything, give it away and follow Me.

44. He went away and did not follow Jesus.

45. A sword.

46. a. The religious leaders. **b.** Government officials. **c.** Members of your own household.

47. a. Confess with your mouth Jesus as Lord. **b.** Believe in your heart God has raised Him from the dead.

48. a. They shall rule and reign with Him. **b.** They shall receive 100 times as much in this present age as they have given up. **c.** They shall receive eternal life in the world to come.

49. He gives them power to become the sons of God.

50. He will come in and fellowship with you.

51. You will be born again.

52. Eternal life.

Study 3: The Power of Water Baptism?

1. a. Repent. **b.** Be baptized. **c.** Receive the Holy Spirit.

2. Make disciples of all nations and baptize them.

3. a. That our body of sin might be done away with. **b.** That we should no longer be slaves to sin.

4. Water baptism

5. Water baptism

6. A sign of the covenant between God and Abraham and his descendants.

7. a. He was cut off from his people. **b.** He has broken God's covenant.

8. Abraham and his descendants.

9. If we belong to Christ, we are Abraham's seed and heirs according to the promise.

10. Those who worship in the Spirit and put no confidence in the flesh.

11. The circumcision of the heart.

12. He will take away the heart of stone.

13. Water baptism.

14. They were baptized in the cloud and the sea.

15. They were all circumcised.

16. Because they had not been circumcised in the wilderness.

17. He had rolled away the reproach of Egypt from them.

18. a. Through water baptism we receive the circumcision of Christ. **b.** Removal of the body of flesh.

19. a. Burial. **b.** Resurrection.

20. a. In the likeness of His resurrection. **b.** He will remove the heart of stone.

21. a. To render the devil powerless. **b.** To deliver those who were subject to slavery.

22. To bring us to God.

23. They were baptized.

24. They were baptized.

25. He desired baptism.

26. He went down into the water (immersion).

27. He was baptized.

28. Immediately.

29. The same day.

30. In the name of the Father, Son and Holy Spirit.

31. a. In the name of Jesus Christ. **b.** In the name of the Lord Jesus. **c.** In the name of the Lord. **d.** In the name of the Lord Jesus.

32. We are baptized into Jesus Christ.

33. The baptism of repentance.

34. He told him to wash seven times in the Jordan.

35. He was furious and insulted.

36. If the prophet had told you to do some great thing, you would have done it. How much more should you do this simple thing. So Naaman washed and was cleansed.

37. The heavens opened and the Spirit of God came upon Him like a dove

38. We have been buried with Him in baptism.

39. We are seated with Christ in heavenly places.

40. Who shall separate us from the love of Christ? Shall tribulation, or distress, or persecution, or famine, or nakedness, or peril, or sword? For I am persuaded that neither death nor life, nor angels nor principalities nor powers, nor things present nor things to come nor height nor depth, nor any other created thing, shall be able to separate us from the love of God which is in Christ Jesus our Lord.

Study 4: What is the Baptism in The Holy Spirit?

1. a. Repent. **b.** Be baptized. **c.** Receive the Holy Spirit.

2. To wait in Jerusalem until they received the promise of the Father and were clothed with power from on High.

3. He presented Himself alive and by many convincing proofs appeared to them over a period of 40 days, speaking to them of things concerning the kingdom of God.

4. The baptism of the Holy Spirit.

5. They would receive power to be His witnesses.

6. Jesus fulfilled His ministry under the anointing of the Holy Spirit and power.

7. As for me, I baptize you with water for repentance, but He who is coming after me is mightier than I; *He will baptize you with the Holy Spirit and fire.*

8. Living water.

9. a. You will never thirst again. **b.** Eternal life.

10. If anyone is thirsty let him come to me and drink. Whoever believes in me, out of his innermost being will flow rivers of living water.

11. We must believe in Him and ask Him for it.

12. Jesus was talking about the Holy Spirit who those who believe in Him were to receive.

13. The Holy Spirit was not given because Jesus was not yet glorified.

14 . Everything lived wherever the waters flowed. There were many fish and fishermen. Many trees grew beside the river whose leaves were for healing. The marshes from the river provided salt.

15. Your body is the temple of the Living God and the Holy Spirit dwells in you.

16. Peter caught so many fish, the nets were breaking.

17. From now on you will catch men.

18. He showed me a river of the water of life, clear as crystal, coming from the throne of God and the Lamb. On either side of the river was the tree of life, bearing twelve kinds of fruits, yielding every month. the leaves of the trees were for the healing of the nations. There will no longer be any curse.

19. God is everywhere present. There is no place high enough or deep enough to get away from God's spirit. God even saw me when I was being created in my mother's womb.

20. God is not far from any one of you because in Him you live, move, and have your being.

21. a. In Your Presence is fulness of joy. **b.** A day in your Presence is better than a thousand elsewhere. I would rather be a doorkeeper in the house of the Lord than to dwell in the tents of wickedness.

22. Do not cast me away from Your Presence and take not Your Holy spirit from me.

23. I will pray and ask the Father to send you another Helper or comforter that He may abide with you forever, the

Spirit of Truth.

24. The Holy Spirit, you know Him for He dwells with you, but He will dwell in you.

25. The true place of worship is neither mountain or temple. The time is coming when true worshipers will worship the father in spirit and truth.

26. He will give the Holy Spirit to those who love Him and keep His commandments.

27. a. Comforter **b.** Helper **c.** Intercessor **d.** Advocate **e.** Strengthener **f.** Standby

28. a. The Spirit of your Father. **b.** The Spirit of His Son.

29. a. He will lead you into all truth **b.** He will show you what is to come.

30. a. People will have dreams **b.** See visions **c.** Prophesy.

31. a. Ananias had a vision to go lay hands on Paul to receive his sight. **b.** Paul had a vision of a man named Ananias coming to pray for him. **c.** Peter had a vision which directed him to go and preach to the Gentiles. **d.** Paul had a vision of a man from Macedonia calling for help and concluded that God was telling them to go preach there. **e.** Paul had a night vision and was instructed to stay and preach in Corinth a preach because God had many people there to save, so Paul stayed and preached 2 years. **f.** Paul was saved and called through a vision. **g.** John received the entire book of Revelation through a vision.

32. a. Things that eye has not seen and ear has not heard. **b.** God reveals them to us by His Spirit.

33. a. You don't need anyone to teach yo, what is true. The Holy Spirit teaches you. **b.** Remain in fellowship with Christ.

34. The love of God.

35. We are transformed from glory to glory into the image of Jesus Christ.

Study 5: How to Receive the Baptism in the Holy Spirit

1. Power to be a witness.

2. We are not to worry about what we will say when we are called up to witness. The Holy Spirit will give us the words to say.

3. Peter was filled with the Holy Spirit.

4. He explained that the miracle was done by Jesus' name, not by his own power. Then He preached the gospel to them in all boldness.

5. They were amazed at Peter's boldness and knowledge and took note that he had been with Jesus.

6. Those who preached the gospel to you did it by the Holy Spirit sent from heaven.

7. I will never leave you though everyone else does. I will die fighting for you.

8. As Jesus was on trial, Peter denied three times that he knew Jesus. The last time he denied Him with cursing.

9. His Gospel was not in persuasive words, but in the demonstration of the Spirit and of power.

10. a. Your faith should not rest on the wisdom of men. **b.** Your faith should rest in the power of God.

11. a. Jesus was anointed with the Holy Spirit and power. **b.** He went about doing good and healing all who were oppressed by the devil. **c.** Because God was with Him.

12. a. To bring Good New to the poor. **b.** To proclaim release to the captives. **c.** To make the blind see. **d.** To set the oppressed free. **e.** To proclaim the favorable year of the Lord.

13. The women, Mary the mother of Jesus, His brothers.

14. 120.

15. In the temple.

16. Jews from every nation under heaven.

17. a. There came from heaven a noise like a violent rushing wind that filled all the house.

b. Tongues of fire appeared on them. **c.** They began to speak with tongues as the Spirit gave them utterance.

18. The multitude of Jews there gathered around them, each hearing them speak in their own language.

19. a. He explained it as the out-pouring of the Holy Spirit spoken of by the prophet Joel. **b.** 3000 were saved.

20. The baptism of fire.

21. He will baptize you in the Holy Spirt and fire.

22. My Word is like fire and like a hammer which shatters the rock.

23. You will turn the people from their evil ways and their evil deeds.

24. It is like a burning fire that can't be held in.

25. He describes it as separating the wheat from the chaff, tossing it up continually until all impurities have been separated from the wheat.

26. The Lord will be like fuller's soap and a refiner's fire. He will purge and purify believers that they may offer unto the Lord offerings of righteousness.

27. To transform us into the same image of the Lord from glory to glory.

28. We have the mind of Christ.

29. My sheep know My voice and they follow Me. They will not follow the strangers voice but will flee from Him.

30. The Holy Spirit fell on them as they heard Peter's preaching.

31. They heard them speak with tongues and exalt God.

32. Through the laying on of hands.

33 Through the laying on of hands.

34. They spoke in tongues and prophesied.

35. I will put My Spirit within you and cause you to walk in My ordinances.

36. Unto you and your children and to all who are afar off, even as many as the Lord our God shall call.

37. To all His children who ask for it.

38. No.

39. a. In my name they will cast out demons. **b.** They will speak with new tongues. **c.** they will pick up serpents. **d.** If they drink any deadly thing it will not hurt them. **e.** They will lay hands on the sick and they will recover.

40. The Spirit makes intercession for us according to the will of God.

41 a. Let everyone who is thirsty come and drink of the water of life without cost. **b.** The Spirit and the bride say come.

Study 6: What are the Gifts of the Holy Spirit?

1. A gift.

2. It is given as a pledge of our inheritance with a view to the redemption of God's own possession.

3. To know the one true God.

4. Spirit of adoption as sons entering into a Father-Son relationship.

5. That we are children of God.

6. Those who are being led by the Spirit of God.

7. a. The lame were healed. **b.** Unclean spirits were cast out. **c.** People with palsies and the lame were healed. **d.** Dead were raised.

8. By the power of the Spirit.

9. By the Spirit of God.

10. a. They shall cast out demons. **b.** They shall speak with new tongues.

c. They shall pick up serpents. **d.** If they drink any deadly poison, it won't hurt them.

e. They shall lay hands on the sick and they shall recover.

11. The preaching of the Word.

12. Speaking with tongues.

13. Prophecy.

14. a. Speaks to God. **b.** Speaks mysteries. **c.** Edifies himself.

15. The Spirit.

16. No.

17. a. The Spirit intercedes for us according to God's will. **b.** We build ourselves up.

18. He wanted all to speak in tongues and he spoke in tongues more than anyone else.

19. Prophecy.

20. a. He is convicted. **b.** Called to account. **c.** The secrets of his heart are disclosed.

d. He will fall on his face and worship God. **e.** He will declare that God is among you.

21. The testimony of Jesus.

22. a. Revelation. **b.** Knowledge. **c.** Teaching.

23. Tongues with an interpretation.

24. a. Psalm. **b.** Teaching. **c.** Revelation. **d.** Tongue and interpretation.

25. Sing in the Spirit.

26. a. Varieties of gifts. **b.** Varieties of ministries. **c.** Varieties of effects.

27. a. Word of wisdom. **b.** Word of knowledge. **c.** Faith. **d.** Healing. **e.** Effecting of miracles. **f.** Prophecy.

g. Distinguishing or discerning of spirits. **h.** Tongues. **i.** Interpretation of tongues.

28.a. Faith, healing, and miracles. **b.** Word of knowledge, distinguishing of spirits, word of wisdom.

c. Faith, healing, miracles. **d.** Discerning of spirits, faith, miracles. **e.** Word of knowledge, prophecy.

f. Tongues and interpretation of tongues.

29. Word of wisdom.

30. a. Apostles. **b.** Prophets. **c.** Evangelists. **d.** Pastors. **e.** Teachers. **f.** Workers of miracles. **g.** Gifts of healings. **h.** Helps. **i.** Administrations. **j.** Various kinds of tongues.

31. a. Service. **b.** Exhortation-encouragement. **c.** Giving. **d.** Leading-giving aid. **e.** Showing mercy

f. Contributing to the needs of the saints. **g.** Practicing hospitality.

32. 1) Love. **2)** Joy. **3)** Peace. **4)** Patience. **5)** Kindness **6)** Goodness. **7)** Faithfulness **8)** Gentleness.

9) Self-control.

33. We are nothing.

34. We should earnestly desire spiritual gifts especially prophecy

35. a. Prophecy. **b.** Visions. **c.** Dreams.

36. For the common good.

37. From your innermost being shall flow rivers of living water which shall be a well of water springing up to eternal life.

Study 7: The Power of The Covenant Supper

1. a. And they continued steadfastly in the apostles' doctrine **b.** Fellowship, **c.** The breaking of bread (the Lord's Supper) **d**. Prayers **e.** They worshiped together at the Temple each day

2. Passover

3. "This is my body, given for you. Do this in remembrance of me."

4. This cup [is] the new covenant in My blood, which is shed for you.

5. The New Covenant

6. "I am the bread of life."

7.a. He who comes to Me shall never hunger. **b.** He who believes in Me shall never thirst.

8. a. You will have eternal life. **b.** You will be raised up at the resurrection. **c.** You will have life in you. **d**. It is true food and drink. **e.** You will abide in Him.

9. From that [time] many of His disciples went back and walked with Him no more.

10. a. "Do you also want to go away?" **b.** "Lord, to whom shall we go? You have the words of eternal life. Also we have come to believe and know that You are the Christ, the Son of the living God."

11. Do this in remembrance of Me.

12. a. He had to bring blood to make atonement for sins. **b.** The tree of life. **c.** a cherub

13. The veil of the temple was torn from top to bottom.

14. My physical body is the temple of the living God.

15. Uzzah reached out his and to steady the Ark and he died.

16. The priests were to carry the Ark on poles on their shoulders. After 6 steps they sacrificed 7 bulls and 7 rams.

17. We enter into the holiest by the blood of the lamb and through the veil, that is His flesh.

18. On the night that Jesus was betrayed.

19. Jesus

20. a. Kill a lamb. **b.** Put blood on the doorposts of your house. **c.** Eat the lamb.

21. There was none sick or feeble among them.

22. If you will listen to My voice and do what is right and obey my commandments, I will put none of the diseases on you I put on the Egyptians. For I am the Lord who heals you.

23. a. He was wounded for our transgressions **b.** He was bruised for our infirmities **c.** Chastised for our peace. **d.** By His stripes we are healed.

24. Jesus

25. Jesus is High Priest after the order of Melchizedeck.

26. Bread and wine.

27. a. God had promised that Abraham and His descendants would be the heir of the world.

28. The promise belongs to those who belong to Christ - Abraham's true seed. We are heirs of the earth.

29. We proclaim Christ's death until he comes.

30. The God of heaven will set up a kingdom which will never be destroyed. It will break in pieces all other kingdoms, but it itself will endure forever.

31. Kings and priests to God or a kingdom of priests.

32.a. Jesus **b.** Forerunner

33. The cup of blessing

34. a. We become unified in Him. **b.** We are transformed into what He is.

35. a. You drink damnation to yourself. **b.** Sickness. **c.** Death

36. We should examine ourselves and judge ourselves.

37. Their eyes were opened and they recognized Jesus. He was recognized through the breaking of the bread.

38. a. Behold I stand at the door and knock. If anyone opens the door I will come in and eat with him and He with Me. **b.** Blessed and Holy is the one who is called to the marriage supper of the Lamb. **c.** Let all who will come and drink of the water of life without cost.

Study 8: How to Have Intimate Fellowship with Jesus and Learn to Hear His Voice

1. It is to your advantage that I go away, for if I do not, the Comforter or Helper will not come.

2. Jesus promised that He would not leave them as orphans, but would come to them through the person of the Holy Spirit and would disclose Himself to them. They would continue to see Him although the world would not, and because of Him, they would live.

3. a. That they might be with Him. **b.** That He might send them out to preach. **c.** To have authority to cast out the demons.

4. Eternal life is knowing the only true God and Jesus Christ Whom He has sent.

5. Paul proclaimed that the most valuable thing on earth is to know Jesus Christ.

6. a. Spiritual wisdom and understanding, (the spirt of wisdom and revelation) so that you might grow in your knowledge of God. **b.** I pray that your hearts will be flooded with light so that you can understand the wonderful future He has promised to those he called. **c.** I want you to realize what a rich and glorious inheritance He has given to his people. **d.** I pray that you will begin to understand the incredible greatness of His power for us who believe Him and the authority he has and the church has over principalities and powers. **e.** To understand that the church is His body; it is filled by Christ, who fills everything everywhere with His presence(to know His Presence).

7. John explained that he and the disciples preached what they had personally heard, seen, experienced, beheld and touched concerning the Word of Life that was manifested in Jesus Christ. They proclaimed the eternal life which was manifested in Jesus. In short, they preached what they had personally experienced.

8. The purpose for the preaching of the gospel was so that men and women could enter into fellowship with the Father and with His Son Jesus Christ

9. You will seek Me and find Me when you search for Me with all your heart.

10. As the deer pants for the water brooks so my soul pants and thirst after God.

11. One day in God's courts and in His presence is better than a thousand spent elsewhere. I would rather stand at the threshold or be a door keeper in the house of my God than dwell in the tents of wickedness.

12. Jesus was always withdrawing from the multitudes to spend time in prayer with His Father.

13. Jesus did nothing of His own initiative, but He only did those things which the Father told Him to do, and He only said those things which the Father told Him to say. He only did those things which pleased the Father.

14. True worship is of the heart and spirit and has nothing to do with outward form.

15. Israel had revolted against God and did not know Him.

16. a. They have abandoned the Lord. **b.** They have despised the Holy one of Israel.

c. They have turned away from Him.

17. a. He was convicted of sin. **b.** He repented of sin. **c.** He was cleansed from sin.

d. He was called by God. **e.** He responded to God's call.

18. As we behold Him, we will be changed into the same image from glory to glory by the Spirit.

19. Those who have His commandments and keep them are the ones who love Him.

20. To love the Lord with all your heart, and with all your soul, and with all your mind. Love your neighbor as yourself. Love one another as I have loved you.

21. He will be loved by Jesus and His Father and Jesus will disclose or reveal Himself to him.

22. Jesus was transfigured before them. His face shone like the sun and His garments were as white as light. Moses and Elijah appeared and talked to Jesus. The voice of God spoke from the cloud saying, "This is My beloved Son, with whom I am delighted. Listen to Him!"

23. Leaving the other disciples behind, He took Peter, James, and John with Him to pray.

24. He began to show them his distress and told them, "My soul is deeply grieved to the point of death. Remain here and keep watch."

25. Greater love has no man than this, that one lay down his life for his friends.

26. He will tell them His secret and make known His covenant.

27. Mary remained at the tomb still seeking for Jesus.

28. Jesus appeared to her, and greeted her, and gave her a message for His disciples.

Study 9: The Power and Authority of God's Word

1. a. Inspired by God. **b.** Men moved by the Holy Spirit spoke from God.

2. a. Teaching. **b.** Reproof. **c.** Correction. **d.** Training in righteousness.

3. a. Desire the sincere milk of the Word. **b.** Study to be approved by God a master workman, dividing the Word accurately.

4. We will grow in respect to salvation.

5. The Word of God.

6. Why do you call me Lord, Lord, and do not do the things that I say?

7. We must destroy speculations and everything raised above the knowledge of God, bringing every thought captive to the obedience of Christ.

8. Every Word that proceeds from the mouth of God.

9. Blinded the minds of the unbelieving.

10. By the renewing of your mind by the washing of the water of the Word.

11. He will put his laws in our heart and write them on our minds.

12. a. A glorious church without spot or wrinkle. **b.** Holy and blameless.

c. In the same image of Jesus.

13. Ignorance of the Word.

14. For the lack of knowledge.

15. God will reject us from being His priests and forget our children.

16. A lamp to my feet and a light to my path.

17. a. Makes us wiser than our enemies. **b.** Gives us more insight than our teachers.

c. Gives us more understanding than the aged.

18. By keeping God's Word and treasuring it in your heart.

19. a. Liberty. **b.** Boldness.

20. God's Word is sweeter to him than honey.

21. The joy and rejoicing of his heart.

22. More than his necessary food.

23. a. Forever Thy Word is settled in heaven. **b.** The sum of Thy Word is truth. **c.** God will not lie, but will do what He has spoken. **d.** Heaven and earth will pass away, but My Word will not pass away.

24. a. Give attention to God's Word. **b.** Incline your ear to His sayings. **c.** Do not let them depart from your sight. **d.** Keep them in the midst of your heart.

25. a. He will be like a tree firmly planted by streams of water. **b.** He will yield fruit in season. **c.** His leaf will not wither. **d.** Whatever he does shall prosper.

26.a. The Word shall be in your mouth. **b.** Meditate on it day and night. **c.** Be careful to do it.

27. a. Impress these words in your heart and soul. **b.** Bind them as a sign on your hand. **c.** Bind them on your forehead. **d.** Teach them to your sons. **e.** Talk of them when you sit in your house, when you are walking, lying down, and when you rise up. **f.** Write them on the doorposts of your house and on your gates.

28. a. That your sons may fill the land and remain in it forever. **b.** The Lord will drive out all your enemies before you. **c.** Every place on which the sole of your foot treads shall be yours. **d.** No man shall be able to stand before you. The fear and dread of you shall fall on all people.

29. The sword of the Spirit.

30. a. It is living, active and sharper than any two-edged sword. **b.** It divides the soul and spirit, joints and marrow. **c.** It is able to judge the thoughts and intentions of the heart. **d.** All things are revealed before it and nothing can hide from it.

31. By the Word of God.

32. By keeping His Word.

33. The wise man hears the Word of God and does it. Through the storm and flood, his house stands because it is founded on the rock.

34. The foolish man hears the Word of God and does not do it. His house falls when the storm comes because it was built on sand.

35. Those who hear the Word of God and do it.

36. a. Builds you up. **b.** Gives you an inheritance among the saints. **c.** Through it you partake of the divine nature. **d.** Through it you escape the corruption that is in the world by lust.

Study 10: Praise, Worship, and Prayer

1. He is worthy to be praised.

2. To declare His praise.

3. Continually.

4. Everything that has breath.

5. He who offers a sacrifice of thanksgiving.

6. a. Clap your hands. **b.** Shout joyfully c. Sing praises.

7. a. Trumpet. **b.** Harp. **c.** Lyre. **d.** Timbrel. **e.** Stringed instruments. **f.** Pipe. **g.** Loud and resounding cymbals.

8. a. With a new song. **b.** With dancing.

9. The high praises of God.

10. The Power to bind the satanic hosts.

11. The enemy was routed and they began to destroy one another.

12. The Lord is enthroned upon our praises.

13. The fallen tabernacle of David.

14. The last days started on the day of Pentecost.

15. Among men.

16. Praise and worship.

17. Your body is the temple of the Living God.

18. Those who worship Him in spirit and truth.

19. In reverence.

20. Bowing before Him.

21. a. They sang praises with joy. **b.** They bowed down and worshiped.

22. Holy array-the beauty of holiness.

23. a. Ask in My name. **b**. You shall receive. **c.** So that your joy may be full.

24. Not to use meaningless repetitions.

25. Because they suppose that they will be heard for their many words.

26. He knows your need before you even ask.

27. We must forgive those whom we have something against.

28. a. Ask according to His will. **b.** We will know that He hears us. **c.** We will receive what we have asked for.

29. They shall be granted unto you.

30. a. Because you do not ask. **b**. Because you ask with wrong motives.

31. a. Regarding iniquity in your heart. **b.** Wavering--doubting. **c.** Not giving honor to your wife.

32. a. One who is God-fearing. **b.** One who does God's will.

33. To pray and not lose heart.

34. He gave her the request because she kept bothering him.

35. He will not delay over the prayers of His elect, but will bring about justice for them speedily.

36. Faith.

37. a. Ask and you shall receive. **b.** Seek and you shall find. **c.** Knock and it shall be opened unto you.

38. He will give what is good to those who ask Him.

39. The prayer of the upright.

40. The sacrifice of the wicked.

41. Ask what you will and it shall be done.

42. Let your requests be made known to God.

43. In prayer.

44. The blood of Jesus.

45. Intercedes for us according to God's will.

46. Fasting.

47. It shall be done for them.

48. Pray for kings and all who are in authority.

49. a. That we may lead a tranquil and quiet life in all godliness and dignity. **b.** That all men may have an opportunity to be saved and come to the knowledge of the truth.

50. a. Lift up holy hands. **b.** Avoid wrath and dissension.

51. Always, without ceasing.

Study 11: What is God's Provision for Healing?

1. Because man sinned.

2. The devil.

3. He would allow none of the diseases of the Egyptians (the world) to come upon them.

4. By His scourging, or stripes, we are healed.

5. By His wounds, we were healed.

6. To destroy the works of the devil.

7. a. Bless their bread and water. **b.** Take sickness away from them.

8. a. Forgave him of all his iniquities. **b.** Healed all his diseases.

9. All of them.

10. For all those who hate God's people.

11. For those who do not obey God's Word and those who do not fear His name.

12. a. Extraordinary plagues (severe and lasting). **b.** Miserable and chronic sicknesses. **c.** All the diseases in Egypt. **d.** Every sickness and every plague.

13. That we might choose the blessing and choose life.

14. a. Love the Lord. **b.** Obey His voice. **c.** Hold fast to Him.

15. a. No evil will befall you. **b.** No plague will come near your dwelling.

16. a. Health and healing. **b.** He will reveal to them an abundance of peace and truth.

17. To do good and heal all who were oppressed by the devil.

18. All of them.

19. All kinds.

20. The unbelief of the people.

21. a. They recognized the Lordship of Jesus. **b.** They had faith in His Word.

22. His Word.

23. Only say the word and my servant shall be healed.

24. a. He had never seen greater faith. **b.** He received what he had believed for.

25. Faith.

26. Through faith in Jesus' name, this man had been healed.

27. a. Heal the sick. **b.** Raise the dead. **c.** Cleanse the leper. **d.** Cast out demons.

28. a. The things that He did. **b.** Even greater works.

29. a. In the name of Jesus. **b.** Laying on of hands.

30. Yes.

31. a. Pray over him. **b.** Anoint with oil in the name of Jesus.

32. a. Heal him. **b.** If he has committed any sins, they will be forgiven.

33. The prayer of faith.

34. Sin.

35. His body wasted away and his vitality was drained.

36. He walked before the Lord in truth with his whole heart and did what was right in God's sight.

37. The Lord heard his prayer and added 15 years to his life.

38. He followed the Lord, but not fully, for he put his trust in the arm of the flesh-in men and not in God. He also imprisoned the seer of the Lord.

39. He became seriously diseased in the feet.

40. He failed to seek the Lord and he died.

41. In the world you will have tribulation.

42. Ask anything in My name and I will do it.

43. Your joy will be full.

44. If you love Him you will keep His commandments.

45. a. Do not worry about your provisions or worry about tomorrow. **b.** Seek the kingdom of God first and His righteousness. **c.** Everything you need will be given to you.

46. The kingdom of God is righteousness, peace and joy in the Holy Spirit.

47. a. Be anxious for nothing. **b**. But in everything by prayer and supplication make your request be made known to God. **c.** The peace of God will rule your heart and mind.

48. No. God has given us a spirit of power, love, and a sound mind.

49. Perfect love casts out all fear. We are to trust in the Lord and not be afraid.

50. Cast all your are upon Him.

51. Humbling yourself before God.

52. They have not asked.

53. They asked.

54. Ask in faith and you shall receive, that your joy may be full.

55. Healing.

Study 12 : What is God's Plan for Inner Healing and Deliverance?

1. Mentally confused, sick at heart, full of raw wounds, bruised, with welts not healed, full of sin, in bad health, festering wounds, mourning, benumbed, badly crushed, agitated in the heart, full of anxiety.

2. a. He desires to restore our soul. b. Body, soul, and spirit.

3. Your body is the temple of God.

4. a. The person who is joined to the Lord is one-spirit with Him. b.By the power of the Blood of Jesus, He will cleanse your conscience from dead works to serve the living God.

5. The law of the spirit of life in Christ Jesus has made me free from the law of sin and death.

6. a. Present your body as a living sacrifice. **b.** Don't copy the ways of the world, their behavior or customs.

7. By the washing of the water of the Word.

8. a. To preach the good news to the meek. **b.** To bind up the broken hearted. **c.** To proclaim liberty to the captives. **d.** To open the prison to those who are bound. **e.** To proclaim the favorable year of the Lord.

9. A glorious church without spot or wrinkle.

10. a. The insides were washed with water. **b.** The washing of the water of the word.

11. Truth.

12. Confess your faults to each other and pray for each other that you may be healed.

13. The favorable year of the Lord.

14. a. Awake and clothe yourself in strength and beautiful garments. **b.** Shake yourself from the dust, o captive. **c.** Loose yourself from the chains around your neck.

Section 1 - Inner Healing

1. He desires for them to be pressed out, bandaged and softened with oil or ointment.

2. It is like purified oil or ointment poured forth.

3. By the revelation of the Lord.

4. He will reveal it.

5. The word of knowledge.

6. a. Confess your sins one to another. **b.** Pray for one another that you may be healed.

7. Must be willing to forgive that person who has hurt him.

8. He bore our griefs and carried our sorrows.

9. a. To bind up the broken-hearted. **b.** To comfort all who mourn. **c.** To set at liberty those who are bruised.

10. a. Beauty for ashes. **b.** The oil of joy for mourning. **c.** The garment of praise for the spirit of heaviness.

11. I will heal him, restore comfort and peace to him, and create praise in his lips.

Section 2 - Deliverance

1. He rendered powerless the devil that we might be delivered from bondage.

2. Cast them out.

3. The name of Jesus.

4. His iniquities will capture him and he will be held by the cords of his sin.

5. Lack of instruction.

6. Woe to those who drag iniquity and sin around with them.

7. Falsehood.

8. Because of the lusts of deceit.

9. They shall not prosper.

10. Confess and forsake them.

11. Those who had believed kept coming, confessing and disclosing their practices.

12. a. Take away all the strong man's armor on which he has relied. **b.** Distribute his plunder.

13. The coming of the kingdom of God.

14. a. Being overcome by a certain sin or habit. **b.** Unforgiveness. **c.** The iniquities of the fathers.

15. The Lord hands them over to the torturers.

16. You must forgive from your heart.

17. He will not forgive you.

18. a. You lay aside the old manner of life which is corrupted by the lust of deceit. **b.** You become renewed in the spirit of your mind. **c.** You put on the new self which is in the likeness of God.

19. a. Created in the likeness of God. **b.** Created in righteousness. **c.** Created in holiness of the truth.

20. a. Bitter jealousy. **b.** Selfish ambition.

21. The root of bitterness.

22. a. Knowledge of the Word of God. **b.** Supernatural revelation of the Lord.

23. a. Word of knowledge. **b.** Discerning of spirits.

24. a. To proclaim liberty to the captives. **b.** To proclaim freedom to the prisoners.

Section 3 - Breaking of Curses.

1.a. He became a curse for us.

2. a. That the blessing of Abraham might come upon the Gentiles through faith. **b.** "If any one does not love the Lord he is cursed."

3. a. Blessed are those whose lawless deeds have been forgiven. **b.** Blessed are those whose sins have been covered. **c.** Blessed is the man whose sin the Lord will not take into account.

4. a. Life and prosperity-the blessing. **b.** Death and adversity-the curse.

5. If they went and served other gods.

6. The third and fourth generations of those who hated God.

7. Blessings and loving kindness to a thousand generations.

8. a. Idolatry-witchcraft. **b.** Dishonoring father and mother. **c.** Moving your neighbor's boundary mark (cheating your neighbor). **d.** Misleading a blind person (being cruel to the disabled).**e.** Those who distort justice due to an alien, orphan, or widow (taking advantage of the helpless). **f.** Lying with your father's wife. **g.** Lying with an animal. **h.** Incest. **i.** Lying with your mother-in-law. **j.** Striking your neighbor in secret. **k.** Accepting a bribe. **l.** Refusing to obey the Lord or to keep His commandments.

9. They will be a sign and a wonder upon your descendants forever.

10. Through ignorance.

11. a. Cursed in the city and in the country. **b.** Your food supply shall be cursed. **c.** Your children, your animals, and the produce of your ground shall be cursed. **d.** You shall be cursed when you come in and when you go out. **e.** Confusion. **f.** Rebuke. **g.** You shall not prosper. **h.** Oppressed and robbed continually. **i.** Others shall eat up your labors. **j.** You shall be oppressed and crushed continually.

12. a. Boils. **b.** Hemorrhoids. **c.** Scab. **d.** Itch. **e.** Sore boils on knees and legs. **f.** Boils from head to foot. **g.** Severe, lasting, extraordinary plagues. **h.** Miserable and chronic sicknesses.

13. a. Madness. **b.** Bewilderment of heart. **c.** Feelings of being driven mad. **d.** Despair of soul (sorrow of mind).**e.** Doubt, dread and fear.

14. The curse of bad and oppressive governments.

15. The curse of adultery and divorce.

16. The curse of illegitimate birth to ten generations will be rejected by the assembly of the Lord.

17. You will serve your enemies in hunger, thirst, nakedness and the lack of all things and He will put an iron yoke on your neck until He has destroyed you.

18. a. Rebuilding the ancient ruins. **b.** Raising up the former devastations. **c.** Repairing the desolations of many generations.

19. As one who has lifted the yoke from us and fed us.

20. 1) "Blessed *shall* you *be* in the city, and blessed *shall* you *be* in the country.

  2)"Blessed *shall be* the fruit of your body, the produce of your ground and the increase of your herds, the increase of your cattle and the offspring of your flocks.

  3) "Blessed *shall be* your basket and your kneading bowl.

  4) "Blessed *shall* you *be* when you come in, and blessed *shall* you *be* when you go out.

  5) "The Lord will cause your enemies who rise against you to be defeated before your face; they shall come out against you one way and flee before you seven ways.

  6) "The Lord will command the blessing on you in your storehouses and in all to which you set your hand, and He will bless you in the land which the Lord your God is giving you.

7) "The Lord will establish you as a holy people to Himself all peoples of the earth shall see that you are called by the name of the LORD, and they shall be afraid of you.

8) And the Lord will grant you plenty of goods, in the fruit of your body, in the increase of your livestock, and in the produce of your ground.

9) The Lord will open to you His good treasure, the heavens, to give the rain to your land in its season .

10) The Lord will bless all the work of your hand.

11) You shall lend to many nations, but you shall not borrow.

12) And the Lord will make you the head and not the tail; you shall be above only, and not be beneath,

21. Your descendants will be recognized as the offspring which the Lord has blessed.

22. My soul will exult in God, He has clothed me with the garments of salvation, a robe of righteousness.

Study 13: What is My New Life in Christ Like?

1. God will write these laws in your heart and mind.

2. 1) Attitude - poor in Spirit. **Blessing-** theirs is the kingdom of heaven.

2) Attitude –those who mourn. **Blessing-** they shall be comforted.

3) Attitude-the gentle. **Blessing-**they shall inherit the earth.

4) Attitude- those who hunger and thirst after righteousness. **Blessing-**they shall be filled

5) Attitude- the merciful. **Blessing-**they shall receive mercy.

6) Attitude-the pure in heart **Blessing-**they shall see God.

7) Attitude-the peacemakers. **Blessing-**they shall be called sons of God.

8) Attitude-those who are persecuted for righteousness sake. **Blessing-**theirs is the kingdom of heaven.

9) Attitude- people will insult you, persecute you, and falsely say evil against you because of Jesus.

Blessing-great is your reward in heaven

3. a. Adultery. **b.** Murder

4. No, let your statement be yes or no.

5. Evil.

6. We will be held accountable on the day of judgment.

7. By our words.

8. What is in the heart.

9. Do not resist him but turn the other cheek.

10. He did not revile or threaten but committed Himself to God.

11. You are to rejoice and be exceedingly glad.

12. Love your enemies and pray for them.

13. He sends sun and rain on the evil men and on the good men.

14. Be merciful as the Father is merciful.

15. No.

16. a.love your enemies, do good, and lend. **b.** Expect nothing in return. **c.** Your reward shall be great. **d.** Your shall be called Sons of the Most High.

17. *The Offense* | *The Guilt*

17. *The Offense*	*The Guilt*
a. Angry with your brother	Guilty before the court
b. Calling your brother "Raca"	Guilty before the Supreme Court
c. Calling your brother a fool	Guilty enough to go into hell fire

18. You will be judged.

19. By the same standard with which you judge others.

20. a. Do not pass judgment and you will not be judged. **b.** Do not condemn and you will not be condemned. **c.** Pardon and you will be pardoned.

21. Go and first be reconciled to your brother, then come and offer your gift.

22. Beware of practicing your righteousness before men to be noticed by them.

23. a. You should give secretly. **b.** The Lord will reward you openly.

24. He will not forgive you.

25. 70 times 7.

26. As we would have them treat us.

27. a. Whoever takes your coat, give him your shirt also. **b.** Whoever takes away what is yours, do not demand it back. **c.** Lend expecting nothing in return.

28. Be on guard against every form of greed.

29. He who is faithful in a very little is also faithful in much.

30. He who is unfaithful in a very little is also unfaithful in much.

31. The humble attitude.

32. He will be humbled.

33. Become a servant.

34. He did not come to be served but to serve and give His life for many.

35. No, take the last place for yourself.

36. The poor, the crippled, the lame, the blind, and those who do not have the means to repay.

37. To lay down your life for your friends.

38. Shepherd My sheep and tend My lambs.

39. a. Feed the hungry. **b.** Give water to the thirsty. **c.** Invite in the stranger.**d.** Clothe the naked. **e.** Visit the sick. **f.** Visit those in prison.

40. Let us not love in word but in deed and truth.

41. a. Think clearly, exercise self control, obey God. **b.** Be holy in every thing you do because God is holy. **c.** We will be judged or rewarded by what we do. **d.** Have reverent Fear toward God. **e.** We were ransomed by the Precious blood of Christ the Sinless, Spotless Lamb of God.**f.** Deeply love each other with all your heart.

Study 14: God's Perfect Choice

1. Marriage.

2. God.

3. God.

4. Beautiful and a virgin.

5. She was willing to go.

6. Meditating.

7. No.

8. He loved God's choice.

9. Keep clear of all sexual sin. Treat each other with holiness and honor, not in lustful passion as the pagan. Do not cheat your Christian brother by taking his wife.

10. We are disobedient to God who gives the Holy Spirit.

11. Trust in the Lord and he will give you the desire of your heart.

12. a. Lust of the flesh. **b.** Lust of the eyes. **c.** Boastful pride of life.

13. The one who does the will of God abides forever.

14. a. Flee from youthful lusts. **b.** Appeal to younger men as brothers, younger women as sisters in all purity. **c.** Flee immorality. **d.** Conduct yourself in holiness, not lustful passion.

15. The things of the Lord, how you may please the Lord. Seek first the kingdom.

16. Do not be conformed to this world. Live sensibly, righteously, and godly in this present age.

17. God will give good to those who ask Him.

18. a. Delight yourself in the Lord, commit your way to Him, rest in Him, wait patiently for Him. **b.** He who finds a wife finds a good thing and obtains favor from the Lord. **c.** No good thing will He withhold from those who walk uprightly. **d.** A prudent wife is from the Lord.

19. The will of God.

20. I know whom I have believed. I am convinced that He is able to guard what I have entrusted to Him.

Study 15: What is Commitment to The Body of Christ?

1. If we have love for one another.

2. To love one another as He has loved us.

3. Laying down your life for our brothers.

4. a. Loyalty and fervent devotion to each other. **b.** Restraint from backbiting and devouring one another. **c.** Esteeming your brother better than yourself. **d.** The strong are to bear the burdens of the weak. When one member suffers, all suffer with it. When one member is honored, all members rejoice with it. **e.** Loving your enemies. **f.** Opening your life and sharing your life-your victories and defeats before all with all. **g.** Loving in deed and if any has need, your abundance is available to supply their wants.

5. The unity of the Spirit in the bond of peace.

6. A house divided against itself fails and a kingdom divided against itself is laid waste.

7. Go and be reconciled to your brother, then come and present your offering.

8. Receive, forgive and love everyone as Christ has received, forgiven and loved you.

9. One body.

10. The body is not one member, but many.

11. No.

12. In the body, just as He desired.

13. No.

14. For the common good.

15. By that which every joint supplies.

16. Proper working order.

17. The body will grow and build itself up in love.

18. We are living stones, and we are growing into a holy temple in the Lord and are being built together into a dwelling of God in the Spirit and a spiritual house for a holy priesthood.

19. He is building His church and the gates of hell shall not overpower it.

20. A glorious church.

21. a. Apostles **b.** Prophets **c.** Teachers **d.** Miracles **e.** Gifts of healings **f.** Helps **g.** Administrations **h.** Varieties of tongues.

22. Through the church.

23. The vine.

24. The branches.

25. Abide in Jesus and in relationship with His body.

26. They received the Word, were baptized, continually devoted themselves to the apostles' teaching, to fellowship, to the breaking of bread and prayer. Many signs and wonders took place as they continually felt a sense of awe. They had all things in common, distributing to those who had need. They were with one mind, with gladness and sincerity of heart praising God. The Lord was adding to their number day by day.

27. The property was yours to sell or keep. After you sold it the money was yours to give away.

28. Oppressive governments take what belongs to you. The king will take your fields and the best of your vineyards and the best of your olive yards and give them to his servants. He will take a tenth of your vineyards and give them to his officers and servants. He will take a tenth of your sheep and you will be his servants.

29. a. Do not be deceived. God is not mocked. Whatever a man sows, this he will also reap." **b.**"A little sleep a little slumber a little folding of the hands to rest and suddenly poverty will come upon you." **c.** "If you don't work, you don't eat."

Study 16: What is God's Government and Order for The Church?

1. a. Apostles. **b.** Prophets. **c.** Evangelists. **d.** Pastors. **e.** Teachers.

2. a. To equip the saints for the work of service. **b.** To build up the body of Christ.

3. Until we attain unto the unity of the faith, the knowledge of the Son of God, to a mature man and the measure of the stature of the fullness of Christ.

4. We will no longer be children who are tossed and deceived, but will speak the truth and grow up into Him.

5. Elders.

6. **a.** Be on guard for the flock. **b.** Shepherd them. **c.** Watch over their souls. **d.** Give an account.

7. To see the sword coming and warn the people.

8. The watchmen are held accountable.

9. Those who refuse to listen.

10. **a.** Obey them. **b.** Submit to them

11. Do not Lord it over others or exercise authority over them. Be a servant to all and do not seek to be served, but serve others and give your life for others as Christ gave his.

12. Elders should always desire that the will of God be done and not Lord it over others, but be an example to the believers.

13. Teaching the law but not obeying it. Sought the honor of men. Wanted to be called teacher.

Christ is to be recognized as Father, Leader, and Teacher. The greatest among you must be the servant of all. We are all brothers.

14. In the mouth of 2 or 3 witnesses let every fact be confirmed. There is safety in the multitude of counselors.

15. Observe their way of life and imitate their faith.

16. He left the 99 and went in search for the one which had gone astray.

17. a. If a brother sins, go and reprove him. **b.** If he refuses to listen, take one or two more with you. **c.** If he refuses to listen to them, take it to the church. **d.** If he refuses to listen to the church, let him be as a Gentile and sinner.

18. Do not receive an accusation against an elder except in the presence of two or three witnesses.

19. a. He should be restored in a spirit of gentleness with humility. **b.** Look to yourself so that you are not tempted.

20. Evil and sin, like leaven, filters through the whole lump.

21. Clean out the old leaven of malice and wickedness.

22. Any so-called brother who is immoral, covetous, idolater, reviler, drunkard, swindler.

23. Elders who rule well are worthy of double honor. Do not rebuke an elder.

Young Men - treat as brothers **Older Women** treat as mothers. **Younger Women** treat as sisters in all purity.

24. a. We are to judge those who are within the church. **b.** God judges those who are without the church; the sinners.

25. Remove the wicked man from among yourselves.

26. It is better to get rid of even the most important members of the body than to cause the whole body to go into Hell because of the spreading wickedness.

27. They fled, 36 men were killed.

28. They took some things under the ban, both having deceived and stolen.

29. God said that His Presence would not remain among them unless they destroyed the things that were taken that were under the ban.

30. The things from under the ban and the people who took them were to be burned with fire.

31. That God loves us and that we are His sons.

32. a. For our good. **b.** That we may share His holiness.

33. For the moment it seems not to be joyful, but sorrowful

34. It yields the peaceful fruit of righteousness.

35. He divided them into 1,000, 100, 50, and 10 and put leaders over each of them.

36. He alone was counseling the people from morning till evening and the people had to wait for long hours. He and the people were wearing themselves out.

37. a. They must know the statutes, laws and ways of God. **b.** Able men who fear God. **c.** Men of truth. **d**. Hate dishonest gain. **e.** Wise. **f.** Discerning. g. Experienced.

38. To settle every minor dispute and help bear Moses' burden.

39. Every difficult and major dispute.

40. a. With no partiality, for the judgment is God's. **b.** Not by what the eyes see or what the ears hear. **c.** With righteousness and fairness.

41. 1) blameless **2)** the husband of one wife **3)** temperate **4)** sober-minded **5)** of good behavior **6)**hospitable, **7)** able to teach **8)** not given to wine **9)** not violent **10)** not greedy for money **11)** gentle **12)** not quarrelsome **13)** not covetous **14)** one who rules his own house well, having his children in submission with all reverence **15)** not a novice, lest being puffed up with pride he fall into the same condemnation as the devil **16)** Moreover he must have a good testimony among those who are outside, lest he fall into reproach and the snare of the devil.

42.1) Reverent **2)** Not double-tongued **3)** Not given to much wine **4)** Not greedy for money **5)** Holding the mystery of the faith with a pure conscience **6)** Let these also first be tested then let them serve as deacons, being found blameless **7)** Their wives must be reverent, not slanderers, temperate, faithful in all things. **8)** Be the husbands of one wife. **9)** Ruling their children and their own houses well.

43.1) Must not quarrel **2)** Be gentle to all **3)** Able to teach, **4)** Patient **5)** In humility correcting those who are in opposition, if God perhaps will grant them repentance, so that they may know the truth,

44. The older women. (Note: this is not necessarily older with age, but older in spiritual maturity.)

Study 17: What is God's Plan for Prosperity and Giving?

1. **a.** Pay God His tithes and contributions. **b.** Seek the kingdom of God first and His righteousness.

2. In tithes and offerings or contributions.

3. The tenth.

4. **a.** The land. **b.** The seed of the land. **c.** The fruit of the tree. **d.** The herd and the flock.

5. It is determined according to the willingness and leading of the heart.

6. We come under a curse.

7. In the storehouse where it is to be given to the priests and Levites.

8. Food for God's house and to provide for the needs of the ministry and those who perform the service of the Lord.

9. Yes.

10. He will open the windows of heaven and pour out a blessing until there is no more need.

11. The devourer.

12. He gave Melchezidek a tithe of all.

13. Men receive our tithes here, but God receives our tithes in heaven.

14. He was blessed in every way and was rich in flocks, herds, silver, gold, men servants, maidservants, camels, and donkeys.

15. Your barns will be filled with plenty and your vats will overflow with wine.

16. **a.** Protection. **b.** Food. **c.** Clothing.

17. He promised to give God a tenth of all.

18. Jacob gave Esau two hundred female goats, twenty male goats, two hundred ewes, twenty rams, thirty female camels with their young, forty cows, ten bulls, twenty female donkeys, and ten male donkeys.

19. No, it was a freewill offering from the heart.

20. Gold, silver, and bronze; blue, purple, and scarlet thread, fine linen, and goats' hair;
ram skins dyed red, badger skins, and acacia wood ;oil for the light, and spices for the anointing oil and for the sweet incense; onyx stones, and stones to be set in the ephod and in the breastplate.

21. The people gave more than enough for the building of the tabernacle and Moses had to asked them to stop giving.

22. **a.** The Lord will bless everything you do. **b.** He will command the blessing on you and your storehouses. **c.** You will abound in prosperity and be plenteous in goods, flocks and children. **d.** He will bless your land with rain and bless all the work of your hands. **e.** You will lend to many nations and shall not borrow. He will make you the head and not the tail.

23. Obey God's commandments and walk in His ways.

24. **a.** Disobedience to God's commandments and for not serving God with a joyful heart. **b.** You will serve your enemies in hunger, in thirst, in nakedness and the lack of all things.

25. A good land of flowing streams, pools of water, with springs that gush forth in the valleys and hills. It was a land of wheat and barley, of grapevines, fig trees, pomegranates, olives,milk, and honey. Food was plentiful and nothing was lacking, where iron is as common as stone, and copper was abundant in the hills.

26. If you belong to Christ you are Abraham's seed and heirs according to the promise.

Study 18: The New Covenant and Prosperity Economics

1. He became impoverished and suffered hunger and the lack of all things.

2. A robe was put upon him, a ring was placed upon his finger, he was invited to a great feast and received back into sonship and the wealth of his father's house.

3. The Lord taught them to profit.

4. Give and it will be given to you in good measure, pressed down, shaken together, and running over.

5. In the same measure that you give.

6. He who sows sparingly, reaps sparingly.

7. Do not give grudgingly or under compulsion.

8. God loves a cheerful giver.

9. a. To give you a sufficiency in everything. **b.** To give you an abundance for every good deed.

10. a. Seed to the sower. **b.** Bread for food.

11. Every form of greed.

12. The abundance of possessions.

13. He was greedy and God required his life.

14. The man who lays up treasure for himself is not rich toward God.

15. Riches being hoarded by the owner for his own hurt.

16. The deceitfulness of riches.

17. a. Those who give out of their surplus. **b.** Those who give sacrificially, giving all that they have to live on.

18. The widow who gave sacrificially.

19. Do not set your heart upon them.

20. Where your treasure is.

21. Lay up treasures in heaven rather than on earth.

22. The love of money.

23. a. They fall into temptation and a snare and many foolish and harmful desires which bring ruin and destruction. **b.** It has caused some to wander away from the faith. **c.** They have pierced themselves with many sorrows.

24. He will be prosperous.

25. a. You will be enriched in everything for all liberality **b.** Many thanksgivings will be given to God by those whose needs have been met by your giving. **c.** You will be fully supplying the needs of the saints.

26. a. The servant with 5 talents did business with them and gained 5 more. **b.** The Master said, "Well, done good and faithful servant. You have been faithful over a few things, I will make you ruler over many things. Enter into the joy of the Lord.

27. a. The servant with 2 talents did business with them and gained 2 more. **b.** The Master said, "Well, done good and faithful servant. You have been faithful over a few things, I will make you ruler over many things. Enter into the joy of the Lord.

28. a. The servant with one talent was afraid and hid the talent and returned it to the master when he came. **b.** the Master called him wicked and lazy and told him he could have at least gained interest from the money. **c.** His money was taken away and The master cast him into the darkness where there is weeping and gnashing of teeth.

29. No, he took the money away from the man who didn't use it and gave it to the man with ten.

30. For to everyone who has, more will be given, and he will have abundance; but from him who does not have, even what he has will be taken away.

31. Don't invite your friends who can repay you. Invite the poor, crippled, the lame, the blind. At the resurrection of the godly, God will reward you for inviting those who could not repay you."

32. He lifts the poor from the ash heap, makes him sit among princes, and inherit the throne of glory.

33. a. Being lazy, sleeping and resting when you should be working causes poverty. **b.** Poverty comes to those who refuse to be corrected. **c.** Good planning and hard work lead to prosperity, but hasty shortcuts lead to poverty. **d.** A person who gets ahead by oppressing the poor or by showering gifts on the rich will end in poverty. **e.** Carousing with drunkards and gluttons along with too much sleep leads to poverty.

f. Hard workers have plenty of food; playing around brings poverty. **g.** A greedy person tries to get rich quick, but it only leads to poverty. **h.** Whoever gives to the poor will lack nothing. But a curse will come upon those who close their eyes to poverty.

34. Do not be deceived, God is not mocked. Whatever you sow this you will also reap. In due season you will reap if you don't get discouraged and quit.

35. If anyone doesn't work, they don't eat.

36.a. Don't worry about what you will drink. **b.** Don't worry about what you will eat. **c.** Don't worry about what you wear.

37. Gentiles - the unbelievers.

38. Seek first the kingdom of God and His righteousness.

39. All these things will be added unto you.

40. Seek the things above.

41. Jesus replied, "I assure you that everyone who has given up house or brothers or sisters or mother or father or children or property, for my sake and for the Gospel will receive now in return, a hundred times over, houses, brothers, sisters, mothers, children, and property--with persecutions. And in the world to come they will have eternal life.

42. I wish above all that you would prosper and be in health even as your soul prospers.

43. He feared God and the Lord was with him.

44. His soul will abide in prosperity.

45. He was blameless, a man of complete integrity. He feared God and stayed away from evil.

46. So the LORD blessed Job in the second half of his life even more than in the beginning. For now he had fourteen thousand sheep, six thousand camels, one thousand teams of oxen, and one thousand female donkeys. He also gave Job seven more sons and three more daughters. In all the land there were no other women as lovely as the daughters of Job. Job lived 140 years after that, living to see four generations of his children and grandchildren.

47. a. God granted him wisdom and knowledge and **b.** God gave him riches, wealth and honor.

48. Every good thing.

49. Everything they need so that there is no lack.

50. a. He does not walk in the counsel of the wicked. **b.** He does not stand in the path of sinners.

c. He does not sit in the seat of scoffers. **d.** He delights in and meditates in the Word day and night. **e.** He is like a tree planted by streams of water, producing fruit in its season; his leaf does not wither.

51. The Lord is my shepherd I shall not want. He gives me food and water and prepares a table for me. My cup runs over with blessing. Surely goodness and mercy will follow me all the days of my life and I will dwell in the house of the Lord forever.

Study 19: What is the Great Commission?

1. Follow Me, and I will make you fishers of men.

2. Repentance and the Gospel of the kingdom of God.

3. a. To preach repentance and the forgiveness of sins to all nations. **b.** Making disciples of all nations. **c.** Baptizing them. **d.** Teaching them to observe all that I have commanded you.

4. a. Cast out demons. **b.** Speak with new tongues. **c.** Handle snakes with safety. **d.** If they drink poison it will not hurt them. **e.** They will lay hands on the sick they shall recover.

5. A poisonous snake bit him and he was not hurt, a man was healed of a fever and dysentery, people were healed, people spoke in tongues.

6. How can they hear without a preacher and how will they go unless someone is sent.

7. Jesus and the resurrection of the dead.

8. To be a witness for Him to all men.

9. He testified to both small and great.

10. Power to be His witnesses.

11. Wins souls.

12. He became all things to all men that he might save some. He did all things for the sake of the Gospel.

13. Once I was blind, but now I see. If He were not from God, He could do nothing.

14. They put him out of the synagogue.

15. a. Religious leaders. **b.** Government officials. **c.** Members of our household.

16. It shall be given you what you shall speak.

17. The Spirit of your Father.

18. Don't be afraid of those who can kill you. Fear God. A sparrow can't fall without His notice. You are more valuable. The hairs on your head are numbered.

19. They were unable to cope with the wisdom and the spirit with which he was speaking.

20. a. Make known His deeds among the peoples. **b.** Speak of all His wonders.

21. Do not be afraid, but go on speaking and do not be silent.

22. It brings a snare.

23. Blessed are you when you are persecuted for righteousness sake for yours is the kingdom of heaven. Blessed are you when you when men speak evil against you for so they persecuted the prophets before you.

24. Stand in the temple and speak to the people the whole message.

25. We must obey God rather than men.

26. Do not be ashamed, but join me in suffering for the gospel according to the power of God.

27. He will confess us before the Father.

28. He will deny us before the Father.

29. a. What I tell you in darkness, speak in the light. **b.** What you hear whispered in your ear, proclaim upon the housetop.

30. Stand in God's counsel, listen to His words, announce His words to the people. They will be turned back form the evil of their ways.

31. God's Word is like fire and like a hammer which shatters the rock.

32. The Holy Spirit.

33. He did not shrink back from declaring to them the whole purpose of God.

34. He did not consider his life as dear to himself in order that he might finish his course and the ministry which God had given him.

35. **a**. I have fought the good fight. **b**. I have finished the course. **c**. I have kept the faith.

d. There is laid up for me a crown of righteousness.

36. The crown of righteousness.

37. They will shine as the stars forever and ever.

38. **a**. Save the sinner's soul from death. **b**. Cover a multitude of sins.

39. **a**. They shall reap with joyful shouting. **b**. They shall return bringing their sheaves with them.

40. There is more joy in heaven over one sinner that repents than over 99 righteous who need no repentance.

41. He felt compassion for them for they were distressed and downcast like sheep without a shepherd.

42. The harvest is plentiful but the workers are few.

43. Pray for the Lord of the harvest to send out workers into His harvest.

44. **a**. Those who sow beside all waters. **b**. Those who send forth disciples or workers freely.

45. Do not put it off, for the fields are ripe now, ready for harvest.

46. One sows, another reaps, one plants, another waters, but it is God who gives the increase.

47. Each will receive his own reward according to his own labor.

48. As his share is who goes down to the battle, so shall his share be who stays with the baggage.

49. They have entered into the labor of others.

50. Rejoice together.

51. **a**. By the blood of the Lamb. **b**. By the word of your testimony. **c**. Loving not your life even unto death.

52. They stoned Paul until he was dead and drug him out of the city. The people gathered around him and Paul got up from the dead and went on preaching.

53. Continue in the faith. Through much tribulation you enter the kingdom of God.

54. Paul and Silas were arrested. They were beaten severely and thrown in prison. At midnight they were singing praise to God. There was an earthquake. The prison doors flew open and the chains fell off all the prisoners. The jailer was saved and his household and the church at Philippi was started.

55. 200 soldiers, 200 spearmen and 70 horsemen.

56. We should suffer hardship as a good soldier.

57. We should avoid entangling ourselves with the affairs of everyday life.

58. **a**. An athlete **b**. A hard-working farmer.

59. We should endure all things for the sake of those who are chosen that they may obtain salvation.

60. Jesus will tell you where to fish and the results will be great.

Study 20: What is the Second Coming of Jesus and What is the Eternal Judgment?

1. He will come again in the same manner as you have watched Him go.

2. **a**. The dead in Christ will rise first. **b**. Those who are alive and remain will be caught up to meet the Lord.

3. The physical body will be changed to an immortal and imperishable body.

4. Death.

5. **a**. Until He has put all enemies under His feet. **b**. He is waiting for all his enemies to be put underneath His footstool.

6. Death.

7. Transformation into the likeness of Jesus.

8. No; the change is from glory to glory.

9. a. A church in all her glory. **b.** Having no spot or wrinkle. **c.** Holy and blameless.

10. By the washing of the water of the Word.

11. To be conformed to the image of the Son.

12. To put on the new self.

13. The bride has made herself ready.

14. The righteous acts of the saints.

15. a. Feed and clothe fellow Christians in need. **b.** Abraham offering up Isaac on the altar. **c.** Rahab received the Israelite spies and sent them home another way, before the Lord destroyed Jericho

16. a. Give drink to the thirsty. **b.** Give food to the hungry. **c.** Take in the stranger. **d.** Clothe the naked. **e.** Visit the sick. **f.** Visit those in prison.

17. They purify themselves just as He is pure.

18. a. Deny ungodliness and worldly desires. **b.** Live sensibly, righteously and godly.

19. a. The church going forth into the world as Jesus went forth. **b.** The same unity that Jesus had with the Father. (This unity will be between each member of the body for one another and between each believer and God.) **c.** The same glory that Jesus had. **d.** Perfection into a unity.

20. a. He did nothing of Himself, but only what He saw the Father doing. **b.** The Father showed Him all things. **c.** He judged as He heard from God. **d.** He did not seek His own will, but the will of God. **e.** He did not speak His own words, but only what the Father told Him to speak. **f.** Those who beheld Him, beheld God. **g.** The world found no guilt in Him.

21. a. Those whose name are not written in the book of life. **b.** But cowards who turn away from Me, and **c.** Unbelievers **d.** The corrupt **e.** Murderers **f.** The immoral **g.** Those who practice witchcraft **h.** Idol worshipers **i.** All liars. **j.** Those who say Jesus is not the Christ (the Messiah) the Son of the Living God. **k.** Fornicators **l.** Idolaters **m.** Adulterers **n.** Effeminate(having or showing characteristics regarded as typical of a woman; unmanly.) **o.** Homosexuals.(Sodomites) **p.** Thieves **q.** Covetous **r.** Drunkards **s.** Revilers **t.** Swindlers (extortioners)

22. He will not erase our name out of the book of life.

23.a. Whoever believes that Jesus is the Christ is born of God. **b.** If we love God, we love those who are His children. **c.** We will keep His commandments.

24. a. Whoever is born of God overcomes the world. **b.** Our faith and trust in Christ to give us the victory. **c.** We win the battle against the world by believing Jesus is the Son of God.

25. a. We have the witness in our heart. **b.** God's promise that we have eternal life in His Son. **c.** If you have God's Son you will have life.

26. Be dressed in readiness, keeping your lamps alight, waiting and watching.

27. Faithful Servant: Faithful and sensible steward who was feeding the flock and doing the Master's will.

Reward: He is put in charge of all the master's possessions.

Drunken Servant: He says that the Master won't come for a long time. He mistreats others and is a glutton and drunkard satisfying his own lusts.

Reward: The Lord will come on a day which the slave will not know about. He will cut him in pieces.

Lazy Servant: He knew his Master's will, but did not do it or get ready and did not act according to God's will.

Reward: He shall receive many lashes or blows.

Ignorant Servant: He did not know the Master's will and committed deeds worthy of flogging. **Reward:** He will receive a few lashes.

28. Those who were prepared, ready and on the alert.

29. a. You are the light of the world, don't hide your light. **b.** Let your light shine before men that they may see your good works and glorify your father who is in heaven.

30. As a thief in the night.

31. Not as a thief; for we are not of the darkness, but of the light.

32. He will do nothing unless He reveals His secret counsel to His servants the prophets.

Study 21: The End of the Old Age - The Beginning of the New

1. The last days

2. Jesus opened up a new and living way into the holy place by the blood of Jesus, which He inaugurated for us through the veil, that is, His flesh.

3. The prophets sought to know what person or time the Spirit of Christ was indicating as He predicted the sufferings of Christ and the glories to follow. It was revealed to them it was for a future generation.(Note: Daniel even was given the exact time period.)

4. The destruction of the temple. Not one stone will be left upon another.

5. a. Your house will be left to you desolate - destruction of the temple and the Jewish nation.

b. "For the days will come upon you, when your enemies will set up a barricade around you and surround you and hem you in on every side and tear you down to the ground, you and your children within you. And they will not leave one stone upon another in you, because you did not know the time of your visitation."

6. Those who are in Judea must flee to the mountains. Whoever is on the housetop must not go down to get the things out that are in his house. Whoever is in the field must not turn back to get his cloak. Pray that your flight will not be in the winter, or on a Sabbath.

7. God's judgment is coming against the rich who trust in their riches and have cheated those who worked for them holding back their pay while they lived in luxury. You have condemned and murdered the just and fattened yourself for the day of slaughter. The coming of the Lord in judgment is near. Behold the Judge stands at the door.

8. By these regulations the Holy Spirit revealed that the entrance to the Most Holy Place was not freely open as long as the Tabernacle and the system it represented were still in use. Under the Old Covenant the high priest could only enter there once a year.

9. So Christ has now become the High Priest over all the good things that have come. He has entered that greater, more perfect Tabernacle in heaven, which was not made by human hands and is not part of this created world. With his own blood—not the blood of goats and calves—he entered the Most Holy Place once for all time and secured our redemption forever. There is now no need for priests to offer up sacrifices.

10. a. The cares of this life **b.** with satisfying the lust of the flesh.

11. The wicked.

12. The wicked.

13. The righteous.

14. a. The upright and blameless will remain. **b.** The wicked and treacherous will be cut off and rooted out of the earth.

15. The sinners.

16. The gentle.

17. The things that cannot be shaken.

18. The kingdom which cannot be shaken.

19. **a**. The sinners and the godless. **b**. The righteous and sincere.

20. **a**. Those whose hearts are weighted down by carousing (drunken partying) **b**. drunkenness and **c**. the worries of life.

21. Be on the alert and pray that you may have strength to escape these things and to stand before the Son of Man.

22. That they not be taken out of the world, but kept from the evil one.

23. Remember Lot's wife. Do not grasp for earthly things.

24. **a**. False Messiah and false prophets. **b**. Great international wars. **c**. Famines and earthquakes. **d**. Christians killed and hated. **e**. Many will fall away and betray one another. **f**. Lawlessness will increase. **g**. People's love will grow cold. **h**. The Good News of the Kingdom will be preached to all nations.

25. We know that the whole creation has been groaning as in the pains of childbirth right up to the present time waiting to be delivered from corrupt into the freedom and the glory of the sons of God.

26. Until the period of restoration of all things about which God spoke by the mouth of His holy prophets from ancient time.

27. **a**. The nations turning to Jesus, His resting place (the church) will be glorious. **b**. Recovering of the dispersed Jewish people from the four corners of the earth.

28. The Lord who brought up and led back the descendants of Israel from the North and from all the countries where He had driven them.

29. The New Covenant.

30. The city of Jerusalem shall be rebuilt never be plucked up or overthrown any more.

31. **a**. Judah will be saved. **b**. No

32. **a**. Hosea **b**. "Those who were not My people, I will now call My people, and I will love those I never loved before. Once they were told, 'You are not My people.' Now He will say, 'You are the children of the living God.'"

33. The throne of David

34. Israel will be a long time without king and sacrifice, without city, temple, priests or idols, but afterward they will return to the Lord their God and the descendant of David their King. (Messiah)

35. When the fullness of the Gentiles has come in, all of Israel will be saved and grafted back in.

36. Multitudes will be saved, nations and kings will come into the kingdom of God.

37. They will recognize Him whom they have pierced, who is Jesus, and they will mourn for Him as one mourns for his only son.

38. They were cut to the heart, they realized that they had crucified Jesus and cried out," What must we do to be saved?"

39. **a**. A fountain for sin and for impurity for the house of David. **b**. If we walk in the Light as He is in the light, the blood of Jesus cleanses us from all sin.

40. When they say, "Blessed is He Who comes in the name of the Lord."

41. Those who overcome and have forsaken all to follow Him.

42. Until the times of the Gentiles is fulfilled.

42. God watches over His Word to perform it.

Study 22: The Advancing Kingdom-Christ's Victory in the Nations

1. a. God gave Adam and Eve dominion over the earth. **b.** He commanded them to be fruitful, and multiply, and replenish the earth, and subdue it.

2. Jesus called Satan the prince of this world and said Satan's judgment was at hand and that he was going to be cast out.

3. If I be lifted up from the earth, I will draw all men unto Me.

4. Paul called Jesus the last Adam and the second man.

5. He took on flesh and blood so that through death He might destroy him that had the power of death, that is, the devil; and deliver those who through fear of death were all their lifetime subject to bondage and slaves to the fear of dying.

6. a. Make disciples of all nations **b.** Baptize them **c.** Teach them to obey everything that He taught. **d.** All authority has been given to Him in heaven and earth.

7. a. I saw Satan fall like lightning from heaven. **b.** I give you the authority to trample on serpents and scorpions, and over all the power of the enemy, and nothing shall by any means hurt you.

8. He has the keys of hell and death.

9. The earth is the Lord's and all the people who live on it.

10. Abraham and his seed, who are the children of God through faith in Jesus Christ, have been made heirs of the world.

11. Jesus will remain in heaven until the restoration of all things spoken by God's Holy Prophets since time began.

12. a. All the ends of the earth will remember and turn to the Lord, and all the families of the nations will worship before You. **b.** He will cause wars to cease and He will be exalted among the nations. **c.** All the nations will flow into kingdom of God and they will learn war no more. **d.** Of the increase of His government and of His peace there will be no end. **e.** He has been promised the nations as His inheritance

13. And in the days of these kings the God of heaven will set up a kingdom which shall never be destroyed; and the kingdom shall not be left to other people; it shall break in pieces and consume all these kingdoms, and it shall stand forever.

14. a. The time is fulfilled. **b.** The kingdom of God is at hand. **c.** Repent, and believe in the Gospel." **d.** They wondered if John was the Christ. **e.** Are you the Messiah(Christ)? **f.** I am the voice of one calling in the wilderness, "Make straight in the desert a highway for our God." **g.** If you are the Messiah (Christ) tells us plainly.

15. a. Fall on this stone and be broken, or it will fall on you and it will grind you to powder. **b.** The stone represents the kingdom of God on earth that the God of heaven will set up.

16. The kingdom of God will shatter all opposition and will fill the whole earth. The kingdom and dominion and the greatness of the kingdoms under the whole heaven shall be given to the people, the saints of the Most High. His kingdom *is* an everlasting kingdom and all dominions shall serve and obey Him.

17. The gates of hell shall not prevail against the Church.

18. He ascended into heaven in a cloud.

19. "I ascend to My Father and to your Father, to My God and to your God."

20. Daniel saw one like the Son of man coming on the clouds of heaven and He came and stood before the Ancient of Days.

21. He came on the clouds of Heaven.

22. a. To Him was given dominion, glory, and a kingdom. **b.** that all nations and tongues should serve and obey

Him. **c.** His kingdom is an everlasting dominion that shall not pass away or ever be destroyed.

23. a. You are my Son. Today I have begotten You. **b.** Ask of me and I will give you the nations for Your inheritance, the ends of the earth for your possession. **c.** You will break them with a rod of iron and smash them like clay pots.

24. a. Serve the Lord with reverent fear. **b.** Submit to God's son or you will be destroyed. **c.** Joy and blessing is found in trusting Him.

25. We are children of God, heirs of God, joint heirs with Christ.

26. God's glory.

27. It is the Father's good pleasure to give you the kingdom.

28. An unshakeable, unmovable kingdom.

29. No, eventually all of Israel will be saved.

30. a. He must reign until all enemies are put under His feet. **b.** The last enemy to be destroyed is death.

31. At the last trumpet.

32. The seventh angel then blew his trumpet, and there were mighty voices in heaven, shouting, "The dominion (kingdom, sovereignty, rule) of the world has now come into the possession and become the kingdom of our Lord and of His Christ (the Messiah), and He shall reign forever and ever (for the eternities of the eternities)!"

33. The earth is waiting for God's sons to be revealed so it can be delivered from its bondage to corruption.

34. Those who are led by the Spirit of God, these are the sons of God.

35. a. To preach the gospel to the poor . **b.** To heal the brokenhearted. **c.** To proclaim liberty to the captives. **d.** To proclaim recovery of sight to the blind. **e.** To set at liberty those who are oppressed

f. To proclaim the year of the Lord's favor

36. The anointing from the Spirit of the Lord.

37. Jesus promised that the Holy Spirit would flow out of the believer in rivers of living water.

38.a. The tree of life was there. **b.** On either side of the river there were trees whose leaves were for the healing of the nations. **c.** There is no more curse.

39. The Baptism of the Holy Spirit will give you Power to be a witness.

40. The rider on the white horse had a bow in his hand a crown on his head and went for conquering and to conquer.

41. The One sitting on the white horse was named Faithful and True. He judges fairly and then goes to war. His eyes were bright like flames of fire, and on His head were many crowns. A name was written on Him, and only he knew what it meant. He was clothed with a robe dipped in blood, and His title was the Word of God. The armies of heaven, dressed in pure white linen, followed him on white horses. From His mouth came a sharp sword, and with it he struck down the nations. He ruled them with an iron rod, and He trod the winepress of the fierce wrath of Almighty God. On His robe and thigh was written this title: King of Kings and Lord of Lords.

Study 23: How to Have Great Faith in God

1. a. Repentance from dead works. **b.** Faith toward God. **c.** Instruction about washings. **d.** Laying on of hands. **e.** The resurrection of the dead. **f.** Eternal judgment.

2. Without faith, it is impossible to please God.

3. God has given to every man the measure of faith. **4. a.** You must believe that God is (exists).**b.** You must believe that He is a rewarder of those who diligently seek Him.

5. It is by grace, through faith.

6. Faith comes by hearing the Word of God.

7. a. Hear the Word. **b**. Confess that Jesus is Lord. **c**. Believe in your heart that God raised Him from the dead.

8. He was to tell him words by which he and his household would be saved.

9. Paul: 1. He preached the Gospel. **2**. He perceived that the man had faith to be healed.

   3. He told the man to stand up and walk. **The man: 1**. He heard Paul preach. **2**. He had faith to be healed

   3. He leaped and walked.

10. He heard the words that Paul spoke.

11. Faith is the assurance of things hoped for, the conviction of things not seen.

12. By faith God made the world by His Word, so that what is seen was not made out of things that are visible.

13. a. Confess or say it. **b**. Do not doubt in your heart. **c**. Believe that what you say is going to happen.

 d. Receive-it shall be granted.

14. a. God brooded over the water, envisioning what He wanted to create . **b**. He said it. **c**. It happened or came to pass - it materialized.

15. a. Do not doubt in your heart. **b**. Believe that you have received what you ask for **c**. Forgive others

16. a.I will do whatever you ask in my name **b**. You may ask me for anything in my name, and I will do it **c**. If you abide in me and my words abide in you ask what you will and it shall be done.**d**. Ask and you will receive so your joy will be full.

17. Thomas had seen the nails pierce Jesus' hands and the spear thrust into His side. His physical senses told him that Jesus was dead. 'Thomas was using head knowledge rather than faith.

18. Thomas believed when he had seen.

19. Blessed are they that have not seen, and yet have believed.

20. a. He believed God, who calls things into being which do not exist. **b**. Against hope, he believed that which God had spoken. **c**. Without becoming weak in faith, he did not consider the circumstances. **d**. He did not waver in unbelief, but grew strong in faith. **e**. He was fully assured that what God had promised; He was able to perform.

21. He considered the Word of God.

22. By receiving God's Word as the word of a friend.

23. Received God's Word as she did the word of her friend.

24. God does not lie, He has spoken it, He will make it good.

Study 24: How to grow in Faith and How to be a Doer of The Word

1. By inclining your ear to His Word and keeping God's Word before your eyes and in the midst of your heart.

2. He refused the circumstances and looked intently at God's promise.

3. God's Word shall succeed.

4. His confession.

5. If we believe what we say shall come to pass, we can have whatever we say.

6. No, we must say it.

7. a. The blood of the Lamb. **b**. The words of our testimony. **c**. Loving not our life unto death.

8. He had given the city of Jericho into his hand.

9. No.

10. Seven priests carry rams' horns before the ark. Go around the city with the army once a day for six days. On the seventh day, march around seven times with the priests blowing the trumpets. When the priests make a long blast with the rams' horns, the people shall shout and the walls will fall. Then go in and take the city, destroying everything.

11. No.

12. They climbed up on the roof, cut a hole in it, and let him down.

13. He saw their faith.

14. He obeyed the Words of the Lord and acted out his faith in that Word.

15. To be a doer of the Word and not a hearer only.

16. By works.

17. By offering up Isaac.

18. He believed that God, who had said that through Isaac his seed should come, was able to raise him from the dead.

19. By preparing the ark, acting on what God had told him.

20. By works.

21. By faith in God David had killed both the lion and the bear from eating his sheep. David believed that the Lord who delivered him from the paw of the lion and from the paw of the bear, would deliver him from the hand of this Philistine.

22. One who looks in the mirror and walks away, forgetting what he looks like.

23. a. Look intently at the Word. **b.** Abide by it. **c.** Be an effectual doer of it.

24. We will be blessed in what we do.

Study 25: The Power of Confessing God's Word

1. We are to go into the world and preach the Gospel.

2. The Lord worked with them and confirmed the Word with signs following.

3. If we believe what we say shall come to pass, we can have whatever we say.

4. Peter took his eyes off Jesus and looked at the winds and the waves and began to sink.

5. Oh you of little faith. Why did you doubt?

6. Jesus couldn't do anything in Nazareth because they did not believe in Him.

7. They gave a bad report saying that people were too strong.

8. They said that they should go up and possess the land for the Lord would give it into their hand.

9. They died by a plague.

10. Their corpses fell in the wilderness and they were not allowed to enter the land.

11. They would be brought into the land; however, they suffered for their father's unfaithfulness and wandered for 40 years in the wilderness.

12. He remained alive, took Moses' place as leader and led the children of Israel into the Promised Land and God granted him success.

13. He entered the land and possessed a mountain for his inheritance and was as strong at 80 as he was at forty.

14. Death and life are in the power of the tongue and man will be filled with the fruit of it.

15. We should fear lest we follow the same example and fail to enter.

16. Because it was not united by faith in those who heard.

17. They saw the giants in the land. Then they saw themselves as grasshoppers.

18. The Israelites were afraid and no one would go out to meet the Philistine giant.

19. Goliath was over 9 feet tall. He wore a bronze helmet and was armed with a coat of mail that weighted 125 pounds. He had bronze armor on his legs and a bronze javelin between his shoulders. The shaft of his spear was like a weaver's beam, tipped with and iron spearhead that weighed 15 pounds; and a shield-bearer went before him.

20. David remembered the lion and the bear that the Lord had helped Him kill while watching his sheep.

21. David said, "You come to me with sword, spear, and javelin, but I come to you in the name of the LORD Almighty--the God of the armies of Israel, whom you have defied. Today the LORD will conquer you, and I will kill you and cut off your head. And then I will give the dead bodies of your men to the birds and wild animals, and the whole world will know that there is a God in Israel! And everyone will know that the LORD does not need weapons to rescue his people. It is his battle, not ours. The LORD will give you to us!" He did just what he said.

22. He took the head of Goliath to Jerusalem.

23. a. She touched the hem of Jesus' garment. **b.** She said, "If I may but touch His clothes, I shall be made whole."

24. She was healed.

25. She told what had happened.

26. Cast down every argument, every high thing that exalts itself against the knowledge of God, and bring every thought captive to the obedience of Christ.

Study 26: How to Become a Bold Confessor

1. Our God whom we serve is able to deliver us from the fiery furnace, but even if He does not, we will not serve or bow down before other gods.

2. They were thrown into the fiery furnace.

3. They were not burned, but were completely delivered.

4. a. Blessed be the God of Shadrack, Mesheck, and Abadnego. **b.** They put their trust in God. **c.** They violated the king's command. **d.** They yielded up their bodies so as not to serve foreign gods.

5. When Daniel knew the document was signed he entered his house and continued to kneel, pray and give thanks to God three times a day.

6. He was thrown into the lion's den and the den was sealed shut.

7. The angel of the Lord shut the mouth of the lions and he was not harmed.

8. a. He is the living God, enduring forever. **b.** His kingdom is one which will not be destroyed.

c. His dominion will be forever. **d.** He delivers, rescues and performs signs and wonders in heaven and on earth.

9. You stiff-necked and uncircumcised in heart and ears, you always are resisting the Holy Spirit. Which one of the prophets did your fathers not persecute? They killed those who announced the Messiah's coming and you have become His, the Messiah's, murderer. Behold, I see the heavens open and the Son of Man standing at the right hand of God.

10. They stoned him to death.

11. The Lord did not hold the sin against them and a young man named "Saul" was forgiven so that he could be saved. Saul later became Paul the great apostle.

12. Through Paul (or Saul) the gospel was taken to the Gentiles.

13. They prayed for boldness and they got it.

14. a. Subdued kingdoms **b.** Worked righteousness **c.** Obtained promises **d.** Stopped the mouths of lions

e. Quenched the violence of fire **f**. Escaped the edge of the sword **g**. Out of weakness were made strong **h.** Became valiant in battle **i.** Turned to flight the armies of the aliens **j.** Women received their dead raised to life again **k.** Died a martyrs death and obtained a better resurrection.

15. They were people of whom the world was not worthy.

16. a. By the blood of the Lamb. **b.** By the word of their testimony. **c.** Loving not our lives unto death.

Study 27: God's Predetermined Purpose and Your Free Will

1. God's ultimate plan will be established.

2. They rejected it.

3. Abraham obeyed and received the land of Canaan as his inheritance.

4. a. Your descendants will be like the dust for multitude. **b.** I will make you a father of many nations. **c.** kings will come from you. **d.** Your descendants will become as numerous as the stars. **e.** Through you and your seed(Christ) all the nations of the world will be blessed.

5. a. To appoint a wife for Isaac. **b.** She had a choice.

6. God's will.

7. a. He was called to ministry and apostleship. **b.** He turned aside.

8. From Rebekah came a nation, and from that nation came the Messiah.

9. Life and prosperity or death and adversity.

10. Life and blessing.

11. No.

12. Appoint a king.

13. They were rejecting the Lord from being their King.

14. No.

15. Bondage and oppression.

16. They would cry and He would not answer.

17. Refused to listen.

18. He gave them their way-a king.

19. God.

20. Serve the Lord or act wickedly and be swept away.

21. To disobey.

22. He would have established his kingdom forever.

23. Saul lost the kingdom and god chose someone else to fulfill His purposes.

24. To destroy all; he disobeyed.

25. *a*.Saul set up a monument to himself.**b.** He was disobedient to God and serving himself.

26. God rejected him from his office as King.

27. He regretted that He had made Saul King.

28. To see what is in his heart-whether you will obey or not.

29. That person must be found faithful.

30. He gave it to someone else to fulfill.

31. For them to repent so He could forgive them.

32. They were not afraid; nor did they repent.

33. Go out and I will spare you.

34. He would build them up in the Lord and plant them in the land. If you go to Egypt, you will die by famine and sword.

35. They went to Egypt and disobeyed.

36. If people repent, God will change His mind.

37. If people do evil, God will not bless them.

38. Yes, God has no pleasure in the death of the wicked. He wants them to repent and live.

39. They would have never be destroyed. They would have had abundant peace and righteousness and their seed would have been like the sand on the seashore, and they would have never been cut off.

40. Abraham believed in the God who brings the dead back to life. Abraham believed God even though such a promise seemed utterly impossible! Abraham never wavered in believing God's promise. In fact, his faith grew stronger, and in this he brought glory to God. He was absolutely convinced that God was able to do anything he promised.

41. God has given to us exceedingly great and precious promises, that through these you may be partakers of the divine nature, having escaped the corruption that is in the world through lust.

42. **a**. Diligence in faith. **b**. Moral excellence. **c**. Knowledge. **d**. Self-control. **e**. Perseverance. **f**. Godliness. **g**. Brotherly kindness. **h**. Christian love.

43. For if these things are yours and abound, you will be neither barren nor unfruitful in the knowledge of our Lord Jesus Christ.

44. For he who lacks these things is shortsighted, even to blindness, and has forgotten that he was cleansed from his old sins.

45. **a.** Be even more diligent to make your call and election sure. **b.** For if you do these things you will never stumble. **c.** An entrance will be supplied to you abundantly into the everlasting kingdom of our Lord and Savior Jesus Christ.

46. **a.** Mark out a straight path for your feet. Then those who follow you, though they are weak and lame, will not stumble and fall but will become strong. **b.** Try to live in peace with everyone. **c.** Seek to live a clean and holy life, for those who are not holy will not see the Lord. **d.** Watch out that no bitter root of unbelief rises up among you. **e.** Make sure that no one is immoral or godless like Esau who traded his birthright for a meal. **f.** See to it that you obey God, the one who is speaking to you. **g.** Be thankful and worship Hm with holy fear and awe.

47. God created them male and female and called them man.

48. There is no male or female in Christ Jesus.

Study 28: Called into His Glory

1.We have been called to gain the glory of the Lord Jesus.

2. To bring many sons to glory.

3. Those who are led by the Spirit, whether they are male or female, are called the sons of God.

4. The whole creation is waiting for the sons of God to be revealed.

5. The creation is waiting to be delivered from their bondage to corruption, so they can enter into the glorious liberty of the sons of God.

6. Where the Spirit of the Lord is their is liberty.

7. a. We are to walk in a manner worthy of God. **b.** He has called us into His own kingdom and glory.

8. He has called us to His purpose.

9. a. He has predestined us to be conformed into the image of His Son. **b.** Jesus is the first born among many brothers and sisters.

10. His glory.

11. a. We have been made right in God's sight through faith in Jesus. **b.** We have peace with God.

c. We stand in the place of the highest privilege. **d.** We look forward to sharing His glory.

12. We are to reign in life by Christ Jesus.

13. Adam and Eve were crowned with glory and honor.

14. They fell short of the glory of God.

15. Jesus declared that He has given us the glory which the Father gave Him.

16. Jesus prayed that we might behold His glory.

17. Moses face shone with the glory of God

18. a. It was so bright that Israel couldn't look at Moses face. **b.** It was a fading glory.

19. The New Covenant is overwhelming because of the greater glory.

20. As we behold His glory, we are changed into His image from one degree of glory to another glory.

21. God has shown His light in our hearts to give the knowledge of the glory of God in the face of Jesus Christ.

22. Trials and tribulations work greater glory.

23. a. He will glorify His glorious house. **b.** He will present the church in all her glory.

24. a. God can do abundantly beyond all you can ask or think. **b.** There will be glory in the church.

25. We should come to God in Reverence, calling Him Father and acknowledge He is the God of Heaven and is Holy.

26. a. Thy kingdom come on earth as it is in heaven. **b.** Thy will be done on earth as it is in heaven. **c.** Give us our daily bread. **d.** Forgive us our sins as we forgive those who have sinned against us. **e.** Keep us from temptation. **f.** Deliver us from evil.

27. God does not tempt people with evil.

28. If you want God to forgive your sins, you must forgive the sins that others have committed against you.

29. For Yours is the Power and the Glory forever.

30. a. Spiritual wisdom and understanding, (the spirt of wisdom and revelation) so that you might grow in your knowledge of God. **b.** I pray that your hearts will be flooded with light so that you can understand the wonderful future He has promised to those he called. **c.** I want you to realize what a rich and glorious inheritance He has given to his people. **d.** I pray that you will begin to understand the incredible greatness of His power for us who believe Him and the authority he has and the church has over principalities and powers. **e.** To understand that the church is His body; it is filled by Christ, who fills everything everywhere with His Presence (to know His Presence).

31. When I think of the wisdom and scope of God's plan, I fall to my knees and pray to the Father, the Creator of everything in heaven and on earth.

32.a. I pray that from his glorious, unlimited resources he will give you mighty inner strength through his Holy Spirit. **b.** I pray that Christ will be more and more at home in your hearts as you trust in Him. **c.** May your roots go down deep into the soil of God's marvelous love. **d.** And may you have the power to understand, as all God's people should, how wide, how long, how high, and how deep his love really is. **e.** May you experience the love of Christ, though it is so great you will never fully understand it. **f.** Then you will be filled with the fullness of life and power that comes from God (vs. 17-19).

33. a. Now glory be to God! **b.** By His mighty power at work within us, He is able to accomplish infinitely more than we would ever dare to ask or hope. **c.** May He be given glory in the church and in Christ Jesus forever and ever through endless ages. Amen

Study the Bible

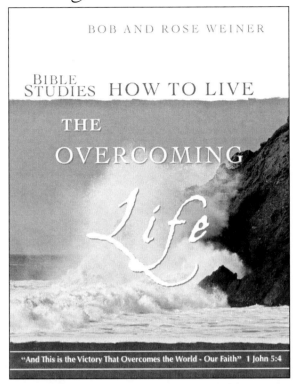

"This is the Victory That Overcomes the World - Our Faith!"
1 John 5:4

Learn how to be an overcomer! Dive into this study in practical Christian living. In *How to Live the Overcoming Life* you will understand the purpose in personal trials and how to get the most out of them for your spiritual growth. Learn how to praise God in every circumstance. Learn how to develop your faith. Understand how to live in the righteousness of Christ and the power of His resurrection that Jesus promised to all who believe in Him. Learn the power the Lord has given to you as a believer to tell others about the Good News of the Gospel.

"For three years now I have taught your books to our high school classes, grades 9th - 12th in our Christian school. I have used them in adult Bible classes, I have even used them to minister to those in prison. I have used your *Bible Studies for a Firm Foundation*, *Bible Studies for the Life of Excellence*, and *Bible Studies on the Overcoming Life*. You have laid these out in such a manner that whether I am teaching high school students or adults, they are greatly received, easy to follow and understand." *- Cheryl Carter*

This easy to use question/answer, fill in the blank format lets the Bible speak for itself. Ideal for personal, group or homeschool study. Size 8.5" x11" - 111 pages. **Order form in the back.**

Discounts available at weinermedia.com

Study the Bible

There is no other book like the book of James in the entire Bible. Written by James, Jesus very own flesh and blood brother, there is no other book so close to the heart of Jesus' teaching in the Sermon on the Mount. From his first hand experience in observing the life of Jesus, James gives us a look at what the Nature of God is really like. What is so stunning about that? This is the very same New Nature that we have inherited from Jesus Christ when we were born again, which makes us sons and daughters of God!

We invite you to the banqueting table to meet Jesus in His Word. Look into the "Glory" and "be transformed" into His image through the power of the Holy Spirit. In *The Life of Excellence - A Study of James*, learn:

- How to Be a Doer of the Word
- How to Become God's Friend
- How to Receive the Wisdom of God
- How to Live in God's Blessing
- How to Live a Life of Faith
- How to Live in the Will of God
- How to Change Your Words and Change Your Life...and much more!

This easy to use question answer workbook, fill in the blank format lets the Bible speak for itself. Ideal for personal, group or homeschool study. Size 8.5" x11" - 120 pages.

Discounts available at weinermedia.com

"The Word of God Implanted in Your Heart Has The Power to Save Your Soul!"- James 1:21

Study the Bible

BOB AND ROSE WEINER

BIBLE STUDIES **PREPARATION** OF THE **BRIDE OF CHRIST**

"Deep Calls unto Deep...
Set Me as a Seal upon Your Heart."
A Psalm of David and a
Song of Solomon

A Study of The Allegories of The Song of Solomon

Study the Allegories of the
Song of Solomon

According to Jewish rabbinical tradition and the teaching of the Church Fathers, Song of Solomon is an allegory revealing at its deepest level the love that God has for His redeemed people. The Ancients held that this book is the Song of Songs in the same way that the holiest place in the tabernacle was the Holy of Holies. This Song of All Songs holds "God's wisdom hidden in a mystery." Its imagery is meant to teach and help us understand the deep union with the Father to which Christ is calling us. Learn how to experience the living Presence of Christ and the fellowship of the Holy Spirit that Jesus has poured out for us to enjoy.

I've been doing this Bible study every year since 1990, and I don't know of a more powerful, supernatural, anointed Bible study. Every time I get into it, I encounter the Lord in the most unique ways. - *Deborah Deonigi*

"This study is truly a spiritual feast. There are so many deep revelations of the love Jesus has for His bride that the language of allegory conveys. What a joy to look into these mysteries and understand the biblical teaching on such a deep subject and learn not only how to deepen your fellowship with the Lord, but actually experience it." *Ellen Russell*

This easy to use question/answer, fill in the blank format lets the Bible speak for itself. Ideal for personal, group or homeschool study. Size 8.5 x11 - 247 pages.

A Study of Philippians
Bible Studies for the Lovers of God

Learn how to live a life full of God's joy and grace, regardless of the circumstances! Paul wrote his letter to the Philippians while he was Nero's prisoner, and yet his epistle fairly shouts with triumphant joy. Gain holy-mindedness as you learn how to set your mind on one thing - the glory of our God and Savior. Learn how to possess the same Christ centered attitude that Paul had when he penned, "For me to live is Christ and to die is gain!"

In *Bible Studies for the Lovers of God*, you will learn what "the prize of the high call of God in Christ Jesus" is that Paul tells us to press toward. Learn how to walk in the example that Jesus gave us of humility and service to others. This is a short study, but it is very profound. Packed full of life changing principles, you will learn truths that will give greater purpose and meaning to your everyday life. Best of all, you will learn how to enter into a deeper fellowship with Jesus.

"Someone gave me this study when I was in prison. I can't tell you how much the truths I found here and the revelation I received from God's Word has changed my life. Thank you for writing *The Lovers of God*. I want to study more of your books and continue to grow close to Jesus." *-T. J., Texas*

This 8.5" x11," 44 page workbook is full of questions and answers - look them up in the Bible and let the Bible speak for itself - then fill in the blanks. This book is ideal for personal, group, homeschool, or family studies.

Study the Bible

"The Bible is the best book ever given to man."
- Abraham Lincoln

BOB AND ROSE WEINER

Bible for the Studies

Lovers of God

"As the Deer Pants for the Water Brooks,
So My Soul Pants for You, O God."
Psalm 42:1

A STUDY OF PHILIPPIANS

Discounts available at weinermedia.com

Book One of the *Trilogy!*

A Must Read!

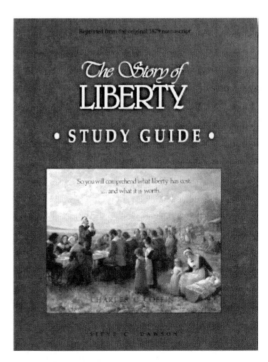

Study the Christian Foundations of Our Nation Before the History Rewrites!

Sweet Land of LIBERTY

Trace the Growth of Christian Liberty

Get the Second Book in Coffin's *Trilogy!*

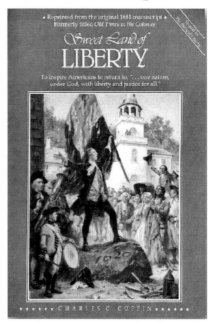

Sweet Land of Liberty is the sequel to *The Story of Liberty* - Originally entitled *Old Times in the Colonies* written in 1881. Coffin traces the growth of Christian Liberty from the beginning of the Pilgrims' first settlement through the growth of the 13 Original Colonies.

Coffin recounts the colonists interaction with the Indians, explains the French and Indian wars, and tells the struggle of two civilizations - the European view of the control of the elite vs freedom of the individual who is able to govern himself according to the laws of God. Coffin shows how man's inhumanity to man gives way to individual freedom and a desire for peace. Coffin shows how the concepts of civil and religious liberty under God were hammered out within the Christian church in the light of the Bible. These principles eventually found their way into the constitution of every state, and were ultimately enshrined in our national constitution.

Coffin explains, "You will see how tyranny and wrong have fought against truth and justice and how tyranny and wrong have gone down before it." An inspiring view of the Providential Hand of God in founding the American Colonies - 458 page paperback, beautifully illustrated.

"Coffin sticks to the facts on each page, so kids get a good dose of history while learning about the true cost of our hard-won freedoms. But what really sets this book apart is Mr. Coffin's genuine Christian world-view." - Conservative Book Club

First Published in 1881

Discounts available at weinermedia.com

Study the Great Ideas of Christian Liberty

Consider and Ponder

Analyze the Development of Christian Self - Government and Religious Freedom

Rose Weiner leads students into a guided study of Coffin's *Sweet Land of Liberty.* Analyze the important events in the development of Christian Liberty and individual freedom. Recognize the Hand of God's Providence moving through historical events as the colonies grow and flourish. Learn how the idea of Christian self-government and freedom of religion, assembly, and freedom of the press were hammered out from the teaching of the Bible. Learn how people raised under bigotry and intolerance broke free from these Old World concepts to embrace the principles of Liberty that are now our heritage.

The Mayflower Compact, John Locke on the Laws of Nature and Civil Government, the First Amendment and other historical documents and patriotic literature are introduced with the text. Poetry and literature that express the ideas of our Founders are brought into the study to make this an intellectual and spiritual feast. Each chapter of this 250 -page guide has fill-in-the-blanks and essay questions to help facilitate personal and group study sessions, classroom, or home schooling classes - Size 8.5"x 11"

A Study of Industry, Courage, and a Determination to Live Free

**Discounts available at
weinermedia.com
ISBN: 978-0-938558-41-5**

Discover How to Know God's Will for Your Life!

FREE Mini Course at:

www.HowToKnowGodsWill.com

"Be Transformed By Renewing Your Mind."

Romans 12:1-2

Have You Ever Wondered How You Can Discover God's Will for Your Life? Your Days of Wondering Are Over!

Rose Weiner leads you through Practical Spiritual Exercises that will help you Understand God's Will, Learn How to Hear His Voice, and Increase the Knowledge of God's Presence in Your Life.

- **Learn How to Tune-In to God's Voice.**

- **Learn How to Change the Way You Think so that God's Thoughts Will Become Your Thoughts.**

- **Learn How to Practice the Presence of God.**

- **Learn How to Ditch Fear, Worry and Anxiety and Walk in the Peace of God.**

- **Learn How to Hear God Speak to You Through the Bible, Through Current Events and in Everyday Circumstances.**

- **Learn How to Renew Your Mind to Experience Greater Spiritual Transformation.**

For Other Inspirational Bible Studies,
Books, and eBooks visit our webstore:

Discounts Available

weinermedia.com

or

Email: weinermedia@gmail.com

Write:

Maranatha Publications/weinermedia

PO Box 1799

Gainesville, Florida

32614

Call: (352) 375-6000